Wildlife
of the
Maltese Islands

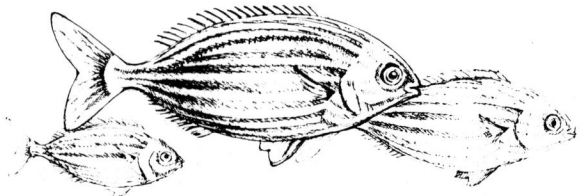

Wildlife
of the
Maltese Islands

Editors
Joe Sultana
Victor Falzon

Authors
Plants
Edwin Lanfranco
Animals
Alfred E Baldacchino
David Dandria
Guido Lanfranco
Sandro Lanfranco
Constantino Mifsud
Patrick J Schembri
Stephen Schembri
Joe Sultana

Illustrated by
Victor Falzon
Guido Lanfranco
Andrew Micallef

Scientific consultants
Edwin Lanfranco
Patrick J Schembri

Translated by
David Dandria

Published by the
Environment Protection Department
Floriana Malta
1996

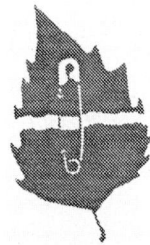

**This is the English edition
of the book *Flora u Fawna ta' Malta*
which was published in 1995
as a tribute to ENCY 95 -
the European Nature Conservation Year.
This work is dedicated
to all those who dedicate their time
to the conservation of nature.**

Cataloguing Data

Wildlife of the Maltese Islands
      editors, Joe Sultana, Victor Falzon;
      authors, Edwin Lanfranco ...[et al.];
      illustrated by Victor Falzon,Guido Lanfranco, Andrew Micallef;
      scientific consultants, Edwin Lanfranco, Patrick J. Schembri;
      translated by David Dandria.
      - Floriana : Environment Protection Department, 1996
          336p. : col. ill. ; 20x26cm.
          Translation of Flora u Fawna ta' Malta, Dipartiment ghall-Harsien ta' l-Ambjent, 1995
        ISBN 9 9909-66-02-1

1. Natural history - Malta

I. Lanfranco, Edwin, 1946-   II. Falzon, Victor, 1962-
III. Sultana, Joe, 1939-

DDC: 508.4585   LC: QH154.M5
Melitensia Classification: MZ37

Foreword

Early in 1994 I was presented with the proposals to publish Flora u Fawna ta' Malta, *the original version of this publication, as a contribution to the Council of Europe's Nature Conservation Year 1995. I did not hesitate to give it the green light for several reasons, and I have done the same for this English version* Wildlife of the Maltese Islands.

I am a great believer in education, and in Flora u Fawna ta' Malta *I could perceive an excellent tool for teachers to help motivate their schoolchildren in nature appreciation. Furthermore I could see that it would arouse awareness towards the beauty and protection of nature in Malta.*

Since I have been occupying the post of Parliamentary Secretary for the Environment, several regulations protecting the flora and fauna have been issued, while a number of nature reserves have also been declared. Malta has also signed and ratified nature conservation conventions such as those of Ramsar, Berne and CITES.

This English edition has a different role. Its main aim is to exhibit Malta's richness in biodiversity to the visitor as well as to nature lovers beyond Malta's shores. We are committed to safeguard this biodiversity for our own and future generations.

Stanley Zammit MD, MP
Parliamentary Secretary for the Environment

A message

Following the great success of Flora u Fawna ta' Malta, *it was natural that by popular demand an English version would shortly follow. It therefore gives me great pleasure to introduce what should be an exceedingly popular publication from my department.*

We wish to provide a much-needed text for environmental education programmes in schools both locally and in Maltese communities abroad. This English version should also reach a wider readership, thereby inspiring more appreciation of the beauty and biodiversity of the Maltese Islands. This variety is further enriched as fresh discoveries of new species are made by members of the scientific community studying the various areas of local flora and fauna.

This publication covers no less than 985 species. I hope that this book will provide an easily understandable and enjoyable exposition of those species which are more common and visible to the casual observer. The Maltese version has filled a much-needed niche in Maltese households. Likewise I hope that this English publication will fill a similar space in the homes of the many guests who visit us throughout the year, lovers of Malta and its natural environment. Certainly none should leave these shores without taking back home an environmental memento of our unique flora and fauna.

Louis Vella MSc
Director - Environment Protection Department

C O N T

The Text

E N T S

The Plates

Introduction

Aims

The principal aim of this book is to display the character, range and beauty of Malta's biodiversity. **Biodiversity** is a term used to indicate the variety of living organisms in existence, and encompasses all forms of plant and animal species, together with their various habitats.

This book also aims to stimulate respect towards nature, as well as to make people aware of the urgent need to safeguard our natural heritage. We hope that this book will also serve as a first step for those who wish to study some branch of natural history in greater depth.

Organisation

Wildlife of the Maltese Islands is divided into three main parts

Part 1: The Islands
Part 2: Plants
Part 3: Animals

There is also a glossary, a list of references, a bibliography for further reading, and indices of names. The book contains 12 colour photographs of Maltese natural habitats, 42 colour plates depicting all the species treated in the text, and numerous line drawings.

Choice of species

Following the first publications on the Maltese flora in the 17th century, many local and foreign authors have written about the various branches of Maltese natural history. Despite the small size of the Maltese Islands, an estimated 10,000 species of non-marine plants and animals occur, of which 4500 have so far been recorded. This figure does not include the species found in the seas around Malta - fish, molluscs, crustaceans and the marine flora. Several groups have yet to be studied: many species of insects and arachnids, for instance, still await identification. This is why the reader will occasionally come across the phrase 'so far recorded'.

Clearly, it was not possible to include all species found in the Maltese Islands, as the work would have run into several volumes. A choice had to be made. The various contributors were therefore asked to select the most familiar and widespread species. They also included certain species of special interest, such as those that are endemic (found only in the Maltese Islands) or restricted to a particular habitat, as well as species of historical or folkloristic interest.

The book includes a total of **985 species**, distributed as follows:

Algae	22	Insects	212
Fungi	21	Crustaceans	49
Lichens	3	Arachnids	20
Vascular Plants	267	Echinoderms	14
Sponges	3	Fish	100
Cnidarians	8	Amphibians	1
Annelids	7	Reptiles	12
Molluscs	101	Birds	124
Myriapods	6	Mammals	15

Some species, especially in the plants section, also carry supplementary information about similar species.

Description of species

Illustrations: Each species is illustrated in colour, which is why the text does not include a detailed description. In the animal illustrations, the whole animal is shown. In the plant section, however, only parts of the plant are shown, such as leaves and flowers, rather than the whole plant. For each species, the page number of the relative illustration is indicated. Several entries are also accompanied by explanatory line drawings.

Nomenclature: Every species is accompanied by its English, Maltese and scientific names. Where several vernacular names were known to exist for the same species, the authors have used the one considered most appropriate. Where no English name could be traced, a new one has been used, often based on the Family or generic name of the species.

Dimensions: Plants of the same species vary greatly in size. Their description therefore lacks information on size, although the heights of certain species are indicated. The size of the animal species, however, is always indicated in millimetres, centimetres or metres as appropriate.

The dimensions given refer to the organisms as found in the Maltese Islands, since in other parts of their range the same species may be smaller or larger. For molluscs, which may take years to reach full maturity, the maximum size is given. In the case of some insects, crustaceans, fish and birds, both minimum and maximum sizes have been given.

The size of birds is given as the length from the tip of the beak to the tip of the tail. For species which are often seen in flight, such as raptors and seabirds, the wingspan is also given. This also applies to bats. In the case of certain mammals, body length and tail length are indicated separately, while for reptiles the length quoted includes the tail.

Where there is a marked sexual difference in size, the dimensions of both sexes are given. In the case of social insects the size of the worker caste, where this is present, is also indicated. Insect lengths are measured from front of head to tip of abdomen, except in the case of butterflies and moths where the measurement is from midpoint of the thorax to the tip of the extended forewing. The size of species such as sponges, sea-urchins and starfish, which tend to have a spherical or globular body, is indicated by the diameter.

Since we are here concerned with living organisms, exceptionally large or small specimens are sometimes encountered. The dimensions quoted in this book refer to specimens falling within the normal size range.

Status: The status indicates the relative abundance of a species. This is given in brief at the end of every entry. For the sake of uniformity, six categories have been used throughout the book: **very common, common, frequent, scarce, rare** and **very rare**.

Some species are common everywhere, while others are common only in a restricted area, sometimes in a single locality. Others are scarce but widespread. The status of each species must therefore be considered in this context. Furthermore, the status of migratory species, such as certain insects, fish and birds, may vary from year to year.

This book treats the flora and fauna of the Maltese Islands. Indications of the number of species in an Order or Family should therefore be taken to refer to the situation in the Maltese Islands, unless otherwise stated. This also holds for statements like 'the largest Family' or 'the smallest beetle'.

For the sake of conciseness, the word 'Malta' in this book refers to all the islands of the Maltese archipelago. When a species is restricted to particular islands, the relevant names are given, e.g. 'found on Comino'; 'occurs on Gozo and Comino'; 'found on the island of Malta'.

The scientific name

The scientific name of a species consists of two words: the **generic** name and the **specific** name (see also note on Classification p13), and it is given in each species' entry below the English name.

Since many species can be subdivided into a number of **subspecies**, it is sometimes necessary to distinguish between them. For this purpose a third word is sometimes added to the scientific name. Thus, for example, the scientific name of the Maltese Freshwater Crab is *Potamon fluviatile*. The name of the subspecies which is endemic to Malta is *lanfrancoi*. The full scientific name of this subspecies is therefore *Potamon fluviatile* ssp. *lanfrancoi*, where **ssp.** is an abbreviation of subspecies.

Some species may have different **forms**. These are denoted by the addition of a third word after the word **form**: e.g. Despott's Top-snail is scientifically known as *Trochoidea spratti* form *despotti*.

In the plants section we also come across **varieties**. Again, a third word is added to the scientific name, e.g. *Olea europaea* var. *sylvestris*, i.e. a variety of the European Olive.

Due to ongoing taxonomic research, scientific names are subject to change. This can create some confusion, especially in the botanical field. In the plants section, therefore, not only is the current scientific name given, but also (in brackets) any other name by which the species was formerly known. This is helpful for cross references with other works.

Some species of cnidarians, annelids, insects, crustaceans, arachnids and echinoderms still await correct identification. Such organisms are therefore only given the generic name. For instance, the Common Robber-fly is referred to as *Serdistus* **sp.** (i.e. a species of the genus *Serdistus*).

The system of classification

The classification of plants and animals involves various levels or taxa, such as Class, Order or Family. Some are primary and others secondary. In this book, however, we have simplified the system of classification.

In the Plants section, the plants are placed in four groups: algae, fungi, lichens and vascular plants. In each group (except lichens) one finds Divisions, which are in turn subdivided into Classes, then Families and finally genera and species. In the Vascular Plants (TRACHEOPHYTA), for example, we find the Division PINOPHYTA, which includes the Class PINOPSIDA. This Class contains the Family Pinaceae, which in turn contains the genus *Pinus*. This genus includes the Aleppo Pine, *Pinus halepensis*. Note that Orders have been omitted from the Plants section.

The Animals section comprises seven major groups or Phyla: sponges, cnidarians (hydroids, jellyfish, sea-anemones and corals), annelids, molluscs, arthropods (myriapods, insects, crustaceans and arachnids), echinoderms (starfish, brittle-stars, sea-urchins and sea-cucumbers) and chordates (fish, amphibians, reptiles, birds and mammals). The hierarchy is similar to that of the plants, except for the inclusion of Orders between Classes and Families, while Divisions are replaced by Phyla. The book assigns a chapter for every Phylum, with the exception of Arthropoda and Chordata, whose Classes are dealt with in separate chapters.

The English version

This English edition covers all the species dealt with in the Maltese publication *Flora u Fawna ta' Malta*. The information has in places been updated and several new line drawings have been added. References and bibliography have been revised, and the indices streamlined for easier use.

Acknowledgments

This book would not have come to fruition without the cooperation, first and foremost, of the contributors Alfred E Baldacchino, David Dandria, Edwin Lanfranco, Guido Lanfranco, Sandro Lanfranco, Constantino Mifsud, Patrick J Schembri and Stephen Schembri. The editors thank them for the patience they have shown. The text, choice of species and a hundred and one other things were discussed at length with the authors. It would have been impossible to collate, edit and present the work of these experts in the final form were it not for their goodwill. For any shortcomings which remain, the editors take the blame.

Thanks go also to the two scientific consultants, Edwin Lanfranco and Patrick J Schembri. Their scientific toothcomb was very fine, and useful advice was certainly not lacking. The same can be said for the two other artists Guido Lanfranco and Andrew Micallef. Their work was carried out with great dedication, and their contribution to this book is indispensable.

There were others who generously offered their expertise in specific fields, namely Paul Sammut (Lepidoptera), Paul Gatt (Diptera), John Borg (Chiroptera) and Mark Borg (Lacertidae).

Alex Casha, Edwin Lanfranco, John Borg, Denis Cachia, Richard Cachia Zammit, Michael Darmanin, Raymond Galea, Joseph M Mangion, Alfred E Baldacchino, Oliver Cardona, Charles Coleiro and Stephen Schembri offered their photographs for selection in Part 1 of the book. Alfred Caruana and Pierre Barbara of Ritescan, who prepared the colour separations, were extremely patient. The editors are also grateful to Frank Spiteri, Frans Jones, Joe Galea, and other staff members at the Gutenberg Press.

The editors feel indebted to Dr. Stanley Zammit, Parliamentary Secretary for the Environment, who approved the publication of this edition without hesitation in the same way he had approved the original Maltese publication. His valuable support was never lacking. Similar encouragement came from Louis Vella and John Grech, Director and Head of Administration respectively of the Environment Protection Department. Thanks are also due to Mario Gauci, Antoine Gatt, Neville Ebejer, Mark Sultana, Ian Mifsud and Dennis Falzon for their assistance.

The task of translating the Maltese text into English was entrusted to David Dandria, who did an excellent job. Desirée Falzon helped the editors to proofread the text.

Last but not least, we wish to thank our wives Lucy and Desirée for their tremendous support.

Joe Sultana
Victor Falzon
Editors

August 1996

A note on Classification

In his 18th century works *Species Plantarum* and *Systema Naturae*, the naturalist Carolus Linnaeus classified plants and animals into groups depending on structure, similarity and inter-relationships. He devised for the first time a classification of species which he based on his perception of their evolutionary links. Modern classification of plants and animals is still broadly based on Linnaeus' system.

The system of nomenclature devised by Linnaeus is binomial, each species being denoted by a 'surname' and a 'name', e.g. *Mustela nivalis* (Weasel), *Pancratium maritimum* (Sea Daffodil) etc. The first word is the **genus** (or generic name) and the second is the **species** (or specific name).

The species is the fundamental unit of classification. When organisms belong to the same species, this implies that they are biologically very similar, so much so that they can interbreed and produce fertile offspring. For example, all Maltese lizards, in spite of variation in size and coloration in the different islands, can interbreed and produce fertile progeny, because they all belong to a single species: *Podarcis filfolensis*.

Organisms of different species cannot interbreed to have fertile offspring. However, different species with strong similarities are placed in the same genus, with the same 'surname'. Thus, Spectacled Warbler *Sylvia conspicillata*, Sardinian Warbler *Sylvia melanocephala* and Subalpine Warbler *Sylvia cantillans* are all three placed in the genus *Sylvia* due to the clear biological similarities between them.

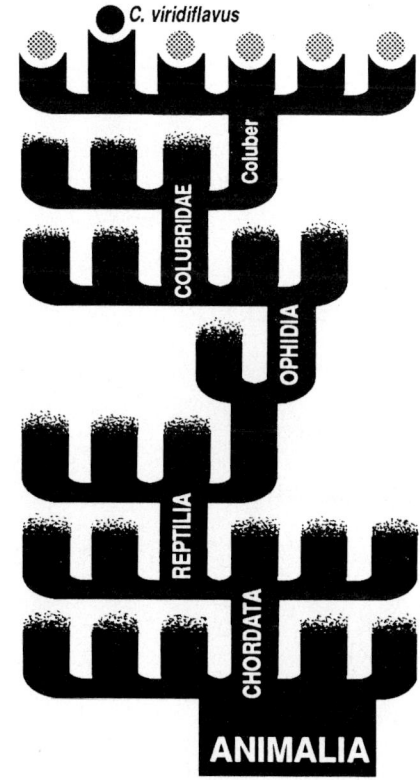

C. viridiflavus

Related genera are grouped together in **Families**. Thus asphodel, tulip, squill and garlic, all plants of different genera, are placed in the same Family (Liliaceae).

This formula is repeated as one ascends the hierarchy of classification. Families are grouped into **Orders**, Orders into **Classes**, Classes into **Phyla** (or **Divisions** in the case of plants) and Phyla into **Kingdoms**.

Thus the Western Whip Snake is *Coluber viridiflavus*. The genus *Coluber* belongs to the Family Colubridae, one of several snake Families in the Order Ophidia. The Ophidia form part of the Class REPTILIA, which is one of the Classes in the Phylum CHORDATA. The Phylum CHORDATA is itself one of a number of Phyla which together form the Kingdom ANIMALIA.

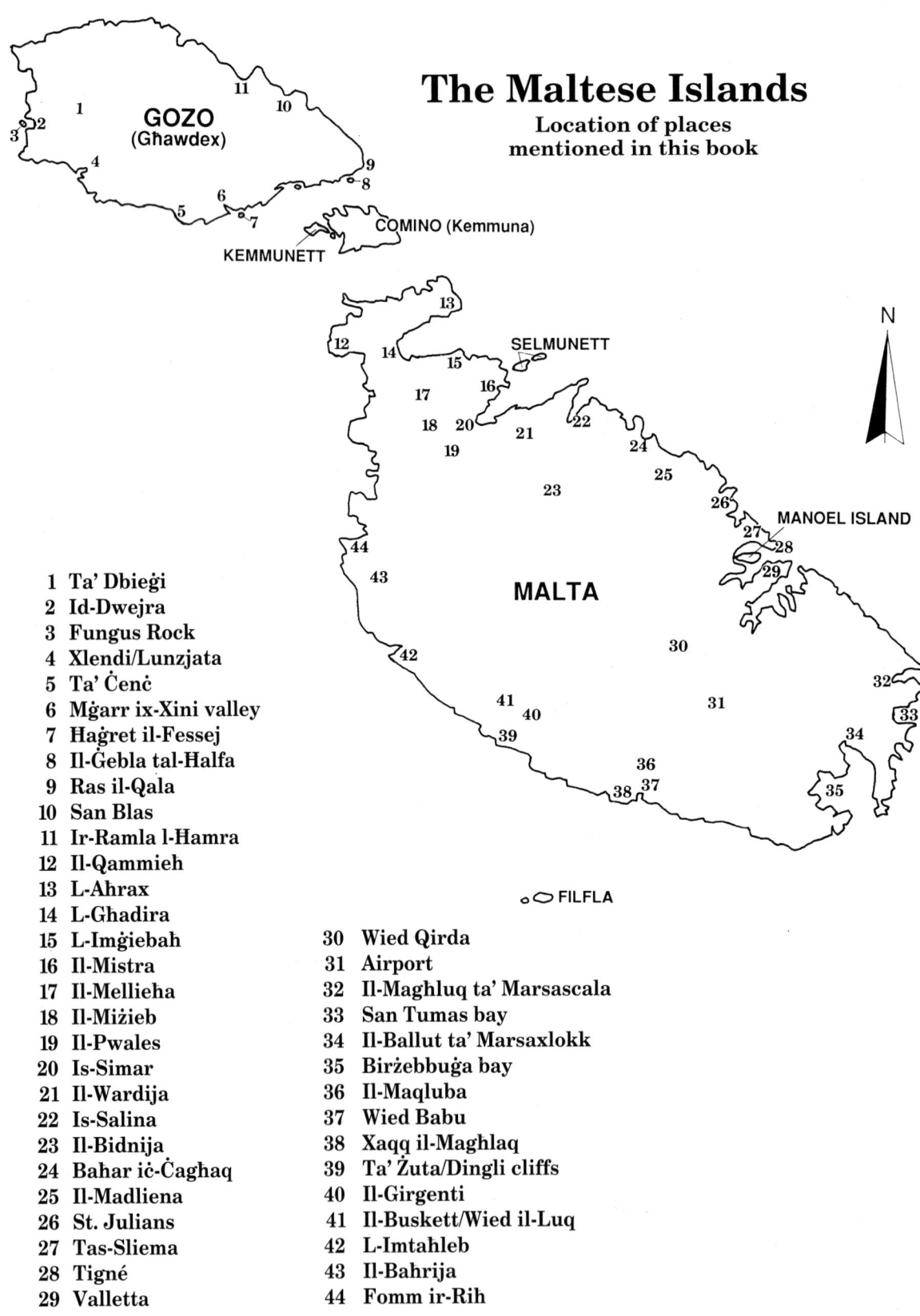

The Maltese Islands

Location of places
mentioned in this book

1 Ta' Dbieġi
2 Id-Dwejra
3 Fungus Rock
4 Xlendi/Lunzjata
5 Ta' Ċenċ
6 Mġarr ix-Xini valley
7 Ħaġret il-Fessej
8 Il-Ġebla tal-Ħalfa
9 Ras il-Qala
10 San Blas
11 Ir-Ramla l-Ħamra
12 Il-Qammieh
13 L-Aħrax
14 L-Għadira
15 L-Imġiebah
16 Il-Mistra
17 Il-Mellieħa
18 Il-Miżieb
19 Il-Pwales
20 Is-Simar
21 Il-Wardija
22 Is-Salina
23 Il-Bidnija
24 Baħar iċ-Ċagħaq
25 Il-Madliena
26 St. Julians
27 Tas-Sliema
28 Tigné
29 Valletta

30 Wied Qirda
31 Airport
32 Il-Magħluq ta' Marsascala
33 San Tumas bay
34 Il-Ballut ta' Marsaxlokk
35 Birżebbuġa bay
36 Il-Maqluba
37 Wied Babu
38 Xaqq il-Magħlaq
39 Ta' Żuta/Dingli cliffs
40 Il-Girgenti
41 Il-Buskett/Wied il-Luq
42 L-Imtaħleb
43 Il-Baħrija
44 Fomm ir-Riħ

The Islands
The Islands
The Islands
The Islands
The Islands

PART 1

The Islands

The
The I
The Is
The Isl
The Isl

Size and position

The Maltese Islands are a group of small, low-lying islands situated almost at the centre of the Mediterranean Sea (35°48'28" to 36°0'0"N; 14°11'04" to 14°34'37"E). They are about 96km south of Sicily and 290km north of the Libyan coast. The sea between Malta and Sicily (the Sicilian Channel) is generally less than 90m in depth, although the maximum depth reaches nearly 200m. The Malta Channel, between Malta and North Africa, is deeper and at some points reaches depths in excess of 1000m.

The Maltese archipelago consists of three inhabited islands, namely Malta, Gozo and Comino, and a number of uninhabited islets: Kemmunett, Filfla, Selmunett (St.Paul's Islands) and Fungus Rock, together with some large rocks, among them Il-Ġebla tal-Ħalfa and Ħaġret il-Fessej. The surface areas are: Malta - 245.7km²; Gozo - 67.1km²; Comino - 2.8km²; Selmunett - 10.1ha; Filfla - 2ha; Fungus Rock - 0.7ha.

Geology

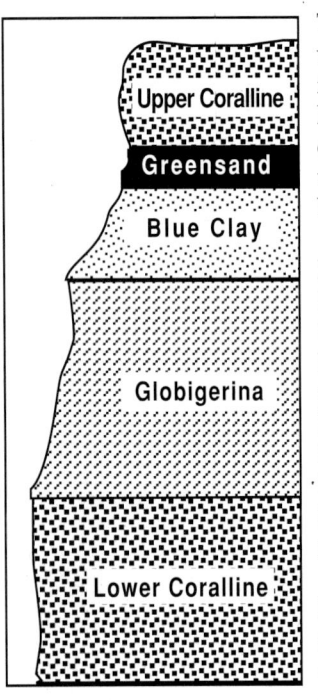

The islands are composed of sedimentary rocks, mostly limestones, which were laid down in the sea during the Oligo-Miocene period. This accounts for the presence of large numbers of marine plant and animal fossils in Maltese rocks. These are the remains of organisms such as algae, molluscs, echinoderms, crustaceans and fish which were preserved in bottom sediments which later became rock. The five principal types of rock exposed are listed below in order of decreasing age:

Lower Coralline Limestone - found exposed in strata up to 140m thick. Formed between 25 and 30 million years ago.
Globigerina Limestone - found exposed in strata of thicknesses ranging between 23 and 207m. It is subdivided into three layers by two intervening pebble layers.
Blue Clay - exposed in layers of varying thickness up to 65m.
Greensand - the thinnest stratum, with exposed thickness up to 12m.
Upper Coralline Limestone - exposed in strata up to 162m thick. This is a complex of calcareous rocks that were laid down not long before the land rose out of the sea about 10 million years ago.

In some localities Quaternary deposits of the Pleistocene Epoch (1.9-0.01 million years ago) are to be found, especially in valleys, on the coast and in caves and fissures. These were formed on land or in fresh water after Malta emerged completely from beneath the sea.

The five main rock strata

Woodland
Il-Buskett
(photograph: Alex Casha)

Maquis
Girgenti
(photograph: Edwin Lanfranco)

Garigue
Comino
(photograph: Joseph M Mangion)

Rocky Steppe
Wardija
(photograph: Edwin Lanfranco)

Clay Slope and Steppe
Qammieh
(photograph: Alex Casha)

Cliff and Boulder Shore
Comino
(photograph: Alex Casha)

Rainwater Rock Pool
Ta' Ċenċ
(photograph: Victor Falzon)

Watercourse
Wied il-Luq
(photograph: John Borg)

Saline Marsh
Ghadira
(photograph: Denis Cachia)

Sand Dune
Ramla l-Hamra
(photograph: Richard Cachia Zammit)

Rocky Shore
Qammieh
(photograph: Raymond Galea)

Seagrass Meadow
L-Ahrax (offshore)
(photograph: Michael Darmanin)

The soil

The material making up the soil is very similar to that forming the rocks. The different soil types present are derived from Coralline Limestone, Blue Clay, Globigerina Limestone and the Quaternary deposits.

Three main soil types are encountered in Malta: Terra soils, Xerorendzina soils and Carbonate Raw soils. Although these can still be found in the areas where they were originally formed from the underlying rocks, extensive movement of soil by humans took place over the years, so that it is now possible to find a mixture of all soil types in the same locality.

Terra Soils are the oldest and were formed during the Pleistocene. They are found mainly on Coralline Limestone, both Lower and Upper. In the natural state, therefore, Terra soils are found mainly in the northern and south-eastern parts of the island of Malta, in the coastal areas of Gozo and on Comino. Xerorendzinas and Carbonate Raw Soils are derived mainly from Globigerina Limestone and Blue Clay. The former are found principally in the central parts of Malta, particularly in the valleys, and were produced mainly from Globigerina Limestone. Carbonate Raw Soils, which are whitish owing to their high calcium carbonate content, were formed mainly from Blue Clay.

Geomorphology

Rain, wind, storms, wave action and ceaseless temperature fluctuations, together with geotectonic movements, have played a great part over the years in the formation of the Maltese Islands as we now know them. Erosion of the different types of rock led to the creation of a characteristic topography.

The Lower Coralline Limestone forms natural bastions of rock in the southern and western parts of the islands. Inland, this type of rock forms flat surfaces riddled with depressions, ridges, holes, crevices and ledges. These were formed when groundwater, slightly acidic because of its carbon dioxide content, dissolved the calcium carbonate. The same thing happened in the case of the Upper Coralline Limestone. Globigerina Limestone, where exposed, gives rise to a different type of landscape with plains of generally smooth rock, while the Blue Clay forms slopes covering the underlying rocks. Greensand is not a very robust rock, and is usually found on clay which easily subsides. Thus much of the Greensand crumbles and rolls downwards, usually with a simultaneous collapse of the Upper Coralline Limestone. This process leads to the formation of screes, with broken rocks and boulders under cliff faces, especially evident on the Gozitan hillsides.

The islands have an inclination from the southwest, where the highest points are found, towards the northeast, where the land slopes gently into the sea. The islands lack mountains, the highest point being Ta' Żuta, near Dingli Cliffs, which is 253m above sea level. The highest point in Gozo - Ta' Dbieġi - has an altitude of 191m. Lakes and rivers are lacking, with only a few freshwater springs to be found.

Geotectonic movements, which started to occur millions of years ago, played an important part in moulding the islands. Large tracts of land were raised, while others subsided, so that faults were created throughout the islands. A major fault is Xaqq il-Maghlaq, which traverses the islands from the northwest to the southeast coasts. Another major fault lies between Madliena and Fomm ir-Rih, while in Gozo the principal fault crosses from Ras il-Qala to Mġarr ix-Xini. Between the two latter faults, several minor faults are to be found running parallel to the major ones. Land subsidence led to the formation of hills and valleys such as the ridges at Wardija, Miżieb, Mellieha and L-Ahrax, and the valleys of Pwales, Mistra and Ghadira in between.

The topography of Gozo is more complex, and is marked by a number of hilly plateaux formed from Upper Coralline Limestone, between which are plains where erosion has exposed the Globigerina Limestone. The hillsides are covered with clay slopes, while the plains slope away into valleys.

The climate

The Maltese climate is typically Mediterranean with mild, wet winters and hot, dry summers. Annual rainfall is very variable, the average for the last 40 years being 53cm. The wet season lasts from October to March, with about 85% of the rain falling in this period. The period from April to September constitutes the dry season.

Temperatures are moderate, the average being 18.6°C, with the monthly average ranging from 12.3° to 26.3°C. Relative humidity is high throughout the year, generally between 65-80%. Malta is renowned for its sunshine, and days in which the sun does not appear are few and far between. The mean daily hours of sunshine is 8.5. Windy conditions are the norm, with only about 8% windless days in the year. The prevailing wind is the *mistral* or northwesterly, which blows on 18% of windy days. Other wind directions are more or less equally represented.

Water resources

Natural water resources are totally dependent on rainwater which percolates through the rock and forms underground reservoirs (aquifers). From here it seeps through cracks and fissures, or else is pumped up by man. It is believed that between 16% and 25% of the annual rainfall finds its way into the rocks to form these natural subterranean water reserves. The major water source is found in the Globigerina and Coralline Limestone layers at sea level. Fresh water percolates through the rock and, being lighter, floats on the salty water which infiltrates from the sea.

Other water reserves are found on clay strata which trap the water percolating through the rocks above. Where the Coralline and Clay layers are exposed together at the surface, water from these reserves seeps out of the aquifer and flows downhill, forming streamlets which meander through the valley watercourses. In the past, many of these springs flowed all the year round, although their output was reduced considerably during the summer months. Nowadays many of them have dried up completely because of over-pumping of water from underground sources or diversion for other uses, mainly irrigation.

During the last fifty years, many valleys have been dammed for the catchment and storage of rainwater for irrigation. More recently, many farmers have excavated large reservoirs over clay strata in order to store rainwater to be used for irrigation during the dry period.

Flora and fauna

Many people are under the impression that Malta is poor in biodiversity. However, when one considers the small size of the islands, together with the limited range of habitats, and the pressure on the natural environment from a relatively large human population, the country is in fact very rich in flora and fauna. It is enough to say that over 4500 species of plants and animals have so far been recorded, not taking marine organisms into account. About 85 of these species are endemic.

Ecosystems

Organisms, together with the environment they inhabit, constitute an ecosystem. Malta has a number of major ecosystems which are widespread, such as garigue, as well as minor ecosystems which are rare, like sand dunes and freshwater pools. Ecosystems can be classified according to their vegetation.

Malta's vegetation, the nature of which is determined principally by the climate, the soil and the degree of disturbance, is typical of low-lying areas of the Mediterranean. The mild temperatures are not detrimental to the flora, but the lack of water has a marked negative impact. The plants growing in Malta are therefore adapted to endure a long dry season.

The most typical vegetation of the Mediterranean is dominated by hard-leaved evergreen trees and shrubs. **Woodland**, with trees such as Evergreen Oak and Aleppo Pine, is the climax of the vegetation series. In Malta this habitat was virtually exterminated following the arrival of humans on the islands. Only some remnants are still to be found in a few areas with small copses of Evergreen Oak. Some of these trees, still existing at Wardija, are possibly between 500 and 900 years old.

Buskett, the major part of which was planted by man, has now acquired the character of a semi-natural woodland, where the trees regenerate naturally. The dominant trees here are Aleppo Pine, together with Evergreen Oak, Olive and Carob. The smaller trees and shrubs include Lentisk, Mediterranean Buckthorn and Hawthorn, as well as a large number of other species. This is the only locality in Malta which represents a mature woodland ecosystem.

Another ecosystem is the **maquis**, characterised by small trees and large shrubs such as Carob, Olive, Lentisk and Bay Laurel, together with climbers which include Ivy, Smilax, Spiny Asparagus and Wild Madder, and large herbaceous species like Bear's Breeches and Lords-and-Ladies. Maquis is typically found on the sides and bottoms of the deeper valleys (*widien*), and at the base of cliff formations.

The **garigue** is an ecosystem which develops on large expanses of limestone bearing numerous depressions and fissures. Here one finds dense, low-growing shrubs, often aromatic, such as Mediterranean Thyme,

Mediterranean Heath, Germander, White Hedge Nettle and Maltese Spurge. Several types of garigue exist, each characterised by different dominant plant species.

The widespread **steppe** is characterised by herbaceous plants, especially grasses (Poaceae), umbellifers (Apiaceae), legumes (Fabaceae) and tuberous or bulbous species like Squill and Asphodel. The steppe is derived from maquis and garigue which have been degraded through various causes, including fire and grazing. Other types of steppe are encountered, including some natural ones formed through climatic factors. These include the **rocky steppe** (a sort of shrubless garigue) and the **clay slope steppe**.

The **cliffs**, found mainly along the southern and western shores, harbour many species of flora and fauna. The plants growing here include various interesting species, among them some endemic forms (occurring in the Maltese Islands and nowhere else in the world). Two of these are the Maltese Rock-centaury and the Maltese Cliff-orache, both belonging to monospecific genera.

In several coastal localities, one finds a number of shallow areas which fill up with water during the winter. Admixture with the salt found in the mud renders the water brackish, leading to the formation of **saline marshlands**. Evaporation during the dry season increases the salinity further and even causes them to dry up completely. In spite of the harshness of such conditions, certain species of plants and animals are restricted to these saline marshes. A short distance inland from the few sandy beaches, the last remaining **sand dune** systems struggle to survive against human interference. These too harbour specialised plants and animals.

Freshwater habitats are also scarce in Malta, especially during the summer months. In winter, water collects in small **rock pools**, and freshwater species live here, albeit for a limited time. A few **freshwater pools** and **springs** are also found in certain valleys, and these are enriched by a number of species, considered rare owing to the scarcity of these habitats.

In spite of the calcareous nature of Malta's rocks, deep **caves** are not frequent. The few examples are home to some specialised organisms. The most well-known are bats, but there are other cave-dwelling species, especially invertebrates. Some are endemic and of great scientific interest.

One must also mention ecosystems which are found on **disturbed ground**. When one considers the high human population density, as well as the extensive land use, one can easily understand why these are widespread. Abandoned fields and countryside road verges fall into this category.

The effects of man

Humans first settled permanently on Malta in Neolithic times, around 7000 years ago. From that day to the present, the face of Malta has seen great changes. The early inhabitants started cutting down trees for firewood and to clear the land for agriculture. They introduced sheep and goats, whose grazing prevented regeneration of the trees. This ceaseless activity eventually led to the destruction of Malta's indigenous woodlands except for a few scattered relics. However, the effects of human activity on the land were never as devastating as in the last fifty years.

The human population of Malta presently stands at 382,506 (1212/km^2). One must also consider the ever-increasing number of tourists, which now exceed one million each year. Progress has meant a significant increase in the effects of human activity. Up to 1985, built-up land accounted for 16% of Malta's area and for 10.1% of that of Gozo. It is estimated that now (1996) some 20% of the surface area of the islands is built up. Much agricultural land, which in 1957 represented 56% of the total land area, was sacrificed to development, and now stands at 34% (1991 figures - Agriculture Dept).

Housing development and road building entail the quarrying of Coralline and Globigerina Limestones. Some of the spent quarries were reclaimed, but many others were abandoned in a derelict state. Meanwhile new quarries were opened, some located in areas of natural importance, such as valleys and close to cliffs. Development also led to an increase in the dumping of waste and rubble in various parts of the countryside.

The terraced slopes of valleys and hillsides, where fodder crops were previously grown, now lie abandoned. The characteristic dry-stone walls are gradually collapsing, leading to the loss of whole tracts of soil through rain-induced erosion. The increase in built-up areas, together with the large number of new roads have led to increased volumes and rates of flow of flood waters, which carry soil to the sea resulting in less water percolating into the ground.

Over the years, development pressures on the natural environment continued to increase and as a result many areas of ecological significance were lost. Several indigenous species of flora and fauna became extinct, while others are now seriously threatened.

The people have also contributed directly to the destruction of nature. Many seem to be unaware of the damage caused when hundreds of shrubs of Mediterranean Thyme are uprooted to decorate Christmas cribs. The sale of wild flowers, such as French Daffodil, Mediterranean Heath and others, has impoverished the countryside, and has led to the near extinction of certain species such as Pheasant's Eye. Groups of children intent on catching frogs (and tadpoles) and freshwater crabs are oblivious to the damage they cause.

Fires started by vandals destroy whole groves, together with their flora and fauna. Hunting and trapping have devastated Malta's avifauna, killing huge numbers of birds every year, especially during spring and autumn migrations. Harpoon-fishing, the use of gillnets in bays and along the coast, trawling with fine-mesh nets, and the illegal use of explosives in the sea have destroyed an appreciable part of Malta's marine life.

The tracts of garigue have not escaped harm. So-called 'land reclamation', which went on unchecked especially in the north of the island of Malta, ravaged large areas of this ecosystem. Birdtrapping sites are also degrading it. The recently popular pastime of driving offroad vehicles on the garigue and in valleys causes great damage to these habitats and to the plants and animals found there. The use of pesticides and herbicides also pollutes many natural habitats.

One must also mention the harm caused by collectors, who divest the countryside of many specimens of flora and fauna, often belonging to rare species e.g. orchids.

Nature conservation

Maltese culture was never one to afford nature respect and appreciation. In the past there was a predominant lack of knowledge about living organisms and about natural processes. Many animal species, such as reptiles and bats, although in reality beneficial, were looked upon with distaste. Anything not directly profitable was expendable. Trees which do not bear edible fruit were considered worthless. Inedible plants were 'weeds', even if some of them were used for medicinal purposes, often based on superstition. Legends and old wives' tales proliferated. Even to this day, some believe that snakes enter the mouths of infants to steal milk, and that geckos can cause skin diseases. Some say that the Large Carpenter Bee portends misfortune, while the day-flying Hummingbird Hawk Moth is a harbinger of good tidings. Fortunately, education is gradually putting an end to these myths.

The advent of good publications and television programmes on many aspects of natural history has brought about a corresponding increase in the appreciation of nature, especially in the immediate past. This was certainly not the case when the first two voluntary environment groups were founded in 1962. The way ahead for what are today BirdLife Malta and the Society for the Study and Conservation of Nature was strewn with difficulties when they started their campaigns for the conservation of nature. They have played a significant role in fostering the awareness we find today, including that of the authorities.

In recent years, the government has also started giving its contribution towards nature conservation. Apart from educational campaigns in schools, certain initiatives were taken, such as the enactment of legislation, the adherence to international conventions on the conservation of the natural environment, and the setting up of the Environment Protection Department and of the Planning Authority.

In the past, few laws concerned with the protection of nature existed. Some 16th century laws protected game for the rich. A Grandmaster's edict banning the gathering of the Malta Fungus sought to ensure that this then precious plant was reserved for the nobility. The first regulations truly concerned with nature conservation were enacted in 1911. These regarded the protection of certain bird species. Over the years these regulations have often been modified, the latest changes being in 1996.

The first regulations regarding the flora were those of 1932 which protected the Mediterranean Thyme. A 1937 Legal Notice gave protection to ancient trees such as the Evergreen Oaks at Wardija. In 1949, the cutting down of coniferous trees (pines and cypresses) without official permit became illegal. In 1992-93 all reptiles, bats, shrews and marine mammals were placed on the list of protected species, as well as Painted Frog, Vagrant Hedgehog, Weasel and Maltese Freshwater Crab. The same regulations also gave protection to several plants, including Winged Radish, Maltese Rock-centaury, Maltese Everlasting, Gozo Hyoseris, Maltese Toadflax, Maltese Cliff-orache, Sandarac, Malta Fungus and two bryophyte species.

Trade in plants and animals was regulated in 1992, and in the following year the government signed the Berne Convention. Furthermore Filfla, Fungus Rock and Selmunett were declared nature reserves in which all species of terrestrial flora and fauna are protected.

The most far-reaching initiative taken by the authorities in recent years was the adoption of a Structure Plan for the Maltese Islands, with the objective of optimising landuse while respecting the environment. This seeks to regulate development such that it takes place in a sustainable manner, at the same time taking appropriate measures for the protection of the countryside and the conservation of Malta's cultural and natural heritage.

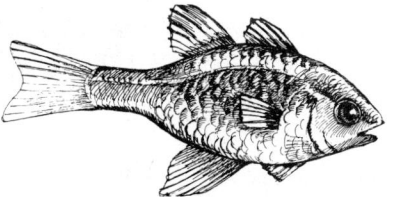

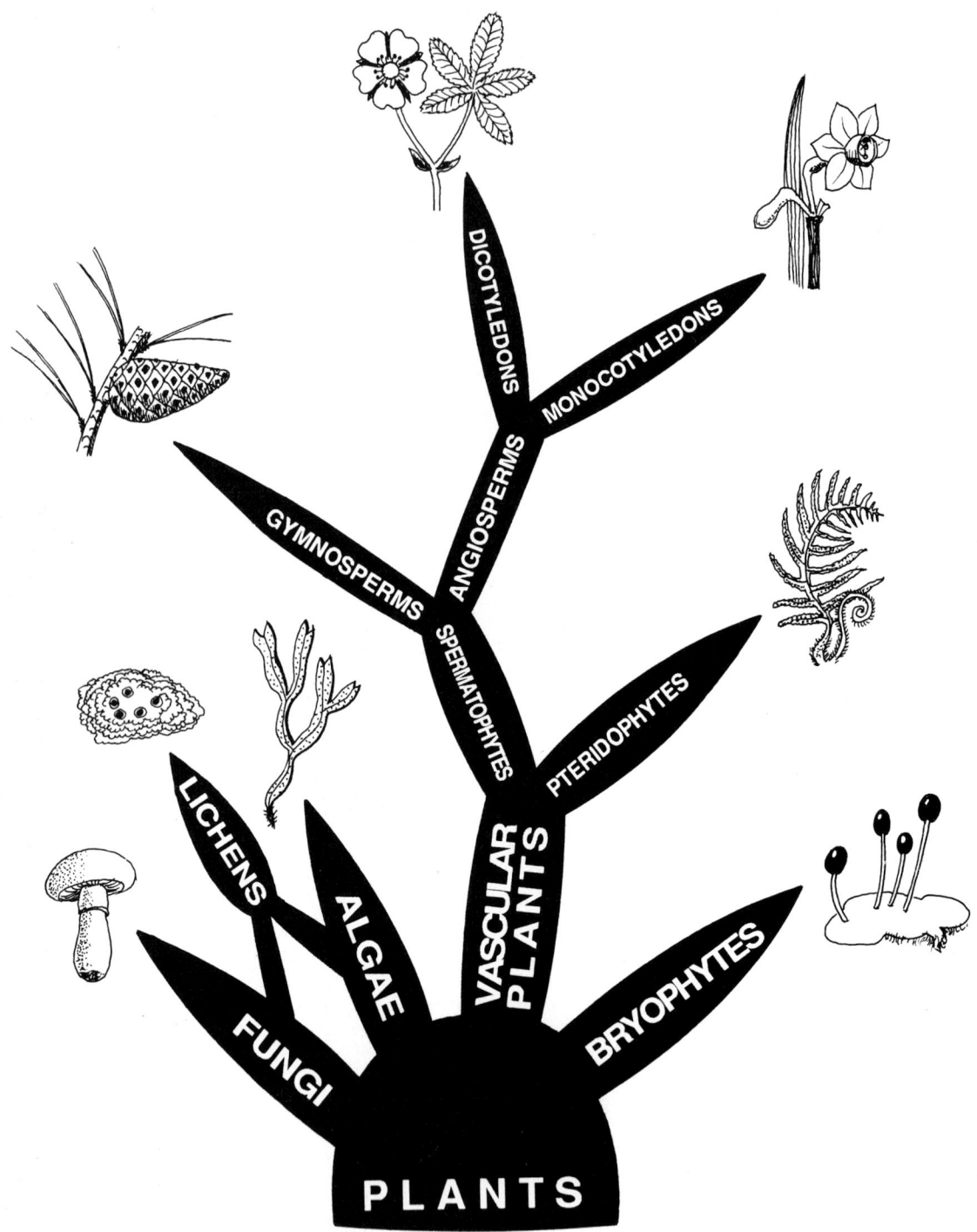

The main Plant subdivisions

Plants
Plants
Plants
Plants
Plants

introduction

Most plants obtain their nutrients by a process known as photosynthesis. They contain **chlorophylls**, green pigments which enable them to utilise light energy to build up the simple organic nutrients they require, using water and carbon dioxide as raw materials. Organisms which do not photosynthesise have to obtain these substances in their organic form in order to live. Plants are therefore essential for the survival of all other organisms. Furthermore, plants release oxygen into the atmosphere during photosynthesis: with the exception of some types of bacteria, oxygen is required by all life forms.

Plants can be divided into algae, fungi, bryophytes and vascular plants. Another group, the lichens, are associations of algae and fungi living in symbiosis.

Algae are normally aquatic plants with a relatively simple anatomy. Fungi are generally terrestrial and are the only plant group which totally lacks chlorophylls. Thus they do not photosynthesise and therefore depend on other organisms for their nutrition.

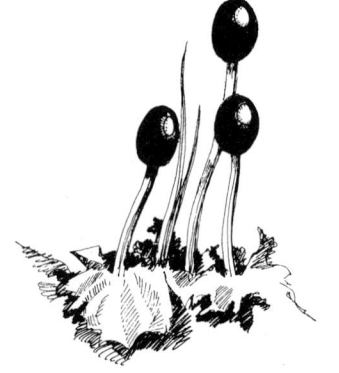

Bryophyte

Bryophytes are small plants which lack vascular tissue and usually grow in a mat-like layer on the ground, soil, rock, or tree trunks. They rarely exceed a height of 1-2cm. Their system of reproduction is more complex than that of the algae, and resembles that of the vascular plants. Over 120 species of bryophytes are known in Malta. The most familiar are the mosses, which form velvety carpets on rocks, walls and roofs. They are not very conspicuous, but when observed with a lens, they reveal a delicate structure of great beauty. Many of them dry up when water is scarce, only to revive after the first rains. Bryophytes are not included in this book.

Vascular plants are generally terrestrial and their reproductive system is quite complex. They have a vascular system consisting of tubular elements through which water and nutrients are transported to various parts of the plant. This is the most familiar group of plants, with a characteristic anatomy consisting of **roots**, **stems** and **leaves**.

Formerly, all plants were classified in a single Kingdom, the Plant Kingdom. In modern systems of classification, however, plants are usually subdivided into the Kingdom PROTOCTISTA (algae, simple fungi and the microscopic protozoa), the Kingdom FUNGI (higher fungi) and the Kingdom PLANTAE (bryophytes and vascular plants).

Plants do not grow individually or haphazardly. Species are adapted to particular habitats with specific environmental factors, with the result that plant communities are formed. These communities together constitute the vegetation of a particular environment.

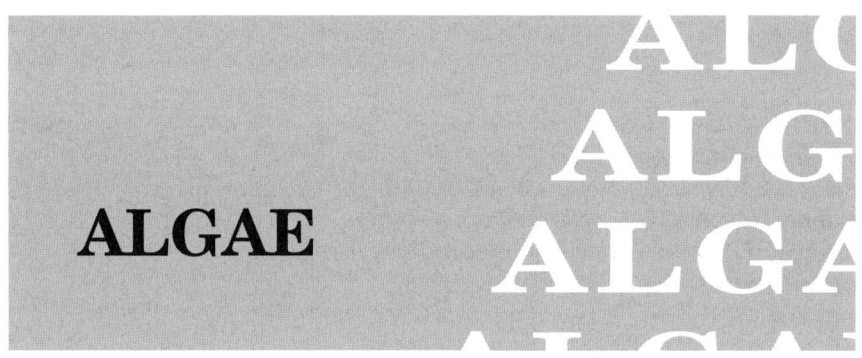

ALGAE

Algae (ALGAE) are generally aquatic plants, common in sea water, fresh water and on damp soil or rock. Many are microscopic. They are split into a number of Divisions. Divisions which include only microscopic forms are not included in this work.

Many species of algae are found in Maltese waters. About 300 of these are not microscopic.

GREEN ALGAE
Division CHLOROPHYTA

Class CHAROPHYCEAE
Family Characeae

Stonewort   **p133**
Chara vulgaris var. *longibracteata*   Kara
Often exceeds 20cm in length. Stems have a number of branches arranged in whorls. Lives in fresh water in valleys and pools. Has an onion-like odour. Very variable. Frequent.

Class ULVOPHYCEAE
Family Ulvaceae

Sea Lettuce   **p133**
Ulva laetevirens (= U. rigida)   Hass il-Bahar
Ranges in size from a few centimetres up to 40cm. Takes the form of a broad, smooth, green translucent sheet. Grows on rocks, pebbles and other seaweeds in shallow water, especially in sheltered, polluted areas. Very common.

Grass-kelp   **p133**
Enteromorpha linza   Enteromorfa
Ranges from a few millimetres up to 15cm. Same habitats as Sea Lettuce. Takes the form of a flattened tube. Very common.
       Several other species of this genus occur, not easily distinguished.

Grass-kelp

Class Bryopsidophyceae
Family Codiaceae

Sponge Seaweed   p133
Codium vermilara   Swaba' tal-Bahar
Length 10-20cm. Diameter 4.5mm. Cylindrical. Dichotomous branches have spongy texture. Grows mainly in sheltered and shady habitats at depths from about 1m. Tolerates polluted waters. Frequent.

Family Udoteaceae

Halimeda   p133
Halimeda tuna   Halimeda
Up to 10cm in length. Calcified. Resembles miniature Prickly Pear. Prefers shaded vertical rock faces in both surface and deep waters, often forming large, dense populations. Common.

Udotea

Udotea   p133
Flabellia petiolata (= Udotea petiolata, U. desfontainei)   Mrewha tal-Bahar
3-10cm. Fan-shaped with dark green fringe. Lives on rocks and other seaweed in shallow to fairly deep water; also in Posidonia meadows. Common.

Family Caulerpaceae

Caulerpa   p133
Caulerpa prolifera   Lsien il-Bahar
Dark green and tongue-shaped. The 'tongues' arise from a much-branched horizontal network of cylindrical branches anchored by root-like structures. Found mostly on muddy bottoms in shallow water. Withstands pollution. Frequent.

Family Dasycladaceae

Mermaid's Cup   p133
Acetabularia acetabulum   Aċetabularja
Takes the form of a slender, whitish stalk. In early summer, tip of stalk gives rise to a saucer-like structure. Grows in shallow water, in sheltered but illuminated situations. Does not resist pollution. Frequent.

Mermaid's Cup

BROWN ALGAE
Division FUCOPHYTA (= PHAEOPHYTA)
Class Fucophyceae (=Phaeophyceae)
Family Scytosiphonaceae

Balloons   **p133**
Colpomenia sinuosa   Bużżieqa tal-Baħar
Diameter 2-10cm. Takes the form of a hollow, irregularly shaped balloon.
Yellowish-brown. Grows on rocky shores in shallow water, especially in
well-illuminated but sheltered situations. Frequent.

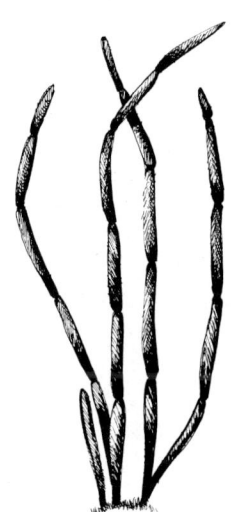

Pinched Seaweed   **p133**
Scytosiphon lomentaria   Alga Maqrusa
10-25cm. Hollow, greenish or yellowish cylinder, pinched at intervals like
a string of sausages. Grows on rocks and pebbles, generally near the surface.
Tolerates pollution. Frequent.

Family Stypocaulaceae

Sea Fern   **p133**
Halopteris scoparia   Felċi tal-Baħar
15-20cm. Dense feather-like branches. Rough in texture, often overgrown
by other species of algae. Dark brown, appearing almost black. Grows in
both shallow and deep waters. Common.

Pinched Seaweed

Family Dictyotaceae

Dictyopteris   **p133**
Dictyopteris membranacea (= *D. polipodioides*)   Ħabaq il-Baħar
Ribbon-like fronds up to 25cm, branching dichotomously, with a structure
resembling a midrib. Yellowish or sometimes darker brown. Grows in clear
seas, especially on steeply sloping rocky bottoms, in depths ranging from
the surface to over 50m. Prefers shady situations. Very common.

Peacock's Tail   **p133**
Padina pavonica   Denb il-Pagun
Whitish, fan-like sheets up to 10cm wide. Grows on sunny, rocky bottoms
or on other seaweeds near the surface. Very common.

Family Sargassaceae

Common Sargasso-weed   **p133**
Sargassum vulgare   Sargassu Komuni
Grows up to 1m in length. Long fronds with short lateral leaf-like branches
and small air-filled bladders at their axils. Grows in sheltered seas from the
surface down to moderate depths. Tolerates some pollution. On the increase.
Common.
> The **Narrow-leaved Sargasso-weed** *S. acinarium* (Sargassu tal-Fond) is
> found at greater depths, with longer, more slender 'leaves'.

Rainbow Bladder-weed   p133
Cystoseira stricta (= C. amentacea)   Ċistosejra Kaħla
20-30cm. Robust . Brown and blue-green iridescent, especially towards tips
of fronds, which bear needle-like branchlets. Lives at the surface on rocky
shores exposed to strong wave action. Does not tolerate pollution. Common.

Flat Bladder-weed   p133
Cystoseira compressa (= C.fimbriata, C.abrotanifolia)   Ċistosejra tal-Frieghi Ċatti
20-60cm. Robust. Brown, sometimes yellowish. Basal branches flat and
smooth. Young plants have rosette-like habit, mature alga has longer,
cylindrical fronds. Grows on rocks near the surface, usually in sheltered
spots. This is the species of *Cystoseira* which best withstands pollution.
Common.

> There are several Mediterranean species of *Cystoseira*; about 10 of them are
> known from the seas around Malta.

RED ALGAE
Division RHODOPHYTA

Class FLORIDEOPHYCEAE
Family Gelidiaceae

Pterocladia   p133
Pterocladia capillacea   Pterokladja
Grows to 14cm with many deep red, flattened fronds. Grows below the
surface, often on wave-swept shores. Withstands pollution. Common.

Family Corallinaceae
> Hard, calcified seaweeds. Some of them, such as Coral Weed and Jania, are
> segmented and flexible, but most are solid, seemingly forming part of the
> rock.

Coral Weed

Coral Weed   p133
Corallina elongata (= C. mediterranea)   Korallina
2-6cm. Hard, segmented fronds. Pink. Grows on rocks at the surface in large
populations. Resists rough seas and moderate pollution. Dried weed
formerly used medicinally, with other red algae, for the treatment of
intestinal worms. Very common.

Jania   p133
Jania rubens   Janja
Like Coral Weed, but paler with thinner, dichotomously branched fronds.
Grows mainly on other algae, often covering them. Very common.

Lithophyllum   p133
Lithophyllum lichenoides   Litofillum
Coral-like, with numerous hard, flattened fronds. Purple with white edges.
Grows at the surface on rocky shores subject to strong wave-action. Exposed
at low water. Populations form rim-like rocky outgrowths. Rare.

Many species, which resemble Lithophyllum in having a stony appearance, are often found coating rocks on the shore, especially in clear, unpolluted waters.

Family Rhodomelaceae

Laurencia   p133
Laurencia papillosa   Lawrenzja
Up to 7cm. Rigid and bears numerous hard bladder-like structures. Olive-green or yellowish, but tip often bleached white when exposed to the air for some time. Grows on rocks at the surface where it is often exposed for long periods. Very common.

Vidalia   p133
Vidalia volubilis (= Osmundaria volubilis)   Vidalja
Up to about 10cm. Like a spirally-coiled, somewhat rigid, ribbon. Dark brownish-red. Grows at depths greater than about 15m. Often cast ashore by rough seas. Common.

Vidalia

FUNGI

Fungi are plants which lack chlorophyll and therefore do not photosynthesise. They feed either by decomposing organic matter, such as the remains or waste products of other organisms, or by attaching themselves to another living plant or animal and absorbing from it the required nutrients. The former are known as decomposers and the latter are parasites. Fungi can be subdivided into two groups: the Lower Fungi and the Higher Fungi. The Lower Fungi are generally minute or microscopic, and many of them live in an aquatic medium (not covered in this book). The Higher Fungi are advanced and almost all are terrestrial. Some of them, known as mushrooms or toadstools, have rather large, fleshy fruiting bodies.

The reproductive system of the Higher Fungi is quite complex. The fungus usually consists of a number of threads or **hyphae** which penetrate the source of food. This mass of hyphae is referred to as the **mycelium**. The **fruiting body**, which is generally rather fleshy, developes from the mycelium and contains a large number of reproductive organs (**sporangia**) in which the **spores** are produced.

Over 400 species of non-microscopic fungi are found in Malta.

ASCOMYCETES
Division ASCOMYCOTA
A large and varied group of generally small moulds, including the yeasts. A few have sizeable fruiting bodies.

Class PYRENOMYCETES
Family Xylariaceae

Cramp Balls   p135
Daldinia concentrica   Ballun tas-Siġar
Resembles a black ball about 5cm in diameter. Lives on branches of dead trees. Rare.

Class DISCOMYCETES
Family Pezizaceae

Early Cup Fungus   p135
Peziza vesiculosa   Skutella ta' l-Art
Irregularly cup-shaped. Lives on dung and other organic matter. Occasionally puffs out a cloud of spores. Frequent.

Early Cup Fungus

Family Morchellaceae

Morel   p135
Morchella sp.   Morkella
One of the few Ascomycetes with a hollow cap and stipe. Cap resembles a sponge. Occurs mainly in gardens. Rare.

BASIDIOMYCETES
Division BASIDIOMYCOTA
A large assemblage of fungi which includes most mushrooms and toadstools. Some of them are small and parasitic on plants, and a few cause damage to agricultural crops. Others have large fruiting bodies. These are usually umbrella-shaped, but some of them can have a bizarre shape. The mycelium of many mushrooms is intimately associated with the roots of trees. They help the trees to acquire nutrients from the soil, while they themselves obtain sustenance from the trees.

Class APHYLLOPHOROMYCETES
Family Hymenochaetaceae

Bracket Fungus   p135
Phellinus rimosus   Lixka
Up to 25cm. Lacks stalk. Reddish-brown with cork-like texture. Resembles a shelf, growing on the trunk of living trees. Scarce.

Class HYMENOMYCETES
Family Boletaceae

Pine Boletus   p135
Suillus collinitus (= Boletus collinitus)   Faqqiegħ taż-Żnuber
Cap diameter about 15cm, brown and sticky . Yellow underneath. Always associated with pine trees. Frequent.

Red-cracked Boletus   p135
Xerocomus chrysenteron (= Boletus chrysenteron)   Faqqiegħ tal-Ballut
Cap diameter about 10cm, with a velvety skin which cracks to reveal pinkish flesh beneath. Grows in association with Evergreen Oak. Rare.

Family Paxillaceae

Scallop Fungus   p135
Paxillus panuoides   Arzella ta' l-Art
Stalk lacking. Cap attached on one side to stumps of dead trees, logs or on sawdust. Scarce.

Family Agaricaceae

Field Mushroom   p135
Agaricus campestris (= Psalliota campestris)   Faqqiegħ Komuni
Cap diameter about 10cm, whitish. Gills pinkish, later turning black. Spore mass dark brown, almost black. Stalk with collar-like annulus. Common.

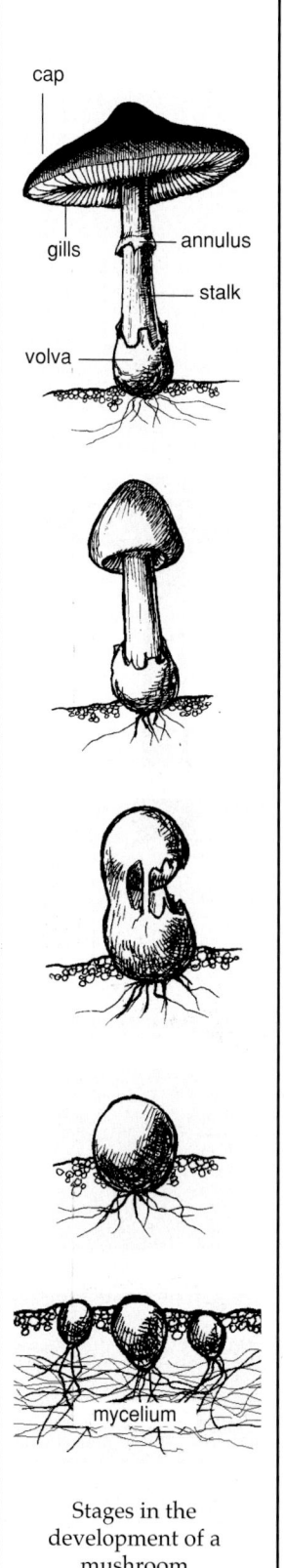

Stages in the development of a mushroom

This genus includes several species which are difficult to distinguish. The **Cultivated Mushroom**, which is commercially available, is *A. bisporus. A. xanthodermus* is very similar, but flesh turns yellow when mushroom is broken. This latter species is slightly poisonous.

Family Pluteaceae

Rose-gilled Grisette   p135
Volvariella speciosa   Faqqiegħ tal-Ġonna
Cap diameter 6-15cm. Whitish or sometimes brownish, especially in the var. *gloiocephala*. Gills white, turning pink. Spore mass brown. Stalk smooth and white with a volva at the base. Frequent in fields and gardens.

Family Amanitaceae

Edible Amanita   p135
Amanita ovoidea   Amanita Tajba
Like Rose-gilled Grissette, but with a larger volva and also has an annulus. Gills and spore mass white. Grows in sheltered localities under trees. Edible, but some varieties are very poisonous. Rare.
   Another species of the same genus is the **Southern Destroying Angel** *A.verna* (Amanita Velenuża), which is very poisonous.

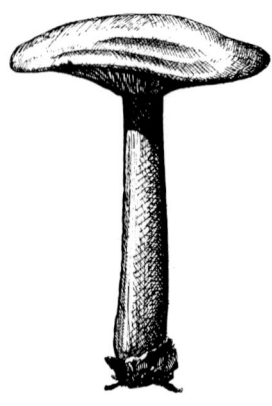
Wood Blewits

Wood Blewits   p135
Lepista nuda (= *Rhodopaxillus nudus, Tricholoma nudum*)   Faqqiegħ Vjola
Cap diameter 6-12cm, cap and gills violet. Spore mass pale pink. Grows under trees. Scarce.

Family Tricholomataceae

Pied Mushroom   p135
Melanoleuca vulgaris (= *M. melanoleuca*)   Faqqiegħ Iswed u Abjad
Cap diameter 4-8cm, blackish above with pure white gills. Spore mass is white. Grows under trees. Scarce.

Pine Clitocybe   p135
Clitocybe pityophila   Faqqiegħ Abjad
Cap diameter 4-10cm.White or cream. Very variable in size and form. Gills envelop upper part of stalk. Often produces basal offshoots. Generally found under pine trees. Poisonous. Scarce.

Family Pleurotaceae

Oyster Mushroom   p135
Pleurotus eryngii var. *ferulae*   Faqqiegħ tal-Ferla
Cap diameter often exceeds 15cm. Stalk relatively short, laterally placed. Only grows in association with the roots of Giant Fennel. Edible, formerly collected for sale. Scarce.

Family Strophariaceae

Stropharia   p135
Stropharia coronilla   Strofarja
Cap yellowish above with deep violet gills. Stalk white with dark annulus. Grows among grass in steppes, garigue and other open habitats. Scarce.

Family Coprinaceae

Shaggy Ink-cap   p135
Coprinus comatus   Faqqiegħ tal-Linka
Tall, with whitish cap on a slender stalk. Cap dissolves at rim as it matures, blackening and dissolving into an inky liquid until it finally disappears. One of the few mushrooms seen in spring, usually among grass in valleys and borders of fields. Scarce.

Family Russulaceae

Blood Milk-cap   p135
Lactarius sanguifluus   Faqqiegħ tad-Demm
Cap diameter 7-10cm. Pinkish, funnel-shaped cap. When broken, a dark, blood-red liquid exudes. Grows in garigue with *Cistus*. Rare.

Pretty Russula   p135
Russula lepida   Faqqiegħ Ahmar
Cap reddish above, with white gills and pale pink stalk. Grows in garigue with *Cistus*. Rare.

Class GASTEROMYCETES
Family Phallaceae

Stinkhorn   p135
Phallus impudicus (= Ithyphallus impudicus)   Fahxija
Cap thimble-shaped. Initially covered with olive-green, gelatinous spore mass, which emits a foul odour. This attracts flies, which assist in spore dispersal. Found in fields and gardens. Rare.

Family Clathraceae

Colus   p135
Colus hirudinosus   Faqqiegħ tal-Gaġġa
Up to 7cm. One of the few fungi found in garigue. Spore dispersal by flies. Scarce.

Family Sclerodermataceae

Earthball   p135
Scleroderma verrucosum   Ballun ta' l-Art
Diameter about 6cm. Ball-shaped. Eventually splits at the top to release spores. Grows under trees. Scarce.

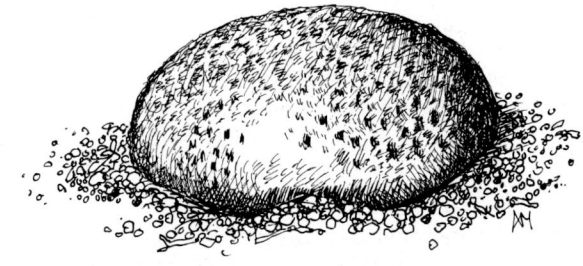

Earthball

LICHENS

Lichens (LICHENES) are plants in which an alga is symbiotically associated with a fungus. The fungus obtains the nutrients it requires from the alga, which produces them by photosynthesis. The association enables the alga to live in places which would otherwise be inhospitable.

The most familiar lichens look like coloured stains on rocks, rooftops or tree-trunks. The most conspicuous are orange, white, grey or black. Lichens are very slow-growing, and many can live for hundreds of years. They are sensitive to air pollution, especially sulphur dioxide.

About 200 species are found in Malta.

Family Teloschistaceae

Wall Xanthoria   p135
Xanthoria parietina   Ksantorja
Flattened, the edge easily peeled off. Bright orange, sometimes greenish. Grows on rocks or tree-trunks. Common.
> Other orange lichens occur, especially on rooftops and rocks. They are very flat and difficult to peel off. They belong to the genus *Caloplaca*.

Family Usneaceae

Ramalina   p135
Ramalina durieui   Ramalina
Looks like tattered, greyish-green leaf. Grows only on the branches of trees, especially at Buskett and Girgenti. Scarce.

Family Cladoniaceae

Karst Cladonia   p135
Cladonia convoluta   Kladonja tax-Xaghri
Resembles tattered leaf, green above and white below. Grows in pockets of soil in rocky steppe and garigue. Common.

Ramalina

VASCULAR PLANTS

Vascular plants (TRACHEOPHYTA) are the largest and the best known plant group. They have evolved a system of tubes which are used for the transport of water and nutrients resulting from the photosynthetic process. Anatomically, vascular plants are made up of **roots, stems** and **leaves**.

The most primitive of vascular plants do not produce true seeds. These are known as **pteridophytes**. They reproduce by means of **spores** which are formed on more or less specialised leaves. Few species are found in Malta. These include ferns, horsetails and clubmosses.

All other vascular plants, known as **spermatophytes**, produce seeds. The seed itself is a complex structure consisting of an embryo surrounded by a food reserve and one or more protective coats. The spermatophytes comprise the **gymnosperms**, which do not produce true flowers and generally bear their spores or seeds in structures known as **cones**; and the **angiosperms** which produce true **flowers**.

In the gymnosperms, male cones produce the **pollen** which are specialised spores, while the seeds develop in the female cones following fertilisation of the ovules. The gymnosperms include the conifers, trees which generally bear hard needle-like leaves. Two indigenous species are found in Malta, although a number of other species are cultivated.

The angiosperms bear true flowers. Externally, flowers generally have **sepals** and **petals**. Internal to these are the **stamens**, which bear the male **sporangia** in the **anthers**. The centrally placed **ovary** contains the **ovules**, which become the **seeds** following fertilisation. The ovary, with the seeds inside, becomes a **fruit**.

Flowering plants can take the form of **trees** or **shrubs**, having woody stems covered with a corky bark. They can also be **herbaceous**, with non-woody stems.

Some herbaceous plants are **annuals**, that is they live for less than one year. Others are **biennials**, living for two years, while a third group are **perennials**, living for more than two years. Biennial or perennial herbs usually have **bulbs**, **tubers** or other underground organs for food storage. All trees and shrubs are perennials.

Leaves, which are always borne at the nodes of the stem, can be **simple**, in which case the leaf is made up of a single blade, or **compound**, where the

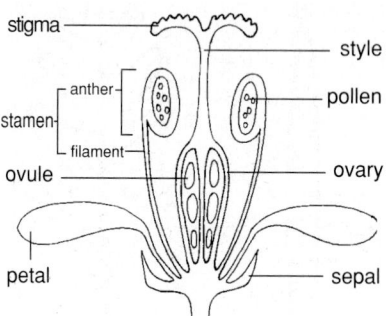

Structure of a flower

simple
pinnate

compound
pinnate

simple palmate

compound palmate

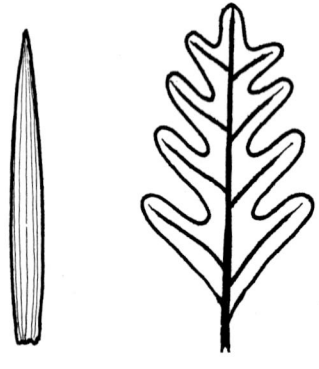

veins
parallel

pinnatifid

leaf is subdivided into a number of secondary leaflets. The venation of the leaves can be **parallel, pinnate** or **palmate**. Pinnate and palmate leaves can be simple or compound. Some simple leaves can be deeply lobed.

About 1000 species of angiosperms occur in Malta, of which some 700 are indigenous.

HORSETAILS
Division SPHENOPHYTA
Class EQUISETOPSIDA
Family Equisetaceae

Branched Horsetail   p137
Equisetum ramosissimum   Denb iż-Żiemel
About 50cm high. The segmented stems and branches are slender and rough. Reproduces by means of spores. Grows in damp conditions, along watercourses and occasionally in irrigated fields close to valleys. This is the only species of this Division found in Malta. Scarce.

LYCOPODS
Division LEPIDOPHYTA
Class LYCOPSIDA
A very primitive class which thrived in the Carboniferous (about 300 million years ago), when lycopods formed entire forests of large trees. Living lycopods are completely different in appearance, being all small moss-like or grass-like plants.

Family Selaginellaceae

Tooth-leaved Clubmoss   p137
Selaginella denticulata   Selaġinella
Small, creeping plant found in humid conditions at the base of shaded rocks together with mosses and lichens in some valleys. Rare.

FERNS
Division FILICOPHYTA
Class FILICOPSIDA
Owing to the dry conditions and the calcareous nature of Maltese soils, few species of fern are to be found. Only one is frequent.

Family Adiantaceae

Maidenhair Fern   p137
Adiantum capillus-veneris   Tursin il-Bir
Small. Grows on damp, shaded rocks in valleys and cave mouths, and also on the sides of wells. Frequent.

CONIFERS
Division PINOPHYTA
Class Pinopsida
Family Pinaceae

Aleppo Pine   p137
Pinus halepensis   Siġra taż-Żnuber
Medium-sized evergreen tree, with paired, needle-like leaves. Male and female cones are borne on the same tree. Male cones are yellowish and hold the pollen, while females are reddish-purple and produce seeds. Seed matures after three years. Typical Mediterranean species. Wild stock extinct, but re-introduced. Common.

Family Cupressaceae

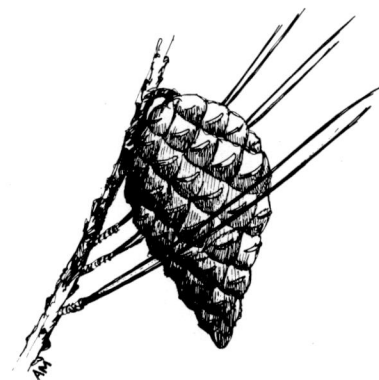

Sandarac   p137
Tetraclinis articulata   Siġra ta' l-Gharghar
Medium-sized evergreen tree, rarely exceeds 10m in height; in the wild up to about 6m. Delicate branches covered with small scale-like leaves arranged in four rows. Male cones about 3mm, terminally borne. Female cones up to 15mm, divided into four segments. Grows in maquis, especially on slopes of coralline limestone. In Europe it only occurs in Malta and southern Spain. Wild specimens occur in very few localities, including Maqluba and Mellieha. The national tree. Very rare.

Leaves and cone of
Aleppo Pine

FLOWERING PLANTS
Division MAGNOLIOPHYTA

Dicotyledons
A large group of Families of plants whose seeds produce two cotyledons (first leaves). Leaf venation is net like, and floral parts are often in fours or fives.

Class Magnoliopsida
Family Salicaceae

White Poplar   p137
Populus alba   Siġra tal-Luq
Large tree. Deciduous. Leaves dark green above and white below due to dense covering of short hairs. They are rustled by the slightest of breezes. Small flowers are borne in catkins, bloom in early spring and are wind-pollinated. Local trees are all males. Grows wild only along watercourses. Rare.

Family Fagaceae

Evergreen Oak   p137
Quercus ilex   Siġra tal-Ballut
Evergreen tree that grows to a considerable height. Leaves rigid, with a thick skin, dark green above and whitish below owing to dense layer of white

White Poplar catkins
male (above) and
female (below)

hairs. Shape of leaves very variable. Leaves growing from suckers are serrated and holly-like. The small flowers in hanging catkins are wind-pollinated. The same tree bears flowers of both sexes, and these bloom in spring. Fruits are called acorns. Typical of Mediterranean woodlands. Grows wild in very few localities, among them Wardija and Imġiebah. The Wardija trees are hundreds of years old. Rare.

Family Moraceae

Fig   p137

Ficus carica   Siġra tat-Tin
Small or medium-sized deciduous tree, rarely exceeding 10m. Leaves palmate. Flowers small and enclosed in the 'fruit', which has a small aperture at the tip allowing the entry of a small wasp of the genus *Blastophaga* which brings about pollination. A number of cultivars are known, bearing fruit which can be round, oval, pale green, yellow, black, dark purple or of mixed hues. A tree which bears male flowers is known as caprifig. Grows in maquis and on disturbed ground. Also grows on rock faces, cliffs, walls and fortifications. Introduced by the first human settlers. Common.

Family Urticaceae

Pellitory-of-the-wall   p137

Parietaria judaica (= P. diffusa)   Xeht ir-Rih
Herbaceous perennial with dark green leaves about 1-4cm long. Stems often reddish. Covered with hairs which, on the leaves, are hook-like, so that the leaves become attached to anything they touch. Flowers small and wind-pollinated. Grows all year round in disturbed habitats, especially in sheltered, shady soils with high nitrate content. Very common.

Large-leaved Stinging Nettle   p137

Urtica dubia (= U. membranacea)   Hurrieq Komuni
Annual. Leaves bear stinging hairs, the tip of which breaks on contact with the skin to inject mild poison. Flowers inconspicuous, wind-pollinated. Male flowers usually borne in the upper part of the plant, forming long inflorescences which are longer than the leaves. Female inflorescences grow lower down and are shorter than the leaves. Grows on disturbed ground, in gardens and neglected areas, especially if sheltered and high in nitrates. Very common.

Two other species of nettle occur.

Family Cynomoriaceae

Malta Fungus   p137

Cynomorium coccineum   Gherq Sinjur
Stocky; very deep red, unbranched, with reduced leaves. Tiny flowers open in spring and cover the upper part. Parasitic on a number of succulent shrubs which grow near the sea. Long thought to be a fungus because of its strange shape. Known mostly from Fungus Rock, and also from Dingli Cliffs.

Malta Fungus

Formerly only known from Fungus Rock, and its rarity and odd appearance caused much interest and attention. Was believed to have medicinal and magical powers, and the Knights of St. John enjoyed a monopoly on its harvesting and distribution; those caught gathering the plant unlawfully were sent to the galleys. In time, it was found growing in other parts of the Mediterranean, especially on small islands. Very rare.

Family Polygonaceae

Willow-leaved Knotgrass   p137
Persicaria salicifolia (= Polygonum salicifolium)   Persikarja tal-Baħrija
Perennial. Grows out of the water. Leaves lanceolate with finely serrated edges. Flowers in summer. Small, pink flowers grow in long, slender but dense inflorescences. Only occurs where water flows all year round. Very rare, except at Baħrija.
> Other species of the closely related genus *Polygonum* occur, mostly rare. The commonest is the **Common Knotgrass** *P. aviculare* (Lewża tar-Raba'), an inconspicuous prostrate plant, with elongate, greyish leaves and small whitish flowers at the leaf axils.

Red Dock   p137
Rumex bucephalophorus   Qarsajja
Low-growing annual, with small flowers forming long inflorescences. Flower stalks swollen and bright red. Grows on garigue, rocky steppes and sandy soil. Spring-flowering. Frequent.

Clustered Dock   p137
Rumex conglomeratus   Qarsajja ta' l-Ilma
Perennial herb with large, lettuce-like leaves. Flowers small, borne in large, dense, many-branched elongate inflorescences, appearing in late spring. Grows along watercourses and in other damp habitats. Frequent.
> Several similar species of *Rumex* occur. Identification is usually based on the structure of the fruit.

Family Chenopodiaceae

Fat Hen   p137
Chenopodium album   Ghobbejra Bajdanija
Annual, often reaching 2m. Leaves greyish. Flowers inconspicuous, in dense clusters. Grows in summer, especially on roadsides, rubble and dumps. Probably not indigenous, but has become widespread in the last 20 years. Common.
> Various species of *Chenopodium* can be found in disturbed habitats.

Shrubby Orache   p137
Atriplex halimus   Bjanka
Very dense shrub. Takes on a hemispherical shape, up to 2m in height. Leaves small (about 2cm), whitish. Small flowers in packed inflorescences. Grows in coastal areas. Frequent.
> Other species of *Atriplex* occur, but unlike Shrubby Orache, are all herbs. The **Halberd-leaved Orache** *A. prostrata* (= *A. hastata*)(Selq il-Bahar) frequently

Halberd-leaved Orache

grows on damp, disturbed ground, especially near the sea. Leaves are arrow-shaped.

Maltese Cliff-orache   **p137**
Cremnophyton lanfrancoi   Bjanka ta' l-Irdum
Dense shrub with whitish, elongate leaves (about 30x4 mm), usually slightly succulent. Flowers small in dense clusters, blooming in early autumn. Fruiting bracts often turn purple. Grows only on cliff sides. The genus *Cremnophyton* contains this single species and is very primitive, probably near to the ancestor of the genus *Atriplex*. Described in 1987 by Sicilian botanists Brullo and Pavone, who named it after Maltese botanist Edwin Lanfranco. Endemic. Rare.

Twiggy Glasswort   **p137**
Salicornia ramosissima   Almeridja
Succulent annual with small, almost imperceptible, flowers. Stems appear to be made up of segments, which are in fact fleshy leaves that completely envelop stem. Often turns red on maturity, at the fruiting stage. Only grows in saline marshes such as Ghadira nature reserve, Salina and Ballut ta' Marsaxlokk. Scarce.
> The **Shrubby Glasswort** *Arthrocnemum macrostachyum* (= *A. glaucum*) (Almeridja tal-Blat), a perennial shrub, also occurs, especially in rocky coastal areas.

Maltese Salt-tree   **p137**
Darniella melitensis (= *Salsola melitensis*)   Xebb
A dense shrub of moderate size (up to 2.5m) with small, cylindrical, fleshy leaves. Flowers very small. The single-seeded fruit has five petal-like 'wings' which serve for its dispersion by wind. Fruits in October-November. Grows mainly on coastal cliffs, but also found in a few inland localities, especially on hillsides in Gozo. The only European species of the genus *Darniella*. Described in 1976. Endemic. Scarce, though locally common.

Smooth-leaved Saltwort   **p137**
Salsola soda   Ħaxixa ta' l-Irmied
Annual, reaching about 1m. Leaves smooth and fleshy. Stems often reddish. Grows rapidly in spring and summer. In autumn, when fruits are mature, it dries up, breaks at the base and is blown about by the wind, thus dispersing the seeds. Occurs near the sea. Frequent.
> The **Prickly Saltwort** *S. kali* (Ħaxixa ta' l-Irmied Xewwikija), with spiny leaves, is found in similar habitats.

Prickly Saltwort

Family Aizooaceae

Lesser Crystal-plant   **p137**
Mesembryanthemum nodiflorum   Kristallina Komuni
Annual. Leaves cylindrical and fleshy, light green at first, turning to brick-red in summer. Covered with layer of large water-filled cells. Flowers 1cm in diameter, with numerous glistening, white petals and yellow stamens. Grows near the sea. Common.
> A rarer species, the **Crystal-plant** *M. crystallinum* (Kristallina Kbira) grows in the same habitat. It has broader leaves whose larger water-filled cells glisten like jewels in the sunlight.

Family Caryophyllaceae

Several species of the Family Caryophyllaceae occur. Many of them are common, especially on street pavements. Mostly small, inconspicuous plants.

Red Campion   p137

Silene colorata   Lsien l-Ghasfur

Annual with opposite, somewhat hairy leaves. Flowers about 2cm in diameter with five bright pink petals, each of which is bifid, thus giving the appearance of having ten petals. Sepals united to form purple-striped tube. Flowers in winter and spring. Grows everywhere, but probably originated in sandy areas. Common.

Family Ranunculaceae

Love-in-a-mist   p139

Nigella damascena   Sieq il-Brimba

Delicate annual with leaves divided into many narrow sections. Flowers pale blue, appearing in spring. Fruit swollen and shaped like a lantern with five apical horn-like processes. Grows mainly in steppes and on disturbed ground. Common.

Winged Larkspur   p139

Delphinium halteratum   Sieq il-Ħamiema Vjola

Annual, 25-30cm high, with slender, rigid stems and deeply-cut leaves. Purple flowers bloom in summer and form an elongate inflorescence. Found mainly on cultivated soil, especially in sunny gardens, fields and road verges. Frequent.

Red Campion
showing bifid petals

Crown Anemone   p139

Anemone coronaria   Kahwiela

Perennial, spending the summer months underground as a tuber. Leaves deeply-cut. Flowers large, about 5cm in diameter, generally violet, with black stamens. Winter-flowering. Grows in sheltered spots in maquis and garigue. Frequent.

Evergreen Traveller's Joy   p139

Clematis cirrhosa   Kiesha

Climbing perennial. Leaves generally trifid, shiny and evergreen. Petioles, which curl like tendrils, serve to attach the plant to the surface on which it is climbing. Flowers yellowish-white with four petals. Flowers produce a number of small, single-seeded fruits, each with a feather-like process for wind dispersal. Flowers in autumn. Grows mainly in maquis. Scarce.

Pheasant's Eye   p139

Adonis microcarpa   Ghajn is-Serduq

Annual. Leaves delicate, finely dissected. Flowers bright red, appearing during winter and spring. Grows mainly in cultivated land. Formerly common, but was widely gathered for decoration, a practice which prevented seed production. Rare.

Evergreen Traveller's Joy
showing trifid leaves

Lesser Celandine p139

Ranunculus ficaria   Fomm l-Gheliem

Perennial, spending the summer underground as tuberous roots. Leaves shiny. Flowers are 4-5cm across, with numerous shiny, bright yellow petals. Blooms in winter and early spring. Grows in shady, damp places in valleys, ditches and maquis. Frequent.

Autumn Buttercup p139

Ranunculus bullatus   Ċfolloq

Perennial herb with tuberous roots. Leaves form a rosette. Flowers shiny yellow, about 2cm across, appearing in autumn. Grows in maquis, garigue and rocky steppes, always on relatively undisturbed ground. Common.

Sanicle-leaved Water Crowfoot p139

Ranunculus saniculaefolius   Ċfolloq ta' l-Ilma

Annual water-plant with two kinds of leaves: those floating at the surface broad and flat, those underwater very finely divided. Flowers have white petals with yellow base, blooming in winter and spring. Grows in rainwater pools in garigue areas. Formerly confused with *R. baudotii* and *R. peltatus*, which do not occur. Frequent.

> The **Three-leaved Water Crowfoot** *R. trichophyllus* (Ċfolloq tal-Wied), which lacks floating leaves, occurs in watercourses.

Family Lauraceae

Bay Laurel p139

Laurus nobilis   Siġra tar-Rand

Evergreen tree with hard, dark green, aromatic leaves with slightly wavy edges. Produces small white flowers in late winter. Fruit black, oval berry 10-15mm long. Grows in humid valleys and in maquis, such as Wied il-Luq and Wied Qirda. Indigenous: leaves have been found fossilised. Also cultivated as ornament. Scarce.

Bay Laurel

Family Papaveraceae

Opium Poppy p139

Papaver setigerum   Xahxieh Vjola

Annual, reaching 1m in height, with somewhat bluish-grey leaves. Petals pale violet with darker base. Flowers mainly in spring. Usually grows on rubble, disturbed soil and neglected corners in urban areas. Probably introduced. Frequent.

Common Poppy p139

Papaver rhoeas   Pepprin

Annual, generally smaller than Opium Poppy. Leaves green and hispid. Petals bright red, often with black spot at base; sometimes paler. Anthers bluish. Fruit is an oval capsule, about 1-2cm. Flowers in spring. Grows mostly in cultivated fields, often covering the entire surface. Very common.

> Various other species of Poppy occur. The **Long-Headed Poppy** *P. dubium* (Pepprin tal-Frotta Twila) and the **Mediterranean Poppy** *P. pinnatifidum* (Pepprin ta' l-Istami Sofor) both have elongate capsules, the former having violet and the latter yellow stamens. The **Bristly Poppy** *P. hybridum*

(Pepprin tal-Lanżit) has more divided leaves, smaller, claret flowers and bristly fruit. All are common.

Yellow Horned-poppy   p139
Glaucium flavum   Pepprin Isfar
Biennial or short-lived perennial. Leaves divided, whitish, often with bluish tinge. Fruit very elongate, horn-like. Flowers in spring and summer. Grows by the sea, especially on sand and disturbed ground. Common.

Italian Fumitory   p139
Fumaria gaillardotii   Dahnet l-Art Kbira
Annual. Delicate plant with weak, sometimes climbing, stems. Leaves finely divided. Flowers pink, deep purple at the tip, about 12mm long. Flowers in winter and spring. Grows mainly on cultivated ground and in road verges. Common.

> The genus *Fumaria* includes many species which are difficult to separate. The **Fine-leaved Fumitory** *F. parviflora* (Dahnet l-Art Żghira) is the most common among species with flowers shorter than 6mm. The **Common Fumitory** *F. officinalis* (Dahnet l-Art Medja) is the commonest of the species with flowers measuring 8-9mm, while the Italian Fumitory is the most common of the species with flowers 10-14mm in length.

Bristly Poppy

Family Capparidaceae

Caper   p139
Capparis orientalis (= C. rupestris, C. spinosa var. inermis)   Kappara
Perennial. Leaves almost round, borne on numerous slender stems which curve or hang down. Flowers white with numerous violet stamens. Blooms in summer. Grows mainly on cliffs, walls and fortifications. Found also in garigue and maquis. The edible flower buds are pickled in vinegar. Common.

Family Brassicaceae (= Cruciferae)
> A large Family which includes many plants of agricultural importance. The flowers have four petals in a cross formation (hence Cruciferae). Seeds are borne in pods, known as siliquae, of various forms.

London Rocket   p139
Sisymbrium irio   Libsiena Komuni
Delicate-looking annual with smooth, pale green, pinnatifid leaves. Flowers very small, pale yellow. Flowers in spring, eventually producing numerous long, slender siliquae. Grows in urban areas, especially along roadsides and in neglected corners. Probably not indigenous. Common.

Slender seed pod (siliqua)

Maltese Stocks   p139
Matthiola incana ssp. *melitensis*   Ġiżi ta' Malta
Perennial. Leaves numerous, fleshy, often with wavy edges, densely covered in short hair, giving them a whitish appearance. Flowers pale violet, blooming in spring on coastal cliffs. Subspecies *melitensis* is endemic. Described in 1988. Very rare; less so in Gozo.

> The **Garden Stocks** *M. incana* ssp. *incana* (Ġiżi Komuni) is a non-indigenous race which has escaped from cultivation. Grows mainly on the Valletta, Floriana, Tigné and Manoel Island fortifications. The flowers are generally

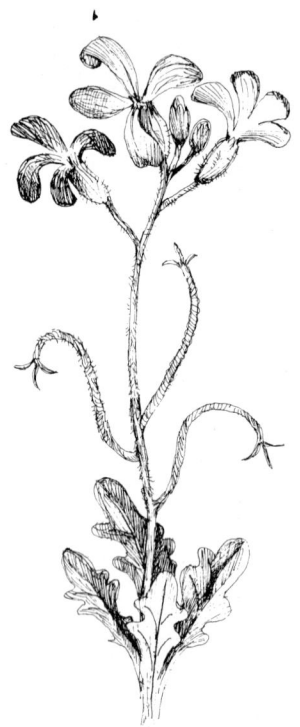

Mediterranean Stocks
showing elongate siliqua

deep violet, white or dappled violet and white. The leaves are not fleshy.

Mediterranean Stocks   p139
Matthiola tricuspidata   Ġiżi tal-Baħar
Annual. Leaves whitish, flowers pale violet. The elongate siliquae end in
three stiff horns. Spring-flowering. Dries up in summer and disperses the
seeds by breaking away at the base and tumbling. Grows mainly in disturbed
or sandy areas near the sea. Formerly found mainly in the extreme eastern
part of Malta, but in the last 20 years has also spread to localities such as
Sliema, Qaliet (near Paceville), Baħar iċ-Ċagħaq. Scarce, but becoming less
so.

Sweet Alison   p139
Lobularia maritima   Buttuniera
Perennial. Low-growing with small greyish leaves and compact bunches of
small white flowers which usually bloom from autumn to midsummer.
Grows everywhere, on disturbed ground, garigue and sandy ground. Very
common.

Shepherd's Purse   p139
Capsella bursa-pastoris   Ġarġir il-Ġemel
Annual. Rather small with tiny flowers (about 2mm), from which develops
heart-shaped siliquae. Flowers from autumn to late spring. Found mostly
in disturbed habitats such as road verges and in cultivated areas. Frequent.

Mediterranean Buckler Mustard   p139
Biscutella didyma   Xeħt il-Forom
Annual with small, pale yellow flowers (4-6mm) which bloom in autumn
and winter. Siliqua resembles two flattened saucers. Grows in garigue,
steppes and disturbed, dry ground. Frequent.

White Mustard   p139
Diplotaxis erucoides   Ġarġir Abjad
Annual. Flowers white, sometimes tinged with violet, about 2cm wide.
Flowers from early autumn to late spring. Seeds borne in long siliquae.
Grows mainly in areas where the soil is frequently worked. Leaves are edible
and can be used in salads. Very common.

Perennial Wall-rocket   p139
Diplotaxis tenuifolia   Ġarġir Isfar
Perennial. Leaves smooth and narrow, more or less divided. The yellow,
scented flowers are about 2cm across and appear virtually all year round.
Grows on disturbed grounds, along roadsides, in tree plantations and in
neglected areas. Leaves used in salads. Very common.

Bargemans's Cabbage   p139
Brassica rapa ssp. *silvestris*   Liftija
Annual. Leaves simple, embracing stem. Flowers similar in size to Perennial
Wall-rocket, but deeper yellow. Blooms in winter and spring. Grows in
cultivated fields. Common.
> The genus *Brassica* includes many familiar crop-plants, such as the **Cabbage**
> *B. oleracea* ssp. *capitata* (Kaboċċa), the **Cauliflower** *B. cretica* ssp. *botrytis*

(Pastarda) and the **Kohl-rabi** *B. rupestris* ssp. *gonglyoides* (Ġidra). The **Wild Cabbage** *B. oleracea* (Kaboċċa Salvaġġa) often grows on rubble in summer and appears to be increasing. It has rather large, bluish leaves and yellow flowers which are slightly paler than those of *B.rapa* ssp. *silvestris*.

Sea Rocket   p139
Cakile maritima   Kromb il-Baħar
Annual. Leaves fleshy. Flowers pale violet, sometimes almost white. Blooms from winter to summer. Grows only on coastal sands. Frequent.

Wild Radish   p139
Raphanus raphanistrum   Ravanell Salvaġġ
Annual. Flowers usually white (sometimes yellowish), with violet veins. Blooms from winter to spring. Grows mainly in disturbed environments. Common.

Yellow Mignonette

Family Resedaceae

White Mignonette   p141
Reseda alba   Denb il-Ħaruf
Herbaceous annual, biennial or short-lived perennial. Leaves much divided. Flowers generally bearing five three-lobed petals, in elongate, dense inflorescences. Flowers from winter to spring. Grows mostly in disturbed areas and steppes. Common.
> The **Yellow Mignonette** *R. lutea* (Denb il-Ħaruf Isfar) is a similar species with pale yellow flowers, and is rather rare.

Family Crassulaceae

Narrow Navelwort   p141
Umbilicus horizontalis   Żokret l-Għaġuża
Herbaceous perennial, surviving summer underground as a tuber. Leaves succulent and glossy, the early ones being round and attached centrally to petiole. Spring-flowering. Grows mostly in rubble walls and in damp, shady crevices in rocks. Frequent.

Mediterranean Stonecrop   p141
Sedum sediforme   Sedum
Evergreen perennial. Leaves fleshy, ranging from greyish-green to bronze-red depending on the amount of sunlight. Flowers in early summer. Grows on garigue especially near the sea and on cliff tops. Frequent.

Blue Stonecrop   p141
Sedum caeruleum   Beżżul il-Baqra
Annual. Leaves small, red and fleshy. Flowers small, usually with seven pale violet petals. Spring-flowering. Grows in garigue and rocky steppes, especially in shallow depressions which fill up with water during the winter, often forming red, carpet-like patches on the rocks. Common.

Family Rosaceae

Bramble
Rubus ulmifolius

p141

Gholliq

Perennial. Climbing and clambering, with thorny stems. Leaves are compound-palmate, generally made up of three or five leaflets. Flowers pink (rarely white). Fruit fleshy, edible. Flowers from spring to autumn. Grows in maquis, especially in valley bottoms, which it often chokes, smothering less aggressive plants. Common.

Evergreen Rose
Rosa sempervirens

p141

Girlanda tal-Wied

A climbing perennial with thorny stems. Leaves compound-pinnate, glossy, evergreen. Flowers white, appearing in spring and early summer. Fruit shiny red. Grows in maquis and on the sides of sheltered valleys. Rare.

Salad Burnet
Sanguisorba minor ssp. *muricata*

p141

Tursin il-Ghul

Perennial with dark green, compound-pinnate leaves bearing numerous leaflets. The small flowers lack petals and are clustered in round or oval heads. Spring-flowering. Grows in garigue and maquis. Frequent.

Creeping Cinquefoil
Potentilla reptans

p141

Frawla Salvaġġa

Creeping perennial. Leaves are compound-palmate with five or seven leaflets. Flowers in spring and early summer. Grows along watercourses. Frequent.

Hawthorn

Hawthorn
Crataegus monogyna

p141

Żaghrun

Small tree or shrub with spiny branches. Loses its leaves in autumn. Flowers in spring, producing red or orange fruits which ripen in autumn. Grows in maquis and in valleys. Frequent.

The **Azarole** *C. azarolus* (Anżalor) is very similar . Formerly cultivated as a fruit tree. Also found in the wild state, although rare. Hybrids between the two species sometimes occur.

Family Fabaceae (= Leguminosae)
A very large Family, with about 100 species. Most have a flower with a large upper petal (the standard), two smaller lateral petals (the wings) and a further two smaller petals below, usually united to form a keel. In some exceptional cases, such as Carob, the flowers lack petals.

Carob
Ceratonia siliqua

p141

Siġra tal-Harrub

Evergreen tree growing to about 10m. Leaves compound-pinnate. Flowers without petals, in small inflorescences carried on the older branches, appearing at the same spot year after year. Male and female flowers occur on different trees, the pods, or locust beans, forming only on female trees. Blooms in autumn, when the strong scent of the male flowers fills the air.

Grows in maquis and in valleys, in cultivated areas and close to rural buildings. Probably native of the Eastern Mediterranean, but introduced in Malta in ancient times. Common.

Milk-vetch   p141
Astragalus baeticus   Kafè Messikan
Annual. Leaves compound-pinnate with numerous leaflets. Flowers whitish in small clusters, giving rise to pods about 3-4cm long. Blooms in winter and spring. Grows in disturbed habitats. Common.

Pitch Clover   p141
Psoralea bituminosa (= Bituminaria bituminosa)   Silla tal-Mogħoż
Perennial with trifoliate leaves. Flowers bluish-violet, in small bunches. Flowers in winter and spring. When bruised, leaves smell of pitch. Found in garigue, maquis and sometimes on disturbed ground. Common.

Common Vetch   p141
Vicia sativa   Ġilbiena Sewda
Annual. Leaves compound-pinnate with terminal tendrils. Flowers in winter and spring. Grows in garigue, steppes and disturbed habitats. Common.
> This species has a number of subspecies, among them *V. s. sativa*, with flowers usually over 1cm long, which, besides being common, is grown as a fodder crop. The commonest subspecies is *V.s. nigra*, with flowers usually less than 1cm long and smaller leaves.

Crimson Pea   p141
Lathyrus clymenum   Ġilbiena tas-Serp
Annual. Stems winged. Leaves compound-pinnate with terminal tendrils. The lower leaves lack leaflets. Flowers in spring. Found in various habitats. Common.

Bushy Restharrow   p141
Ononis natrix ssp. *ramosissima*   Broxka ta' Għawdex
A much-branched, aromatic shrub with dense foliage. Leaves covered with sticky hairs. Flowers yellow, often red-veined. Blooms in spring. Grows in garigue, especially close to the sea. More frequent on Gozo than on the island of Malta, and also grows on Comino and Kemmunett. Formerly collected for firewood, so much so that Grandmaster De Rohan had issued a decree banning its collection prior to a fortnight after the feast of St. John (24 June), in order to allow seed formation and dispersal. Scarce.

Mediterranean Melilot   p141
Melilotus sulcatus   Trew Komuni
Annual with trifoliate leaves. Tiny flowers in small, stalked bunches. Flowers in winter and spring. Found in various habitats. Common.
> Various species of *Melilotus* ,which are difficult to distinguish, are known. The **Small Melilot** *M. indica* (Trew tat-Toroq) has smaller flowers, but in longer and denser bunches. Common, especially at road verges and on garden paths. All species, especially the latter, have a characteristic pleasant odour due to the presence of the chemical coumarin.

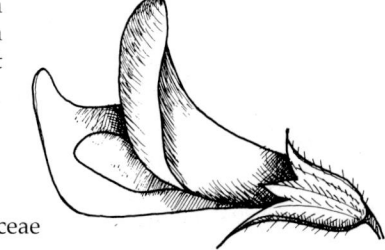

Typical flower of the Family Fabaceae

Pod of Toothed Medick

Pod of Disk Medick

Pod of Sea Medick

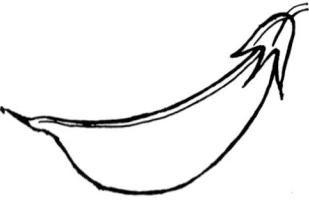

Pod of
Edible Birdsfoot Trefoil

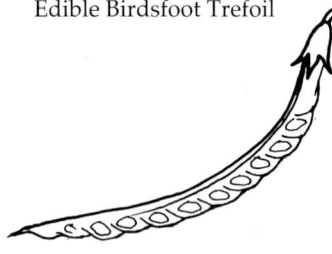

Pod of
Common Birdsfoot Trefoil

Toothed Medick   p141

Medicago polymorpha   Nefel Komuni

Annual with trifoliate leaves. Following pollination, the tiny flowers give rise to spirally-coiled pods bearing hooked teeth along outer margin. The teeth serve for attachment of the pods to the fur of animals for purposes of dispersal. Flowers in winter and spring. Grows in various habitats. Very common.

> Several other species of *Medicago* occur. These are difficult to distinguish, except by comparing the structure of the seed pod, which is almost invariably spirally-coiled. The **Disk Medick** *M. orbicularis* (Nefel Lixx) is the only common species which has entirely smooth pods lacking teeth.

Sea Medick   p141

Medicago marina   Nefel tar-Ramel

Herbaceous perennial, with a covering of velvety, white hairs. Flowers lemon yellow and borne in small dense bunches. Spring-flowering. Found only in sand dunes. Rare.

Star Clover   p141

Trifolium stellatum   Xnien ta' l-Istilla

Annual with hairy, trifoliate leaves. Flowers pale pink. Following fertilisation, sepals enlarge to form a red star with a white centre where the pod is concealed. Spring-flowering. Grows in garigue and steppes. Common.

Hop Trefoil   p141

Trifolium campestre   Xnien Isfar

Annual with trifoliate leaves. Small, pale yellow flowers in dense clusters reminiscent of Chinese lanterns. Spring-flowering. Found in garigue and steppes. Common.

Lesser White Clover   p141

Trifolium nigrescens   Xnien Abjad

Annual with trifoliate leaves. Flowers generally white, often tinged pink, appearing in spring. Grows mostly in garigue and steppes, also frequently occurs in disturbed habitats. Very common.

> Several other species of *Trifolium* are known. Most are rare.

Edible Birdsfoot Trefoil   p141

Lotus edulis   Qrempuċ

Annual, flowering mainly in spring. Grows everywhere. Pod is fleshy and edible. Common.

Common Birdsfoot Trefoil   p141

Lotus ornithopodioides   Qrempuċ tal-Mogħoż

Annual. Flowers in small groups of three to five. Flowers in winter and spring. Grows in almost all habitats. Very common.

Grey Birdsfoot Trefoil   p141

Lotus cytisoides   Għantux tal-Blat

Small shrub with small greyish leaves. Flowers generally yellow, sometimes tinged reddish. Blooms mostly in winter and spring. Grows in garigue, scree and along the coast. Frequent.

Winged Pea   p143
Lotus tetragonolobus (= Tetragonolobus purpureus)   Fiġġiela Ħamra
Annual. Flowers deep red, similar to those of Edible Birdsfoot Trefoil. Pod has four winged angles. Flowers in winter and spring. Grows mainly in garigue and steppes. Common.

Common Kidney Vetch   p143
Anthyllis vulneraria ssp. *maura*   Silla tal-Blat
Herbaceous perennial. Leaves compound-pinnate, terminal leaflet being much longer than lateral ones. Spring-flowering. Found mostly in garigue and rocky steppes. Frequent.

Shrubby Kidney Vetch   p143
Anthyllis hermanniae   Ħatba Sewda
Dense shrub reaching a height of 50cm. Leaves small and dark greyish-green. Small yellow flowers often cover the whole plant. Spring-flowering. Grows in garigue, often the dominant shrub. Mediterranean distribution is localised, e.g. not present in Sicily. Frequent.

Bladder Kidney Vetch   p143
Tripodion tetraphyllum (=*Anthyllis tetraphylla, Physanthyllis tetraphylla)*   Silla tal-Bżieżel
Annual with compound leaves made up of four leaflets. After flowering, sepals expand, becoming bladder-like. Spring-flowering. Found in garigue and rocky steppes. Frequent.

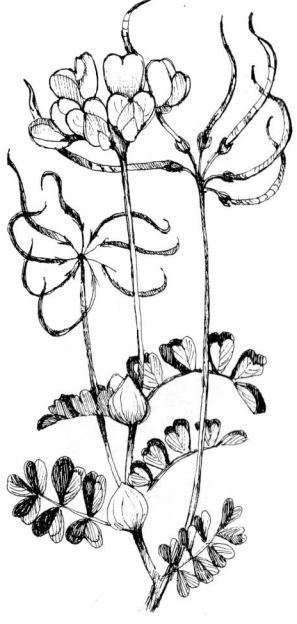

Shrubby Crown Vetch   p143
Coronilla valentina   Koronilla
Poisonous shrub rarely exceeding 1m. Leaves compound, slightly bluish-grey. Flowers yellow and strongly scented. Flowers from late winter to mid-spring. Grows on cliff-like sides of certain valleys such as Wied Babu. Maltese plants are close to the subspecies *glauca*. Rare.

Shrubby Crown Vetch

Common Horseshoe Vetch   p143
Hippocrepis multisiliquosa   Xintilli Komuni
Annual with compound-pinnate leaves and horseshoe-shaped pods. Spring-flowering. Found mainly in garigue and rocky steppes, but also on disturbed ground. Common.

> Two other, less frequent species are known: the **Lesser Horseshoe Vetch** *H. ciliata* (Xintilli tal-Blat) and the **Single-flowered Horseshoe Vetch** *H. biflora* (Xintilli Żghira). The former resembles the Common Horseshoe Vetch, but with smaller flowers, and with the 'holes' of the horseshoe opening on the inner edge. The other species has a straight pod and flowers are borne singly.

Scorpion-tail Vetch   p143
Scorpiurus muricatus   Widna
Annual. Flowers range from yellow to orange-red. Pod has ear-shaped outline. Spring-flowering. Grows mainly in garigue and steppes. Formerly cultivated as animal fodder. Frequent.

Sulla p143

Hedysarum coronarium Silla

Herbaceous perennial. Leaves compound-pinnate. Flowers deep red and shiny. Spring-flowering. Grows wild on clay slopes, but widely cultivated as a fodder crop. Probably not indigenous; several cultivars have been introduced. Frequent in the wild state.

> A scarce species, the **Clustered Clover** *H. glomeratum* (Silla Salvaġġa) with magenta flowers is also found, in garigue and coastal steppes. Species of *Hedysarum* have segmented pods covered in short spines.

Family Oxalidaceae

Cape Sorrel p143

Oxalis pes-caprae (= O. cernua) Haxixa Ingliża

Herbaceous perennial, spending summer as a bulb. Leaves trifoliate with long petioles. Blooms in winter and spring. Grows virtually everywhere. Said to have been introduced at the beginning of the 19th century, probably by Father Carlo Giacinto, a Genoese in charge of the botanic gardens at Floriana. The Maltese name, which means English Plant, probably arose because its introduction coincided with the start of British rule in Malta, although some maintain that it stems from the fact that the first plant was given to Giacinto by an English lady. It spread from Malta to the entire Mediterranean, and even up the Atlantic coast to the British Isles. In South Africa, where the plant is indigenous, three flower forms are known, at least two of which must be present for effective pollination to occur. In Malta and other countries where it was introduced, only one subspecies was established, and so no viable seed is produced. Very common.

> The **Double-flowered Cape Sorrel** (Ingliża Sewda) is a form with multi-petalled flowers which are often reddish externally. The **Sleeping Beauty** *O. corniculata* (Ingliża tal-Ġonna) is a species with smaller flowers and with leaves often tinged violet, commonly found growing in gardens and flower-pots.

Double-flowered
Cape Sorrel

Family Geraniaceae

Dovesfoot Cranesbill p143

Geranium molle Ġeranju Komuni

Annual with palmate leaves and small flowers. Flowers in winter and spring. Found in garigue, steppes and disturbed habitats. Common.

> Several other species of *Geranium* are found, mainly in humid places.

Musk Storksbill p143

Erodium moschatum Haxixa tal-Misk

Annual with compound-pinnate leaves. Flowers pale or deep purple. Flowers in winter and spring. Grows in various habitats. Common.

Glandular Storksbill p143

Erodium malacoides Moxt

Annual. Leaves simple. Flowers purple, appearing in winter and spring. Grows in various habitats. Common.

> Other *Erodium* species occur.

Family Zygophyllaceae

Fagonia   p143
Fagonia cretica   Fagonja
Shrub with small trifoliate leaves and spiny stipules. Spring-flowering. Grows mainly on clay slopes in the western part of the island of Malta. Absent from Gozo. Rare.

Maltese Cross   p143
Tribulus terrestris   Ghatba
Annual which grows flat on the ground; leaves compound-pinnate. Small, yellow flowers develop into a fruit made up of five spiny sections. These become detached and are dispersed as they adhere to the feet of animals. Fruit resembles the Maltese eight-pointed cross, and traditionally believed to grow only on Fort St. Angelo (which is not true). Flowers in summer and autumn. Grows in disturbed habitats, especially in the Inner Harbour area. Frequent.

Family Linaceae

Upright Yellow Flax   p143
Linum strictum   Kittien Isfar
Slender, erect annual. Leaves narrow and elongate. Small, yellow flowers appear in spring. Grows on garigue and rocky steppes. Common.

> Two other species of flax are found: the **Slender Yellow Flax** *L. trigynum* (= *L. gallicum*) (Kittien Irqiq) has yellow flowers and is often found growing with Upright Yellow Flax; and **Pale Flax** *L. bienne* (= *L. angustifolium*) (Kittien Ikhal) with larger (about 1cm) pale blue flowers, which is rare.

Pale Flax

Family Euphorbiaceae

Annual Mercury   p143
Mercurialis annua   Burikba
Annual with small, green, wind-pollinated flowers. Male and female flowers borne on different plants. Male flowers in elongate inflorescences and females in smaller bunches. Blooms from autumn to spring. Found mainly on sheltered disturbed ground with high organic content. Very common.

> *M. annua* ssp. *ambigua* has smaller flowers with both sexes on the same plant. It is generally smaller and grows on garigue and rocky steppes.

Castor Oil Tree   p143
Ricinus communis   Siġra tar-Riċnu
Small tree with large, palmate leaves. Flowers in large, terminal bunches with male flowers below female ones. Following pollination, a round, spiny fruit is formed, which splits into three to expose large, smooth seeds with a marbled pattern. Flowers virtually all year round. Grows chiefly in disturbed habitats, but also invades valley bottoms, especially if they hold water. An African native which was introduced as a medicinal and ornamental species. Seed is poisonous. Can harm natural habitats by smothering native plants. Common.

Pine Spurge   p143

Euphorbia pinea   Tenghud Komuni

Herbaceous perennial. Leaves long and narrow, sometimes reddish. Flowers in regular, yellowish bunches. Very variable, depending on habitat. Flowers all year round. Grows on garigue and rocky steppes, but can withstand disturbance. Often found in neglected areas, gardens and roadsides. Common.

Tree Spurge   p143

Euphorbia dendroides   Tenghud tas-Siġra

Shrub reaching a height of 1-2m. Hemispherical, with numerous, regularly placed branches. Leaves turn red and fall in late May. Flowers in yellow bunches, appearing in winter and spring. A dominant plant in garigue, especially on slopes of coralline limestone, forming one of the most attractive natural communities. Frequent.

Maltese Spurge   p143

Euphorbia melitensis   Tenghud tax-Xagħri

Dense, rounded shrub, about 40-60cm but sometimes over 1m in height. Flowers bright yellow, appearing mainly in March. Fruit three-lobed and spiny. Grows on garigue, where it is often the dominant species. Described in 1846 by Italian botanist Parlatore. Later confused with other species such as *E. spinosa*, which grows in Italy, *E. bivonae* of Sicily and *E. papillaris* of the Egadi Islands. Recent studies have confirmed the separate identity of the Maltese plants. Endemic. Frequent.

Sun Spurge   p143

Euphorbia helioscopia   Tenghud tax-Xemx

Annual. Pale green. Greenish flowers in radially symmetrical bunches. Blooms from autumn to spring. Found in almost all habitats. Common.

> Several other species of *Euphorbia* occur. They all have a milky sap which is poisonous to humans.

Family Rutaceae

Fringed Rue   p143

Ruta chalepensis   Fejġel

Small shrub up to 50cm high. Leaves bluish, strongly aromatic. Flowers in spring. Found in garigue. Frequent.

Family Anacardiaceae

Lentisk   p145

Pistacia lentiscus   Deru

Large, evergreen shrub or small tree. Can reach a height of 6m, but generally below 3m. Leaves compound-pinnate with a characteristic odour. Male and female flowers on separate trees. Flowers from winter to spring. Small, red berries form following pollination. Grows in maquis. In some Mediterranean countries (but apparently not in Malta), oil pressed from fruits was used in oil lamps, while resin was chewed to keep teeth clean and to freshen the breath. Frequent.

Lentisk

Family Rhamnaceae

Mediterranean Buckthorn   p145
Rhamnus alaternus   Alaternu
Large evergreen shrub or small tree. Leaves very variable, but can be easily
recognised as the first two secondary veins arise from the base of the main
vein. Flowers very small, appearing in winter and developing into bunches
of small purplish fruits which turn black. Grows in maquis, valley bottoms
and abandoned fields. Appears to be on the increase, probably due to less
grazing by sheep and goats in recent years. Scarce.

Olive-leaved Buckthorn   p145
Rhamnus oleoides   Żiju
Medium-sized bush which can reach a height of 3m, although usually lower
than 1m. Leaves small, resembling those of the wild Olive. Branches profuse,
terminating in a hard spine. Flowers small, appearing in winter and early
spring, followed by small black fruits. Grows in maquis and garigue (where
it is low-growing). Frequent.

Family Malvaceae

Common Mallow   p145
Malva sylvestris   Ħobbejża Komuni
Herbaceous annual or biennial with palmate leaves. Generally supine, but
sometimes erect. Flowers in winter and spring. Grows in somewhat
disturbed habitats such as country lanes and in built-up areas, also found
in more natural habitats such as garigue and steppe. Common.
> The **Cretan Mallow** *Lavatera cretica* (Ħobbejża Wieqfa) is also common
> and resembles Common Mallow. Usually grows erect (up to 2m), with
> smaller violet flowers.

Cretan Mallow

Tree Mallow   p145
Lavatera arborea   Ħobbejża tas-Siġra
Robust, erect biennial. Leaves palmate, velvety. Flowers large and showy.
Blooms in spring and early summer. Grows on disturbed ground, especially
near the sea. Probably not indigenous, but becoming more widespread.
Frequent.

Large-flowered Mallow   p145
Lavatera trimestris   Ħobbejża tal-Warda Kbira
Annual, generally prostrate. Flowers large, about 10cm in diameter, usually
whitish with pink veins, sometimes darker. Blooms from mid-spring to
early summer. Grows near cultivated fields and country paths, and in
steppes. Frequent.

Family Clusiaceae (= Hypericaceae, Guttiferae)

Egyptian St. John's-wort   p145
Hypericum aegyptiacum (= Triadenia aegyptica)   Fexfiex ta' l-Irdum
Small shrub, sometimes reaching a height of 1m. Foliage dense, small leaves
bluish-grey. Blooms from winter to early summer. Grows on cliff top
garigues and cliff sides. Frequent.

Crisped St. John's-wort p145

Hypericum triquetrifolium (= H. crispum) Fexfiex tar-Raba'
Herbaceous perennial, with spreading branches. Leaves small with wavy edges. Flowers mainly in summer. Grows in cultivated ground and sometimes in other disturbed habitats. Common.

> Also frequent is the **Pubescent St. John's-wort** *H. pubescens* (Fexfiex Sufi),with dense, hairy foliage. A creeping plant, found mainly in rocky steppe and garigue, flowering in spring and early summer.

Family Cistaceae

Hoary Rock-rose p145

Cistus creticus Ċistu Roża
Shrub with sticky leaves. Flowers large, appearing in spring. Found mainly in garigue, occasionally as the dominant species. Very scarce.

Narrow-leaved Rock-rose p145

Cistus monspeliensis Ċistu Abjad
Shrub with sticky, narrow leaves. Blooms in spring. Found in garigue. Only two populations - one on the island of Malta and one on Gozo - are known, where it occurs as the dominant species. Rare.

Mediterranean Sun-rose p145

Fumana arabica Ċistu Isfar
Small prostrate shrub. Leaves small, flowers about 3cm across. Blooms in spring. Grows in garigue and rocky steppes. Frequent.

> The **Thyme-leaved Sun-rose** *F. thymifolia* (Ċistu Żghir) has smaller flowers, about 1cm, and grows with Mediterranean Sun-rose.

Mediterranean Sun-rose

Family Tamaricaceae

African Tamarisk p145

Tamarix africana Siġra tal-Bruk
Medium-sized tree with rough, grey trunk and numerous branches covered with small leaves which resemble those of Cypress. Flowers very small in dense white or pale pink inflorescences. Flowers mainly in spring, also in winter and summer. Grows near the sea, especially at mouths of valleys and in saltmarshes. Tolerates sea spray. Indigenous on Gozo and Comino, and probably also on the island of Malta. Common, but indigenous trees are rare.

> A large number of trees of this and related species have been planted in various localities. They are all very similar and difficult to distinguish.

Family Cucurbitaceae

Squirting Cucumber p145

Ecballium elaterium Faqqus il-Ħmir
Herbaceous perennial. Leaves large, with a harsh surface. Flowers pale yellow. Sexes separate but found on the same plant. Fruit oval and bristly, about 4cm long. When ripe, seeds shoot out at the slightest disturbance. Accompanying liquid is irritating to the eyes. Flowers all year round. Grows in disturbed habitats, especially neglected urban areas, on rubble, and in country lanes. Common.

Family Cactaceae

Prickly Pear   p145
Opuntia ficus-indica   Bajtar tax-Xewk
Large bush. The flattened fleshy pads are in fact the stems. Leaves proper are much reduced, taking the form of spines or bristles. Flowers large with many petals. When stamens are touched by insects, they bend towards the centre of the flower to facilitate pollination. Flowers mostly from late spring to early summer. Planted mostly along field edges, but has also invaded maquis, screes and cliffs. In Gozo it is used as a fodder crop. Probably of Caribbean origin. Introduced for its edible fruit, but escaped cultivation and now forms part of the Mediterranean landscape. Several cultivars occur, and the flesh of the fruit can be orange, pale yellow or red depending on the cultivar. Common.

Family Lythraceae

Creeping Loosestrife   p145
Lythrum junceum (= L. graefferi)   Litrum ta' l-Ilma
Herbaceous perennial. Spreads by rhizomes. Leaves elongate. Flowers in spring and early summer. Grows in watercourses. Frequent.

> The smaller **Hyssop Loosestrife** *L. hyssopifolia* (Litrum ta' l-Ghadajjar) is more frequent. Grows prostrate in freshwater pools in garigue, flowering after pools have dried up.

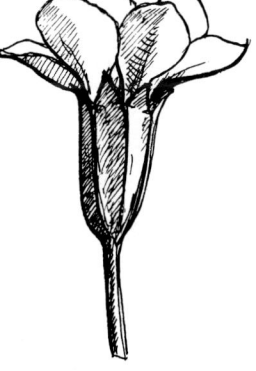

Hyssop Loosestrife

Family Myrtaceae

Myrtle   p145
Myrtus communis   Rihan
Evergreen shrub or small tree. Leaves lemon-scented. Flowers in summer. Fruits are black or white, small berries. Grows in maquis. Rare.

Family Araliaceae

Ivy   p145
Hedera helix   Liedna
Evergreen, perennial climber. Leaves on the non-flowering branches are lobed; leaves of flowering branches are simple. Autumn-flowering. Produces bunches of small black berries. Grows in maquis where it climbs over rocks, walls and trees. Scarce.

Family Apiaceae (= Umbelliferae)

Sea Holly   p145
Eryngium maritimum   Xewk ir-Ramel
Spiny, herbaceous perennial. Leaves rigid, whitish with bluish tinge. Small white flowers surrounded by spiny bracts which are often purplish. Flowers in summer and autumn. Grows only in sand, and hence is vulnerable. Rare.

Alexanders   p145
Smyrnium olusatrum   Karfus il-Ħmir
Biennial, reaching a height of 1m or more. Leaves resemble those of Celery. Umbels of yellowish-green flowers appear in winter and spring. Grows in

maquis and disturbed habitats, especially in sheltered, fertile soil. Very common.

Sea Samphire   p145
Crithmum maritimum   Bużbież il-Bahar
Perennial with succulent leaves. Flowers greenish-yellow. Blooms in summer. Grows in rock crevices along coast. Frequent.

Fennel   p145
Foeniculum vulgare   Bużbież
Herbaceous biennial or perennial. Grows up to about 3m. Leaves finely divided, sweet-scented. Yellow-flowered umbels appear mainly in summer. Grows in various habitats, especially steppes, road verges, country lanes, neglected fields and disturbed ground. Some varieties are cultivated as vegetables. Very common.

Giant Fennel   p145
Ferula communis   Ferla
Herbaceous perennial, grows to over 2m. Leaves finely divided into shiny, curled segments. Flowers yellow, in dense umbels, appearing in spring. Grows on rocky steppes, garigue, maquis and disturbed ground, including abandoned fields. Foliage often gathered for use in floral arrangements. Very common.

Mediterranean Hartwort   p145
Tordylium apulum   Haxixet it-Trierah
Annual, with compound leaves. Fruit saucer-shaped. Flowers in winter and spring. Grows in steppes, garigue and disturbed ground. Common.

Wild Carrot   p145
Daucus carota   Zunnarija Salvaġġa
Biennial. Leaves finely divided, with a delicate lace-like appearance. White or pinkish flowers in umbellate inflorescences, appearing in spring. Grows on steppes and disturbed ground. Several varieties are known, so far insufficiently studied. Very common.

Family Ericaceae

Mediterranean Heath   p147
Erica multiflora   Erika
Bush 50-100cm or more in height. Leaves short, needle-like, dark green, sometimes turning reddish. Flowers pale or deep pink with deep violet anthers, in dense bunches. Blooms in winter, often extending into spring. Grows in garigue and on cliff tops, often the dominant shrub. Common.

Family Primulaceae

Blue/Scarlet Pimpernel   p147
Anagallis arvensis   Harira Kahla/Hamra
Prostrate annual with smooth leaves. Flowers blue or scarlet, rarely violet or white. Grows on fertile soil in valleys, gardens and road verges. Common.

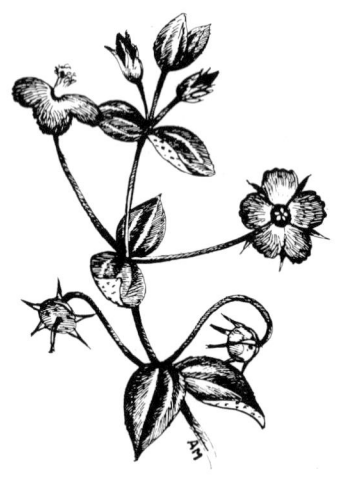

Blue/Scarlet Pimpernel

Family Plumbaginaceae

Maltese Sea-lavender   p147
Limonium melitensis   Limonju ta' Malta
Low shrub. Leaves in a basal rosette. Rigid stems with many regular branches grow annually; these bear pale violet flowers in late summer and autumn. Grows on cliff sides and clay slopes. Endemic. Frequent.

> **Zerafa's Sea-lavender** *L. zeraphae* (Limonju ta' Żerafa), is also endemic and grows in coastal rocky areas. Flowering stems are supine. Named after Maltese botanist Stefano Zerafa. The **Seaside Sea-lavender** *L. virgatum* (Limonju tal-Bahar) has erect flowering stems with slightly arching branches.

Family Oleaceae

Olive   p147
Olea europaea   Siġra taż-Żebbuġ
Evergreen tree. Rigid, dark green leaves are whitish underneath owing to dense covering of short hairs to reduce water loss. Flowers small, white. Fruit is the familiar black olive. Grows in maquis, also cultivated, although locally no longer much-grown for fruit or oil. Wild race *O. europaea* var. *sylvestris* has small leaves and spiny branches. Some trees, hundreds of years old, occur at Bidnija and at San Blas valley in Gozo. Scarce in the wild.

Family Gentianaceae

Common Centaury   p147
Centaurium erythraea   Ċentawrja Kbira
Annual or biennial, flowering mainly in May-June. Grows in garigue and rocky steppes. Frequent (very common on Comino).

> Three other species of *Centaurium* occur, all with smaller flowers.

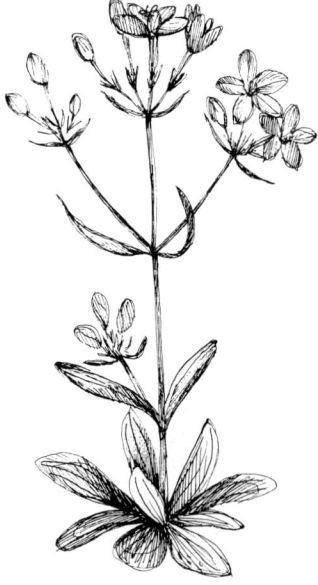

Common Centaury

Yellow-wort   p147
Blackstonia perfoliata (= Chlora perfoliata)   Ċentawrja Safra
Annual. Leaves bluish in opposite pairs which join at base, embracing stem. Flowers mostly in April-May. Grows on garigue and rocky steppes, often with species of *Centaurium*. Frequent.

Family Asclepiadaceae

Wolfbane   p147
Periploca angustifolia   Siġra tal-Harir
Sizeable shrub, often growing to a height of 2 m. Flowers rather unusual in structure. Fruits are pods which resemble a pair of horns. When mature they split open to release seeds carrying fine silky hairs which assist in wind dispersal. Flowers mainly between autumn and spring. Grows in garigue, on cliff tops and maquis. Scarce, but appears to be on the increase.

Family Rubiaceae

Field Madder   p147
Sherardia arvensis   Harxajja Roża
Small annual. Leaves arranged in whorls around stem. Flowers in winter and spring. Found in garigue and steppes, also in cultivated fields and open disturbed areas. Common.

Rock Crosswort   **p147**
Crucianella rupestris   Kruċanella
Low shrub, with many branches along which small, whitish leaves are arranged in whorls of four. Grows on seaside rocks, cliffs and screes. Frequent.

Common Goosegrass   **p147**
Galium aparine   Harxajja Komuni
Annual. Leaves in whorls around the square stem. Stem, leaf edges and fruits bear numerous hook-like hairs. These are used for climbing and for attachment of the fruit to animals' fur for dispersal. Spring-flowering. Found on fertile disturbed soil and in maquis. Common.
> At least three other species of *Galium* occur. All are frequent.

Wild Madder   **p147**
Rubia peregrina   Robbja Salvaġġa
Perennial, evergreen climber. Shiny, dark green leaves arranged in whorls. Flowers small, greenish-white in much-branched inflorescences. Fruits are small black berries containing deep purple, ink-like dye. Flowers in spring and early summer. Found mainly in maquis. Frequent.

Family Convolvulaceae

Mallow Bindweed   **p147**
Convolvulus althaeoides   Leblieb tax-Xaghri
Herbaceous perennial with prostrate or climbing habit. Leaves greyish, deeply lobed. Flowers pink with darker centre, appearing in spring, mostly mid-April to June. Grows in steppes, garigue and disturbed areas. Common.
> The **Slender Bindweed** *C. elegantissimus* (Leblieb tax-Xaghri Ċar) is very similar, but flower centre is white. Flowers earlier, from March. Common.

Mallow Bindweed

Field Bindweed   **p147**
Convolvulus arvensis   Leblieb tar-Raba'
Prostrate or climbing herbaceous perennial. Leaves greyish, arrowhead-shaped. Flowers white, pink or striped white and pink. Blooms from early summer to autumn. Grows mainly in fields and gardens. Roots rhizomatous and very persistent. Very common.

Olive-leaved Bindweed   **p147**
Convolvulus oleifolius   Leblieb tal-Blat
Small or medium dense shrub, up to 50cm high. Leaves slender and silvery due to dense covering of short, silky hairs. Flowers white or pink, appearing from spring to autumn. Grows on garigue, especially along cliff tops. Eastern Mediterranean species, with Malta at the westernmost point of its range. Frequent.
> The **Narrow-leaved Bindweed** *C. lineatus* (Leblieb tax-Xatt) is very similar but smaller, prostrate with smaller flowers. Grows on rocky ground near the sea.

Dodder   **p147**
Cuscuta epithymum   Pittma
Annual. Dense mass of long, red, slender, filamentous stems, sometimes pink or yellow. Leaves absent. Flowers small, pink or white, in small round

bunches about 5mm in diameter. Parasitic on various plants of garigue and rocky steppes, especially on Mediterranean Thyme, Maltese Spurge, Asphodel and Squill. Frequent. Very common on Comino.

Family Boraginaceae

Common Heliotrope   p147
Heliotropium europaeum   Vanilja Bajda
Annual. Leaves greyish. Flowers small, the caterpillar-like inflorescence curved like the handle of a violin. Flowers in summer and early autumn. Found mostly on cultivated ground, in fields and gardens. Very common.

Honeywort   p147
Cerinthe major   Qniepen
Annual. Flowers resemble pendulous bells with bracts which are sometimes deep violet. Blooms in spring. Found mainly in open disturbed habitats and maquis. Increased considerably during this century. Common.

Small-flowered Bugloss   p147
Echium parviflorum   Lsien il-Fart Żghir
Annual. Leaves covered in bristles. Flowers small and tubular, and may be pink or blue on the same plant. Grows practically everywhere. Common.
  The **Sand Bugloss** *E. arenarium* (Lsien il-Fart tar-Ramel) is generally prostrate, with deep violet flowers. Frequent near the sea.

Pale Bugloss   p147
Echium italicum   Lsien il-Fart Abjad
Biennial. Leaves large, elongate, forming flat rosette at soil level. Flowers white or pale pink on long, bristly stems bearing numerous lateral branches. When dry, inflorescences turn white and remain erect, resembling miniature Christmas trees. Grows in steppes, valleys and open, slightly disturbed habitats. Spring-flowering. Frequent.

Large Blue Alkanet   p147
Anchusa azurea (= A. italica)   Lsien il-Fart Ikhal
Herbaceous perennial. Leaves elongate, covered with bristles. Flowers vivid blue, appearing in spring. Found mainly in fields and country lanes. Frequent.
  The **Blue Hound's-tongue** *Cynoglossum creticum* (Lsien il-Kelb) is similar, but with velvety leaves and smaller flowers, which are pink or purple with darker veins. Grows in valleys. Frequent.

Blue Hound's-tongue

Borage   p147
Borago officinalis   Fidloqqom
Annual. Leaves large, covered with spiny bristles. Flowers blue with black stamens gathered together to form central horn-like structure. Flowers in winter and spring. Grows everywhere. Very common.

Family Verbenaceae

Vervain   p147
Verbena officinalis   Buqexrem
Herbaceous perennial. Long erect stalk bears small flowers. Blooms from spring to winter. Grows mainly in disturbed habitats. Common.

Chaste Tree   p147
Vitex agnus-castus   Siġra tal-Virgi
Large, deciduous, hemispherical bush or small tree up to 4m high. Leaves aromatic, compound-palmate with narrow lobes. Flowers bluish-violet (sometimes pink or even white). Fruits round, small, dark grey, like peppercorns. Flowers in summer and early autumn. Grows in watercourses in valleys, especially near the sea. More widespread on Gozo. Also found on Comino. Fruit was believed to suppress sexual urges, hence alternative Maltese name *Bżar tal-Patrijiet* (friars' peppercorns). Stems are used to make bases and handles of Giant Reed woven baskets. Scarce.

Family Lamiaceae (= Labiatae)

Olive-leaved Germander   p149
Teucrium fruticans   Żebbuġija
Dense shrub, about 50-100cm or more. Leaves dark green above and white below, as in Olive. Flowers from nearly white to violet, appearing from winter to late spring. Grows in garigue, on valley slopes and maquis, often the dominant shrub. Common.

Yellow Germander   p149
Teucrium flavum   Borghom Komuni
Shrub with shiny green leaves. Flowers pale yellow, almost white, with pink highlights. Blooms in late spring and early summer. Grows in garigue, on valley sides and maquis. Common.

White Hedge-nettle

Great Sage   p149
Phlomis fruticosa   Salvja tal-Madonna
Bush with greyish-green leaves with dense covering of short hair. Large yellow flowers, velvety in texture. Spring-flowering. Grows in garigue and rocky valley sides on coralline rocks. Frequent.

White Hedge-nettle   p149
Prasium majus   Te Sqalli
Dense shrub with light green leaves. Flowers generally white, sometimes tinged with purple (esp. on Comino). Flowers in winter and spring. Grows in garigue and maquis, often among stones. Tolerates disturbance. Common.

Henbit Dead-nettle   p149
Lamium amplexicaule   Kappilliera
Annual. Leaves round, bases embracing stem. Long tubular flowers are borne at the apex, from winter to spring. Grows mostly on cultivated soil in fields and gardens. Frequent.

Lesser Calamint   p149
Calamintha nepeta ssp. *glandulosa* (= *Satureja calamintha*)   Kammilta
Small prostrate shrub. Leaves small, greyish, strongly aromatic. Blooms from spring to autumn. Grows in garigue, valleys and rocky steppes. Frequent.

Maltese Savory   p149
Micromeria microphylla (= *Satureja microphylla*)   Xpakkapietra
Very small, low-growing shrublet. Stems very slender bearing small leaves,

which are often purplish. Flowers from winter to early summer. Grows in garigue, rocky steppes, rocky valley sides as well as in cracks and furrows among paving stones of large gardens. Restricted to the Puglia region of Italy and islands in the Central Mediterranean. Frequent.

Mediterranean Thyme   p149
Thymbra capitata (= Coridothymus capitatus, Thymus capitatus)   Saghtar
Dense, low shrub. Leaves small, dark green, set in four dense rows. Strongly aromatic. Stems turn white. Flowers in spring and summer. Grows in garigue. Common.

Pennyroyal   p149
Mentha pulegium   Plejju
Herbaceous perennial. Leaves rounded, strongly aromatic. Flowers purple, in dense bunches hugging stem. Blooms in late spring and in summer. Grows where fresh water occurs, such as valley bottoms and garigue rock pools. Common.

Rosemary   p149
Rosmarinus officinalis   Klin
Dense shrub, about 1 m high (sometimes up to 2m). Leaves hard, needle-like. Flowers blue, often very pale. Flowers all year round. Grows mainly in maquis on coralline rocks. Also cultivated as an ornament and for culinary purposes. Scarce.

Wild Clary   p149
Salvia verbenaca (= S. clandestina)   Salvja Salvaġġa
Herbaceous perennial. Most leaves, which are more or less lobed, grow in basal rosette. Flowers from autumn to spring. Grows in practically all habitats, even if disturbed. Common.

Family Solanaceae

White Henbane   p149
Hyoscyamus albus   Mammażejża
Biennial herb, sometimes annual or perennial. Leaves greyish, hairy. Flowers generally pale yellow with brown centre. Flowers all year round. Grows mainly in disturbed habitats, especially rubble, old walls and fortifications. Common.

Black Nightshade   p149
Solanum nigrum   Gheneb id-Dib
Annual. Flowers all year round. Produces small, black, poisonous berries. Grows mostly in sheltered but disturbed areas, along paths, under trees and beside fields. Common.
> The **Hairy Nightshade** *S. villosum* (= *S. luteum*) (Tuffieh is-Serp) is similar but berries are red. Fruit poisonous.

Black Nightshade

Greater Thorn-apple   p149
Datura innoxia (= D. meteloides)   Siġret ir-Rizzi
Annual, 1m high or more. Leaves greyish. Very large tubular white flowers, up to 20cm long. Flowers in summer and autumn. Fruit large and covered

with hard spines. Grows on disturbed ground, especially in gardens. Poisonous. Native of Central America, but naturalised in Mediterranean region. Rare, but on the increase.

Shrub Tobacco   p149
Nicotiana glauca   Tabakk tas-Swar
Small tree up to 4m high. Leaves smooth and somewhat greyish. Flowers yellow, long and narrow, in small bunches. Flowers mostly from spring to autumn. Grows in disturbed habitats, especially in rubble, building sites, old walls and fortifications. Native of South America, becoming naturalised in various Mediterranean localities. Frequent.

Family Scrophulariaceae

Wavy-leaved Mullein   p149
Verbascum sinuatum   Xatbet l-Andar
Biennial. Leaves large, rough, with wavy edges, in a flattened, basal rosette. Blooms in late spring and throughout summer. Flowers bright yellow. Found mainly on disturbed ground. Common.

Greater Snapdragon   p149
Antirrhinum tortuosum (= A. majus ssp. *tortuosum)*   Papoċċi Hamra
Shrub or herbaceous perennial. Flowers all year round. Mature fruit resembles human skull. Grows in many different habitats, both natural and disturbed, but especially in stony situations. Native of Spain, Sicily and Malta, but has now spread to various other Mediterranean localities. Common.

Sicilian Snapdragon   p149
Antirrhinum siculum   Papoċċi Bajda
Small shrub or herbaceous perennial. Closely resembles Greater Snapdragon but the slightly smaller flowers are yellowish-white, often with purplish veins. Flowers all year round and grows everywhere, especially on cliffs, walls and fortifications. Mature fruit resembles human skull. Originally endemic to Sicily and Malta, but is now naturalised in southern Italy, France and Spain. Plants with purple-veined flowers are probably hybrids of *A. siculum* and *A. tortuosum*. Frequent.

Mediterranean
Fluellen

Round-leaved Fluellen   p149
Kickxia spuria ssp. *integrifolia*   Xatbet l-Art Safra
Annual, with a spreading, prostrate habit. Leaves rounded and hairy. Flowers small, similar to those of snapdragon, generally yellow with deep violet markings. Summer-flowering. Grows on cultivated ground, especially gardens and fields. Common.
> The **Mediterranean Fluellen** *K. commutata* (Xatbet l-Art Vjola) is similar but flowers are pale violet with white and/or yellow markings, and is also found in more natural habitats. Frequent.

Maltese Toadflax   p149
Linaria pseudolaxiflora   Papoċċi ta' Malta
Small annual, with slender, more or less supine, stems. Leaves small, generally three at each node in the lower part of the stem. Flowers pale violet or white, appearing in spring. Grows in exposed pockets of soil on rocks.

Endemic to Malta and Linosa. Occurs on all the Maltese Islands. Fast declining. Rare.

Three-leaved Toadflax   p149
Linaria triphylla   Papoċċi tat-Tliet Werqiet
Annual. Generally grows erect, with three rather broad, greyish-blue leaves at each node. Flowers bunched at apex. Spring-flowering. Grows mostly in fields. Frequent.

Water Speedwell   p149
Veronica anagallis-aquatica   Veronika ta' l-Ilma
Herbaceous perennial. Leaves smooth, elongate. Stem generally hollow. Flowers from spring to autumn. Grows in watercourses. Frequent.
   Some small, annual species of *Veronica* also occur in fields and gardens.

Bellardia   p149
Bellardia trixago   Perlina Bajda
Annual, with straight rigid stems. Flowers generally white, often flushed purple. Purple plants particularly common on Comino. Spring-flowering. Semi-parasitic, as it absorbs nutrients from the roots of other plants, usually grasses (Family Poaceae). Found in steppes and garigue. Frequent.
   The **Yellow Eye-bright** *Parentucellia viscosa* (Perlina Safra) is very similar but flowers are yellow. Often found growing with Bellardia.

Three-leaved Toadflax

Family Acanthaceae

Bear's Breeches   p151
Acanthus mollis   Hannewija
Herbaceous perennial. Leaves very large, smooth and shiny. Inflorescence on erect stem which reaches a height up to 1m or more. Flowers in spring and early summer. In summer, seeds are expelled explosively from the fruit with the sound of a pistol shot. Grows in maquis and on sheltered, fertile soil in disturbed habitats. Leaves form the basis of classic ornamental motifs, especially in the capitals of Corinthian columns. Frequent.

Family Orobanchaceae

Dwarf Broomrape   p151
Orobanche muteli   Budebbus ta' l-Ingliża
Annual, only about 10cm high. Stem yellow bearing white flowers, sometimes brown with purple flowers. Blooms in spring. Parasitic on Cape Sorrel. Maltese plants belong to endemic form *melitensis*, which was originally parasitic on various leguminous plants. Common.

Bean Broomrape   p151
Orobanche crenata   Budebbus tal-Ful
Annual. Largest species of broomrape. Spring-flowering and parasitic on Broad Bean, sometimes also on garden geraniums. Common.
   Various species of broomrape are found. The **Hairy Broomrape** *O. pubescens* (Budebbus tal-Lellux) is mostly associated with Crown Daisy and Alexanders. The **Sand Broomrape** *O. densiflora* form *melitensis* (Budebbus tar-Ramel) is a rare endemic which is parasitic on Grey Birdsfoot Trefoil.

Family Plantaginaceae

Hare's-foot Plantain   p151

Plantago lagopus   Biżbula Komuni

Annual. Leaves in basal rosette, very variable in form and texture, generally straight-edged, or with only a few small teeth. Flowers small in dense, hairy inflorescences with long stamens; adapted for wind pollination. Flowers in winter and spring. Grows everywhere. Variable. Very common.

> Several species of *Plantago* are found. The **Toothed Plantain** *P. serraria* (Biżbula tas-Snien) has leaves appressed to the ground with prominent teeth along margins. The **Buck's-horn Plantain** *P. coronopus* (Biżbula tal-Baħar) has rather narrow, toothed leaves. The **Greater Plantain** *P. major* (Biżbula Kbira) has large, attractive leaves with prominent veins and long inflorescences. Rather rare, occurring along springs and watercourses.

Family Caprifoliaceae

Dwarf Elder   p151

Sambucus ebulus   Sebuqa Salvaġġa

Herbaceous perennial. Reaches about 2m and spreads by means of rhizomes. Leaves compound-pinnate. Summer-flowering. Found in certain valleys and fields, more frequently on Gozo than on the island of Malta. Rare.

> The **Common Elder** *S. nigra* (Sebuqa Sewda), a tree some 5m high, flowers in spring. Found mostly on Gozo, but does not appear to be indigenous. Rare.

Evergreen Honeysuckle   p151

Lonicera implexa   Qarn il-Mogħża

Medium-sized to large evergreen shrub. Leaves in opposite pairs. Sometimes assumes climbing or clambering habit. Flowers pinkish, appearing in spring and early summer. Grows in maquis and on rocky valley sides. Frequent.

Family Valerianaceae

Horn-of-plenty   p151

Fedia cornucopiae   Sieq il-Ħamiema

Annual. Rather low-growing with smooth leaves. Flowers in winter and spring. Found mostly in garigue and steppe, sometimes in more or less disturbed areas. Common.

Family Dipsacaceae

Southern Scabious   p151

Scabiosa maritima   Skabjoża

(= S. atropurpurea ssp. *maritima, Sixalix atropurpurea* ssp. *maritima)*

Biennial herb, sometimes perennial. Flowers in pale pink heads. Blooms in spring and summer. Grows practically everywhere. Common.

Family Asteraceae (= Compositae)

A large Family. The flowers (florets) are grouped in dense clusters which look like a single flower. Each of these inflorescences (flower-heads) is surrounded by closely packed bracts which form an involucre. The florets can be of two types: those which have an elongate tongue-like petal (the ray florets) and

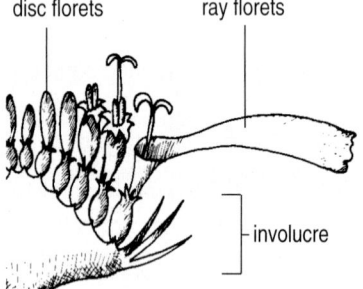

Section of typical flower-head
of the Family Asteraceae

those which are tubular with five more or less equal petals (the disc florets). Flower-heads can consist of either or both of these types. When both are present the ray florets are usually external. Each floret produces a small single-seeded fruit, which is often equipped with hairs or bristles, forming a pappus, for dispersal by wind.

Pappus

Annual Daisy   p151
Bellis annua   Bebuna
Small annual with simple leaves. Flowers in winter and spring. Found in various habitats. Common.

Southern Daisy   p151
Bellis sylvestris   Margerita Salvaġġa
Perennial herb, flowering in autumn and winter. Grows in sheltered spots in valleys and maquis. Common.

Narrow-leaved Aster   p151
Aster squamatus   Settembrina Salvaġġa
Herbaceous biennial, sometimes perennial. Tall, often exceeding 2m. Leaves long and narrow, smooth and dark green. Flower-heads very small, whitish, appearing mostly in summer. Grows in most habitats, especially where water is available, including brackish pools. Native of South and Central America, probably introduced into Malta in the 1930s. Aggressive, often smothering natural vegetation. Very common.

South American Fleabane   p151
Conyza bonariensis (= C. ambigua)   Żagħżigħa Salvaġġa
Annual, reaching just over 50cm. Leaves narrow, often greyish. Flower-heads small, consisting entirely of disc florets. Blooms mainly from spring to autumn. Grows in disturbed habitats, especially in urban areas. Native of South America. Very common.

> The **Greater Fleabane** *C. albida (= C. naudinii, C. sumatrensis, C. floribunda)* (Żagħżigħa Kbira) also appeared during the 1970s. It is very similar to *C. bonariensis* but often exceeds 2m and has broader, green leaves and with flower-heads in large dense bunches. Another South American native.

Pygmy Cudweed   p151
Evax pygmaea   Evaks
Very small greyish annual. Spring-flowering. Grows in steppes and garigue, often along footpaths. Common.

Eastern Phagnalon   p151
Phagnalon graecum ssp. *ginzbergeri*   Lixka Komuni
Small shrub. Leaves dark green above, white below. Flower-heads consist solely of disc florets, surrounded by pointed involucral bracts. Spring-flowering. Grows in garigue, steppes and also on disturbed ground. Common.

> The **Rock Phagnalon** *P. rupestre (= P. tenorii)* (Lixka tal-Blat) is very similar but the involucral bracts are rounded. Frequent in the same habitats.

Maltese Everlasting   p151
Helichrysum melitense (= H.rupestre var. *melitense)*   Sempreviva ta' Għawdex
Bush about 1m high. Leaves white, long and narrow with dense covering of short hair. Involucre and flowers bright yellow. Blooms mostly in May and June. Endemic, growing only on the western cliffs of Gozo and on Fungus

Rock Phagnalon

Rock. Said to have occurred also on the island of Malta, but has not been seen in recent times. Rare.

Golden Samphire   p151

Inula crithmoides   Xorbett
Shrub with narrow, fleshy leaves. Flowers in summer and autumn. Grows by the sea. Common.

Sticky Fleabane   p151

Dittrichia viscosa (= Cupularia viscosa, Inula viscosa)   Tulliera Komuni
Herbaceous shrub. Leaves aromatic, sticky due to numerous glandular hairs. Flowers mainly in summer and autumn. Found practically everywhere. Very common.

> The **Stinking Fleabane** *D. graveolens (= Cupularia graveolens, Inula graveolens)*(Żagħżigħa Safra) is an annual with narrow leaves and yellow flowers, found on disturbed ground. Frequent.

Maltese Fleabane   p151

Chiliadenus bocconei   Tulliera ta' Malta
Small shrub with strong smell of camphor. Leaves coated with fine white hairs in winter and spring, but smaller and green in summer and autumn during the flowering period. Grows mostly in garigue, rocky steppes and cliffs. Also found on bastions and old walls. The first endemic plant to be described, together with the Maltese Sea-lavender, by Sicilian botanist Boccone in 1674. More recent botanists have confused it with another species which does not occur in Malta. Common.

Spiny Ox-eye Daisy

Spiny Ox-eye Daisy   p151

Pallenis spinosa (= Asteriscus spinosus)   Għajn il-Baqra Xewwikija
Annual or biennial. Flowers in spring and early summer. Grows in steppes, garigue and on slightly disturbed ground. The pale-flowered form is common, while the form with deep yellow flowers is rare. Common.

> The aromatic **Seaside Ox-eye Daisy** *Nauplius aquaticus (= Asteriscus aquaticus, Odontospermum aquaticum)* (Għajn il-Baqra tax-Xatt) is similar but shorter with very deep yellow flowers, almost orange. Grows mainly on rocky ground near the sea, especially on the smaller islands like Comino, Kemmunett and Selmunett, where it is frequent.

Maltese Sea Chamomile   p151

Anthemis urvilleana (= A. secundiramea ssp. urvilleana)   Bebuna tal-Baħar
Prostrate annual. Leaves fleshy and shiny, pinnatifid. Flower-heads have gaps among the white ray florets. Blooms in spring. Grows near the sea, often carpeting large areas. This is one of a small group of species found in the small islands around Sicily. Named after the botanist and explorer D'Urville. Endemic. Frequent.

Chamomile   p151

Matricaria recutita (= M. chamomilla, Chamomilla recutita)   Kamumilla
Erect annual. Leaves finely divided. Centre of flower-head somewhat conical, consisting of greenish-yellow disc florets. Fragrant. Flowers in spring. Found mostly on disturbed ground, especially in inhabited areas. Frequent.

> The **Corn Chamomile** *Anthemis arvensis* (Bebuna tar-Raba') resembles Chamomile but is more robust and has larger flower-heads with flattened,

deep yellow discs. Leaves are somewhat greyish. Frequent, especially in disturbed areas in the countryside.

Crown Daisy   p153
Chrysanthemum coronarium (= Pinardia coronaria)   Lellux
Annual. Leaves dark green, deeply divided. Flowers bright yellow, appearing in winter and spring. On disturbed ground in both urban and countryside localities. Very common.

    The variety *discolor*, in which the ray florets are white with a yellow base, often occurs. The **Corn Marigold** *C. segetum* (Lellux tar-Raba') is rather rare and grows in cultivated fields, especially on Gozo. Leaves are broader.

Corn Chamomile

Silvery Ragwort   p153
Senecio bicolor (= S. cineraria)   Kromb il-Bahar Isfar
Shrub, which grows to just over 1m. Leaves rather fleshy, dark green above and greyish-white below due to dense coating of short hairs. Blooms from late spring to mid-summer. Grows especially in seaside localities. Common.

Groundsel   p153
Senecio vulgaris   Kubrita
Annual. Leaves shiny. Flower-heads without ray florets. Flowers in winter and spring. Grows mainly on disturbed ground. Common

Field Marigold   p153
Calendula arvensis   Suffejra tar-Raba'
Annual, blooming from autumn to early spring. Grows practically everywhere. Very common.

Shrubby Marigold   p153
Calendula suffruticosa ssp. *fulgida*   Suffejra Kbira
Herbaceous perennial. Ray florets bright orange. In flower from autumn to early summer. Grows along country pathways, in valleys and slightly disturbed areas. Frequent.

    The variety *gussonei (= C. sicula)* also occurs; it has smaller, yellow flower-heads. Endemic to Sicily and Malta.

Boar Thistle   p153
Galactites tomentosa (= Lupsia galactites)   Xewk Abjad
Annual. Florets all tubular, white, sometimes with a purple tinge. Spring-flowering. Grows everywhere, especially on disturbed ground. White-flowered form is generally the only one found, while the purple-flowered one is more common on the continent. Very common.

Horse Thistle   p153
Notobasis syriaca   Xewk tax-Xitan
Annual, growing to 1.5m or more. Leaves below flower-heads are violet. Blooms in winter and spring. Grows along country paths and in other disturbed habitats. Frequent.

Wild Artichoke   p153
Cynara cardunculus   Qaqoċċ tax-Xewk
Herbaceous perennial. Leaves very large and spiny. Flowers generally in

early summer. Grows in steppes, especially on clay and garigue; sometimes on disturbed ground. The large, deep bluish-violet flower-heads attract many insects. Common.

Milk Thistle   p153
Silybum marianum   Xewk tal-Madonna
Biennial, up to 2m high. Leaves large and broad, with white venation. Spring-flowering. Grows along country paths, on rubble and other disturbed ground. Common.

Southern Star Thistle   p153
Centaurea nicaeensis   Xewk ta' l-Ghotba
Biennial. Leaves harsh, slightly greyish. Blooms mostly from May to July. Found in steppes and fallow fields. Common.

Maltese Star Thistle   p153
Centaurea melitensis   Xewk Malti
Slender, rigid annual. Stem bears longitudinal winged ridges. Flower-heads small, appearing mainly in late spring and early summer. Grows in steppes and fallow fields. Described in 1674 from Malta by Sicilian botanist Boccone, but not endemic. Formerly frequent. Rare.

Maltese Rock-centaury

Maltese Rock-centaury   p153
Palaeocyanus crassifolius (= Centaurea crassifolia)   Widnet il-Bahar
Shrub. Leaves shaped like spoon handle, smooth and rather fleshy. Involucral bracts are smooth, without spines or bristles. Flowers mainly between May and July. Grows on cliffs in the south of Malta and Gozo. A primitive species, probably from the Tertiary Period (66-1.6 million years ago). Probably related to the ancestors of the genera *Centaurea* and *Serratula*. Often cultivated in public gardens and centre-strips. Genus and species both endemic. The national plant. Scarce in the wild.

> The original name *Centaurea spathulata* was given by Zerafa in 1827. However, since the name had already been given to another species, the botanist Bertoloni named it *C. crassifolia*. It is very different from other *Centaurea* species, especially in having succulent leaves and unarmed involucral bracts. In 1975, the Czech botanist Dostál created the genus *Palaeocyanus* for this species.

Woolly Safflower   p153
Carthamus lanatus (= Kentrophyllum lanatum)   Xewk ta' Kristu
Erect annual, growing to 50cm or more. Flowers yellow, appearing mostly in June and July. Grows in steppes, neglected fields and along country lanes and footpaths. Only the ssp. *baeticus* occurs. Common.

Clustered Carline-thistle   p153
Carlina involucrata (= C. corymbosa ssp. *involucrata)*   Sajtun
Herbaceous perennial. Internal bracts of the involucre spread like golden rays. Summer-flowering. Grows in steppes, garigue and abandoned fields. Very common.

Ground Thistle   p153
Atractylis gummifera(=Chamaeleon gummifer, Carlina gummifera)   Xewk tal-Mixta
Perennial herb with large, deep taproot. Flowers in late summer and early

autumn, long after leaves have withered. Found in steppes and garigue. Root contains a sweet but very toxic substance. Common.

Spiny Chicory   p153
Cichorium spinosum   Qanfuda
Small hemispherical shrub with many spiny branches. Flowers blue, opening for a few hours during early morning from May to July. Occurs mainly near the coast. Frequent.

> The **Chicory** *C. intybus* (Ċikwejra, grows to about 2m and is found in disturbed habitats.

Perennial Hyoseris   p153
Hyoseris radiata   Żigland tal-Pizzi
Herbaceous perennial. Leaves smooth, deeply lobed, grouped in basal rosette. Flower-heads are deep yellow and appear in winter and spring. Grows in various habitats, especially in sheltered, sloping situations. Common.

> Many species with yellow flower-heads consisting solely of ray florets (as in Dandelion) occur. Some of these are difficult to distinguish. Species which have a basal rosette include **Early Dandelion** *Taraxacum minimum* (Ċikwejra Salvaġġa), which resembles Perennial Hyoseris but flowers from September, prior to developing leaves, up to early spring. It is restricted to urban areas, especially between kerbstones and beneath walls in the Inner Harbour area. The **Tuberous Hawkbit** *Leontodon tuberosus* (= *Thrincia tuberosa*) (Żigland ta' l-Gherq) has leaves less deeply lobed and blooms in autumn and winter. Common in valleys.

Tuberous Hawkbit

Gozo Hyoseris   p153
Hyoseris frutescens   Żigland ta' Ghawdex
Small evergreen shrub. Leaves fleshy, with numerous rounded lobes. Flowers all year round. Grows on coastal rocks and in cracks in cliffs, especially in sheltered, humid localities. Endemic. Found mainly on Gozo. On the island of Malta it is restricted to only two sites. Probably the most archaic species of *Hyoseris*. Rare.

Smooth Goatsbeard   p153
Tragopogon hybridus (= *Geropogon glaber*)   Lehjet il-Bodbod
Stiff, upright annual. Leaves grass-like. Long involucral bracts. Flower-heads purplish pink. Blooms in April-May and grows mostly on clay soil, often in fallow fields. Scarce.

Smooth Sow-thistle   p153
Sonchus oleraceus   Tfief Komuni
Annual. Leaves soft and smooth, generally deeply divided. Blooms mostly in winter and spring. Grows everywhere on disturbed ground. Very common.

> Various similar species are also common or very common. The **Prickly Sow-thistle** *S. asper* (Tfief Ċar) has pale yellow flowers and stiff leaves with slightly spiny margins. The **Mediterranean Sow-thistle** *S. tenerrimus* (Tfief Fin) is sometimes perennial and has the leaves cut into narrow segments down to the midrib. It has more profusely branched, slender, rigid stems. The **Prickly Urospermum** *Urospermum picroides* (Tfief Xewwieki) is very similar to the Smooth Sow-thistle, but the involucral bracts are in a single row

Mediterranean Sow-thistle

and the ray florets are narrower. The **Common Reichardia** *Reichardia picroides* (Qanċlita) is also similar, but can be distinguished by white-edged involucral bracts.

Great Lettuce   p153
Lactuca virosa   Hass Xewwieki
Annual or biennial, up to 2m high. Leaves quite large, broad and prickly. Produces many small, pale yellow flower-heads. Summer-flowering. Found mainly in disturbed habitats, especially in inhabited areas. Common.

The **Prickly Lettuce** *L. serriola* (Hass tal-Pizzi) is similar but leaves are generally smaller and lobed. Frequent and on the increase.

Maltese Hawksbeard   p153
Crepis pusilla (= Melitella pusilla)   Melitella
Small annual with narrow, shiny leaves forming flattened rosette. Small, sessile flower-heads with very pale yellow florets are borne at the centre of the rosette. Spring-flowering. Grows along country paths. Described from Malta in 1907 by Italian botanist Sommier, who named it *Melitella pusilla*, dedicating the genus to Malta. First foreign occurrence (from Crete) was recorded in 1967, and since then it has been recorded from several other countries (including Australia!) Later transferred to genus *Crepis* in 1968 by German botanist Merxmüller. Very rare.

Monocotyledons
The Monocotyledons comprise those Families of plants whose seeds have a single cotyledon. Most of them have parallel-veined leaves and the floral parts in threes.

Class LILIOPSIDA
Family Alismataceae

Posidonia

Water Plantain   p155
Alisma plantago-aquatica   Biżbula ta' l-Ilma
Herbaceous perennial which grows in water. Leaves smooth. Flowers pink with three petals. Blooms in late spring and in summer, when it often grows higher than 1m. Grows in watercourses. Frequent.

Mediterranean Starfruit   p155
Damasonium bourgaei (= D. alisma ssp. *bourgaei)*   Damażonju
Annual water plant. First leaves are flattened and float on the surface. As the water dries, the later leaves become erect and more robust. Flowers white with three petals, appearing in spring. Grows in temporary rainwater pools in garigue. Rare.

Family Posidoniaceae

Posidonia   p155
Posidonia oceanica   Posidonja
Herbaceous marine perennial. Leaves dark green, ribbon-like, about 1cm

wide. Below the leaves is a brush-like mass of fibres, being the remains of the fibrous bases of old leaves. Flowers in early spring, and forms olive-like fruits in autumn. Plants in flower or bearing fruit are rarely seen. Leaves and rhizomes constitute a barrier breaking the force of the waves and so protect the shore. Its lush underwater meadows provide shelter and food for numerous species, and are also an important breeding ground for fish, cephalopods and crustaceans. Very sensitive to pollution, turbidity and trawling, as a result of which Posidonia meadows are regressing. Slow-growing, with a very long recovery time. The usual Maltese common name *Alka* is confusing since it is in no way related to the Algae. Common.

Family Liliaceae

Branched Asphodel   p155
Asphodelus aestivus (= A. microcarpus)   Berwieq
Herbaceous perennial. Leaves long, bluish-green verging on grey. Roots tuberous. Flowers in winter and spring. Grows mostly in rocky steppes, but can be found in most habitats. Withstands burning and grows even in nutrient-poor soils. Very common.

Mediterranean Meadow Saffron   p155
Colchicum cupanii   Busieq
Bulbous perennial. Flowers light pinkish-violet to almost white, appearing in early autumn after the first rains, before leaves emerge. Grows in garigue and rocky steppes. Frequent.

Wild Tulip   p155
Tulipa sylvestris   Tulipan Salvaġġ
Bulbous perennial. Flowers deep yellow. Blooms for a very short time between late March and early April. Grows in fallow fields, in a single locality on the island of Malta. Very rare.

Autumn Squill   p155
Scilla autumnalis   Ghansar tal-Ħarifa
Bulbous perennial. Very small, with slender, shiny leaves. Flowers very pale pink, almost white, appearing in early autumn before leaf formation. Found in rocky steppes and garigue. Prone to geographical variation in size and flower colour. Common.

Sicilian Squill   p155
Scilla sicula   Ghansar Ikhal
Bulbous perennial. Leaves broad, margins bearing fringe of short, white hairs. Flowers pale bluish-grey with blue stamen filaments and green anthers. Spring-flowering. Grows in garigue, valleys and maquis. Endemic to Malta, Sicily and Calabria, being classed as rare in the latter two localities. Formerly confused with *Scilla peruviana* which has deep blue flowers and is sometimes cultivated. Scarce.

Southern Star of Bethlehem   p155
Ornithogalum narbonense   Ħalib it-Tajr Żgħir
Bulbous perennial. Grows mainly in steppes and neglected fields. Spring-flowering. Frequent.

Wild Tulip

Autumn Grape Hyacinth

Large Star of Bethlehem   p155

Ornithogalum arabicum   Ħalib it-Tajr Kbir
Bulbous perennial. Flowers fragrant, with shiny black, bead-like ovary.
Grows in steppes and neglected fields. Blooms mostly in April and May.
Threatened because it is often gathered in large bunches for sale. Frequent.

Sea Squill   p155

Urginea maritima (= Drimia maritima)   Għansar
Perennial, with a large bulb at the soil surface. Leaves broad, smooth, shiny
green. Flowers white on long, erect stems up to 1m or more. Flowers in
August and September before leaf emergence, which occurs in autumn and
winter. The plant which grows in Malta, Sicily, the circum-Sicilian islands
and the islands of the Western Mediterranean is considered by some to be
a different species, *U. pancration*. Common.

Tassel Hyacinth   p155

Muscari comosum (= Leopoldia comosa)   Basal il-Ħnieżer
Bulbous perennial. Spring-flowering. Found mostly in neglected fields and
steppes. Common.
    The **Autumn Grape Hyacinth** *M. parviflorum* (Ġjaċint tal-Ħarifa), a small
    plant frequently growing on rocky steppes and garigue, has similar violet-
    blue flowers which appear in early autumn after the first rains.

Maltese Dwarf Garlic   p155

Allium lojaconoi   Tewm Irqiq ta' Malta
Bulbous perennial. Very delicate plant which flowers in June and July.
Rather inconspicuous, growing in small depressions in the rocks in steppes
and valleys. Formerly mistaken for *A. parviflorum*, which is endemic to
Sardegna and Corsica. Botanists Brullo, Lanfranco and Pavone dedicated
this species to Sicilian botanist Lojacono-Pojero, who had noticed that the
Maltese plants were different, and whose herbarium contained a specimen
labelled *Allium melitense* which was never published. This name could not,
however, be used as it had already been assigned to a species of leek.
Endemic. Scarce.

Wild Leek   p155

Allium commutatum   Kurrat Salvaġġ
Bulbous perennial. Up to 1m or more in height, with a spherical inflorescence
containing numerous small, purplish flowers. Blooms in May and June.
Grows on rocky ground, steppes and in disturbed habitats. In most
publications on Maltese flora, this plant appears as *A. ampeloprasum,*
another species which is probably absent from Malta. Common.
    The **Maltese Leek** *A. melitense* (Kurrat ta' Malta) occurs on rocky steppes.
    It closely resembles Wild Leek, but is generally smaller (about 30cm) and with
    inflorescences rarely exceeding 3cm. Probably endemic. Very large leeks
    occur on Filfla and Fungus Rock, reaching heights of nearly 2m with 10cm
    inflorescences; they are probably variants of *A. commutatum*. The **Pale
    Garlic** *A. dentiferum* (Tewm Safrani) grows in late spring and early summer
    in neglected fields, along country paths and in other disturbed habitats in the
    open. Inflorescences consist of pale yellowish-brown flowers and have two
    long bracts. In previous publications, it was erroneously referred to as *A.
    paniculatum*, which is not found in Malta. The **Cultivated Leek** is *A.
    porrum*.

Hairy Garlic   p155

Allium subhirsutum   Tewm Muswaf

Bulbous perennial, up to 30cm high. Leaves with a covering of fine hairs. Flowers pure white. Blooms in spring. Grows on rocky ground on garigue and in valleys. Common.

> The **Pink Garlic** *A. trifoliatum* (Tewm tal-Linja Vjola) is similar, but petals have violet midrib and are often pinkish. Frequent in steppes and fallow fields.

Rosy Garlic   p155

Allium roseum   Tewm Hamrani

Bulbous perennial. Generally reaches a height of 30cm. Flowers vary from deep to very pale pink. Spring-flowering. Grows on rocky steppes and garigue. Frequent.

> The subspecies *bulbiferum*, which forms small red bulbils in the inflorescence, sometimes occurs. The **Sweet Garlic** *Nothoscordum inodorum* (= *A. fragrans*) (Tewm tal-Qsari) has white, fragrant flowers and occurs in gardens. Native of America.

Family Asparagaceae

Spiny Asparagus   p155

Asparagus aphyllus   Spraġ Xewwieki

Rambling shrub which reaches 1m, sometimes more. Resembles mass of spines and blooms in autumn. Grows in maquis, valleys and fallow fields. Common.

Family Smilacaceae

Common Smilax   p155

Smilax aspera   Pajżana

Climbing and clambering, thorny perennial. Flowering in autumn is followed by bunches of bright red berries. Grows in maquis and valleys. Very variable in breadth of leaf and thorniness. Frequent.

Family Amaryllidaceae

Sea Daffodil   p155

Pancratium maritimum   Pankrazju

Bulbous perennial. Leaves bluish, twisted spirally. Blooms in summer and early autumn. Grows in sand and found in almost all sandy beaches, the bulbs being deeply buried. Scarce.

French Daffodil   p155

Narcissus tazetta   Narċis

Bulbous perennial. Blooms in autumn and winter. Grows in neglected fields, steppes and on sloping ground. Often gathered in large bunches for sale. Frequent.

> After the first autumn rains, the **Autumn Narcissus** *N. serotinus* (Narċis Imwahhar) occurs. Flowers are about 3cm across and generally borne singly. Frequent in rocky steppes and garigue.

Autumn Narcissus

Family Iridaceae

Barbary Nut Iris   p157

Gynandriris sisyrinchium (= Iris sisyrinchium)   Fjurdulis Salvaġġ
Bulbous perennial. Generally has single very long, prostrate leaf, sometimes two. Spring-flowering. Flowers open in early afternoon and close at sunset. Grows in rocky steppes, garigue and footpaths in open ground. Common.
> A taller variant with larger, earlier flowers, is rare.

Southern Dwarf Iris   p157

Iris pseudopumila   Bellus
Herbaceous perennial with rhizomes. In leaf all year round. Winter-flowering. The colour and form of flowers is different in each population, but generally deep violet or pale yellow. Grows in rocky steppes and garigue. Rare.

Sicilian Iris   p157

Iris sicula   Fjurdulis Sqalli
Herbaceous perennial with rhizomes. Leaves broad, evergreen. Spring-flowering, often reaching a height of 1m. Grows in steppes and maquis. Endemic to Sicily and Malta. Rare.

Field Gladiolus   p157

Gladiolus italicus (= G. segetum)   Ħabb il-Qamħ tar-Raba'
Bulbous perennial. Flowers in spring. Grows mostly in cultivated fields. Evolved along with wheat cultivation in the Middle East and spread westwards. Common.
> The **Southern Gladiolus** *G. dubius* (Ħabb il-Qamħ tal-Wied) grows in rocky valleys. Very similar to Field Gladiolus but can be distinguished by the anthers, which are shorter than the filaments, and by the winged seeds. Rare.

Yellow-throated Crocus   p157

Crocus longiflorus   Żagħfran Salvaġġ
Bulbous perennial. Flowers in autumn, after first rains, up to early December. Grows on garigue and rocky steppes. Rare, but where found it is often abundant.

Sand-crocus   p157

Romulea ramiflora   Żagħfran tal-Blat
Bulbous perennial. Leaves slender, straight or coiled. Blooms from February to April. Grows mostly in rocky steppes and garigue. Common.
> About three other species of *Romulea* are known. These are difficult to distinguish and include **Maltese Sand-crocus** *R. melitensis* (Żagħfran tal-Blat Malti), an endemic which closely resembles Sand-crocus but has very narrow petals.

Family Juncaceae

Sharp Rush   p157

Juncus acutus   Simar Niggież
Herbaceous perennial. Leaves long, needle-like, rigid and very sharply-pointed. Spring-flowering. Flowers have hard petals which persist for a long time when dry. Grows in damp places near the coast, especially in brackish

Sand-crocus

pools. Flower stalks formerly widely used for construction of fish traps. Declining. Very scarce.

Other species of *Juncus* occur. The **Hollow-leaved Rush** *J. subulatus* (Simar ta' l-Ilma) has long, supple leaves and grows in a number of valleys. The **Sea Rush** *J. maritimu*s (Simar tal-Bahar) is rare and grows in saline marshes.

Family Orchidaceae

The Orchids constitute a large and specialised Family. They produce minute seeds, the smallest known, in large numbers. In order to germinate, these seeds have to be infected by a type of fungus which eventually penetrates to the roots. The orchid lives underground for a period which varies from one to several years, after which the leaves emerge. Maltese orchids are all tuberous perennials; they bear two tubers, one of which is swollen and the other shrivelled. This gave rise to the Maltese name *Hajja u Mejta* which literally means 'alive and dead'. Another name is *Bajdet il-Fenek* which means 'rabbit's testicles'. The flowers have three sepals and three petals, one of which is specialised and referred to as the **labellum**. In many species of the genus *Ophrys*, the labellum resembles an insect.

Brown Orchid

Small-flowered Tongue Orchid   p157
Serapias parviflora   Orkida ta' l-Ilsien Żghira
Flowers in spring. Grows in garigue, rocky steppes and abandoned fields. Frequent.

Mirror Orchid   p157
Ophrys speculum (= O. vernixia, O. ciliata)   Dubbiena Kahla
Spring-flowering. Labellum has metallic, mirror-like appearance. Grows in garigue and steppes. On the island of Malta it is very rare, while on Gozo it is scarce but rather widespread. Also found on Comino.

Brown Orchid   p157
Ophrys fusca   Dubbiena
Flowers in winter and spring. Very variable. Grows in garigue, steppes and maquis. In 1993, Belgian botanist Delforge distinguished three different races which he regards as separate species. Frequent.

Yellow Bee Orchid   p157
Ophrys lutea   Żunżana
Spring-flowering. Found in garigue, rocky steppes and maquis. Two subspecies, *lutea* and *minor*, occur. Rare.

Maltese Spider Orchid   p157
Ophrys sphegodes ssp. *melitensis*   Brimba Sewda
Spring-flowering. Grows in maquis, garigue and rocky steppes. Very variable. Was often confused with similar subspecies or species. Endemic. Scarce.

Bumble Bee Orchid   p157
Ophrys bombyliflora   Nahla
Spring-flowering. Grows mostly in garigue and rocky steppe. Frequent.

Fan-lipped Orchid   p157
Orchis collina (= O. saccata)   Orkida Hamra
Winter-flowering. Grows in garigue, rocky steppes and fallow fields. Frequent.

Scented Bug Orchid   p157
Orchis coriophora ssp. *fragrans*   Orkida Tfuh
Spring-flowering. Grows in garigue, rocky steppes and abandoned fields. Colour of flower very variable. Frequent.

Milky Orchid   p157
Orchis lactea   Orkida tat-Tikek
Winter-flowering. Grows in garigue, rocky steppes and neglected fields. Colour and pattern of flowers very variable. Belgian botanist Delforge has recently suggested that the Maltese plants are *O. conica*. Frequent.

Common Pyramidal Orchid   p157
Anacamptis pyramidalis   Orkida Piramidali
Flowers in April and May. Grows in steppes, garigue, maquis, clays and fallow fields. Frequent.

Maltese Pyramidal Orchid   p157
Anacamptis urvilleana   Orkida Piramidali ta' Malta
Flowers from February to April. Grows on garigue and rocky steppes. Resembles Common Pyramidal Orchid, but generally smaller with pale pink or white flowers. Named by botanists Sommier and Caruana Gatto. Endemic, but some plants found recently in the Gargano peninsula in Puglia (Italy) are said to belong to this species. Scarce.

Family Araceae

Friar's Cowl

Italian Lords-and-Ladies   p157
Arum italicum   Garni
Herbaceous perennial. Leaves large, dark green, arrow-shaped. Flowers small, yellow, joined together to form tongue-like stalk which is enveloped in large, light green bract. Flowers mostly in March and April. Grows in maquis and sheltered habitats, even if disturbed. Common.

Friar's Cowl   p157
Arisarum vulgare   Garni tal-Pipi
Herbaceous perennial. Leaves similar to those of Italian Lord-and-Ladies, but smaller. Flower-like bract is pipe-shaped, with green and purplish-brown stripes. Grows in all sheltered habitats which are damp and fertile. Common.

Family Typhaceae

Southern Reed-mace   p159
Typha domingensis (= T. australis, T. angustata)   Buda
Herbaceous perennial, up to 3m tall. Flowers mostly between May and July. Grows out of the water in watercourses. Formerly rare, now on the increase,

growing in various localities where fresh water occurs. Scarce.

Previous publications mention two other species, *T.latifolia* and *T. angustifolia,* but these were probably never present.

Family Cyperaceae
Various species occur, including several of the genus *Carex* (Maltese *Soghda*)

Round-headed Club-rush p159

Holoschoenus vulgaris (= Scirpus holoschoenus) Simar tal-Boċċi
Herbaceous perennial. Long, slender, cylindrical and rigid stems. Flowers are gathered in spherical bunches, and appear in late spring and early summer. Grows in watercourses. Frequent.

Round Galingale p159

Cyperus rotundus Bordi tat-Toroq
Herbaceous perennial, with several small, round tubers. Flowers in summer and autumn. Grows along road verges and in irrigated fields. Probably not indigenous. Frequent.

The **Sweet Galingale** *C. longus* (Bordi tal-Wied) is similar but larger and is frequent in watercourses.

Family Poaceae (= Gramineae)
The largest Family of vascular plants, with about 100 species. Their anatomy is extremely specialised. The flowers are very small and wind-pollinated. They are usually grouped together in small bunches known as spikelets, enclosed in bracts. The spikelets are in turn assembled together to form the inflorescence, which may be loose or compact. Although lacking bright colours, they are nevertheless very elegant plants. Members of this Family are known as grasses.

Large Quaking Grass p159

Briza maxima Beżżulet il-Qattusa
Annual. Spikelets resemble Chinese lanterns. Spring-flowering. Grows in garigue and rocky steppes. Frequent.

Stiff Rye-grass p159

Lolium rigidum Sikrana Komuni
Annual. Spikelets on a rigid axis. Spring-flowering. Grows everywhere. Very variable. Common.

Several other species of *Lolium* occur.

Golden Dog's-tail p159

Lamarckia aurea Xkupilja
Small annual with loose, shiny, golden spikelets. Spring-flowering. Grows in steppes and garigue, often also on disturbed ground. Frequent.

Great Brome p159

Bromus diandrus Bunixxief Kbir
Annual, in flower from autumn to spring. Grows everywhere, especially in disturbed habitats. Very common.

Various other *Bromus* species are found. The **Compact Brome** *B. madritensis*

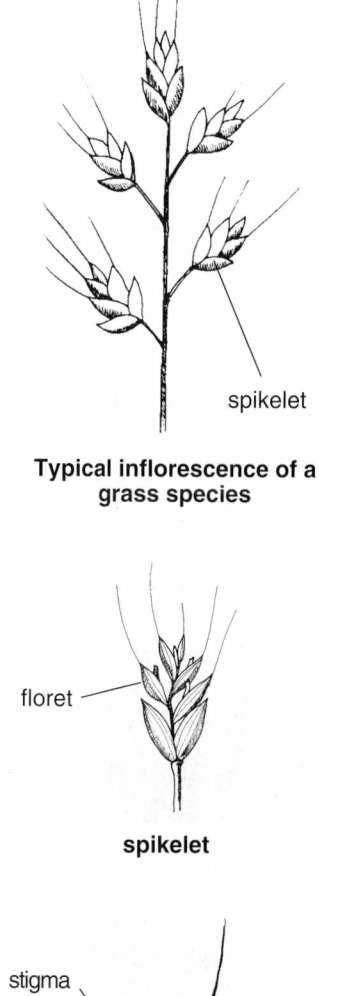

Typical inflorescence of a grass species

spikelet

floret

spikelet

stigma

anther

floret

(Bunixxief Vjola) is very similar to *B. diandrus*, but is smaller and more compact, and often has a purple tinge. Very common.

Goat Grass p159
Aegilops geniculata (= A. ovata) Brimba
Small annual. Spring-flowering. Grows in steppes and garigue. Common.

Hare's-tail Barley p159
Hordeum leporinum Nixxief Komuni
Spring-flowering annual. Grows everywhere, especially on disturbed ground. Very common.
> Various species of *Hordeum* are found, but all are less common. The **Cultivated Barley** is *Hordeum vulgare* (Xghir).

Hare's-tail Grass p159
Lagurus ovatus Denb il-Fenek
Small annual. Flowers in spring. Grows in steppe and garigue, sometimes in disturbed habitats. Frequent.

Annual Beard-grass p159
Polypogon monspeliensis Denb il-Liebru Kbir
Annual, flowering in spring and early summer. Grows mostly in valleys which hold water. Frequent.
> The **Sea Beard-grass** *P. subspathaceus* (Denb il-Liebru Żghir) is smaller, often prostrate, and sometimes tinged with red or purple. It grows in road verges, under walls and in garigue rainwater pools.

Animated Oat p159
Avena sterilis Hafur Kbir
Annual which often exceeds 1m in height. Flowers in spring. Grows everywhere, especially on disturbed ground. Very common.
> The **Barbed Oat** *A. barbata* (Hafur Żghir) is similar, but the spikelets are smaller. Also very common. Other species of *Avena,* which are difficult to distinguish, occur.

Purple Canary Grass p159
Phalaris caerulescens Skalora ta' l-Ilma
Herbaceous perennial. Spikelets assembled in large, elongate spike, which often turns purple. Flowers in spring and early summer. Grows in watercourses. Frequent in suitable habitats.
> The **Lesser Canary Grass** *P. minor* (Skalora Żghira) is an annual and is much more common than *P. caerulescens.* It does not turn purple and grows everywhere. The **Canary Grass** *P. canariensis* (Skalora), which is used as birdseed, often escapes and grows in inhabited areas.

Great Reed p159
Arundo donax Qasba Kbira
Perennial. The largest of the Poaceae, reaching a height of over 4m. Flowers in autumn. Grows along watercourses and in areas where there is underground water. Probably introduced in antiquity. In winter, stems are often cut, dried and used as windbreaks, as well as in basketry and in the manufacture of blinds. Common.

Great Reed

Another species, the **False Reed** *A. plinii* (Għaljun), is about 2m high with narrower but denser leaves. Grows in maquis and fertile valleys. The **Common Reed** *Phragmites australis* (Qasbet ir-Riħ) grows to about 3m where water is present, especially in saltmarshes.

Bermuda Grass   p159
Cynodon dactylon   Niġem
Prostrate, rhizomatous perennial. Flowers from spring to autumn. Grows everywhere, especially in disturbed and unstable habitats. Very common.

Sticky Bristle-grass   p159
Setaria adhaerans   Xrika Komuni
Annual. Generally low-growing. Spikelets bear bristles which are very adherent. Flowers mostly in summer. Occurs on cultivated ground, in gardens, orchards and fields, especially on irrigated land. Very common.
Various other species of Setaria occur.

Mediterranean Steppe-grass   p159
Stipa capensis (= S. retorta, S. tortilis)   Nixxief ta' l-Isteppa
Annual. Leaves narrow, yellowish. Spikelets golden, bearing long bristle with two nodes. Spring-flowering. Grows in all types of steppe. Very common.

Rice-grass   p159
Piptatherum miliaceum (= Oryzopsis miliacea)   Barrum Komuni
Perennial. Flowers in spring and summer. Grows mostly on disturbed ground, especially road verges, country paths and inhabited areas. Very common.

Hispid Beard-grass   p159
Hyparrhenia hirta (= Cymbopogon hirtus)   Barrum tax-Xagħri
Perennial. Grows to nearly 1m. Flowers from spring to autumn. Found in steppes and neglected fields. Common.

Purple Beard-grass   p159
Andropogon distachyus   Barrum Vjola
Perennial. Often found growing with Hispid Beard-grass, but lower and with spikelets grouped on two stalks. Frequent.

Esparto Grass   p159
Lygeum spartum   Ħalfa
Perennial with very tough rhizomes. Leaves slender but persistent. Flowers from winter to summer. Binds the clay on which it grows. Frequent.

Esparto Grass

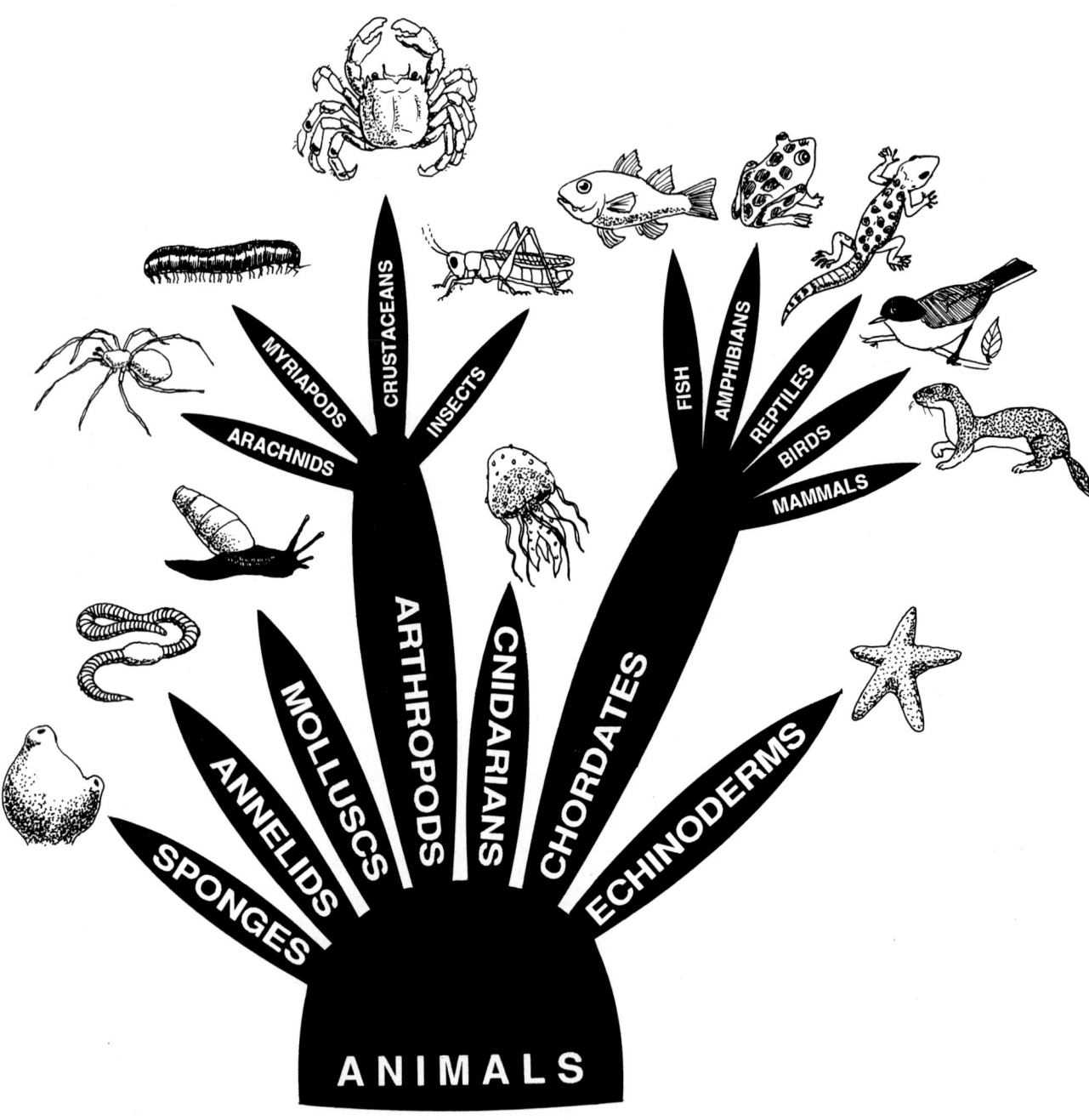

The main Animal subdivisions

Animals
Animals
Animals
Animals
Animals

introduction

More than a million and a half species of animals have so far been described worldwide. New species, especially small ones, are discovered daily.

Until recently, the Animal Kingdom was divided into two: the unicellular (one-celled) Protozoa and the multicellular (multiple-celled) Metazoa. The Protozoa, together with some unicellular organisms previously considered to be plants, have now been placed in a separate Kingdom - the PROTOCTISTA. In modern classifications, the Animal Kingdom (ANIMALIA) includes only multicellular organisms which are unable to make their own food. This has to be acquired from the environment. Animals develop from the zygote that forms when a male sperm fertilises a female ovum.

The Animal Kingdom as we now know it is divided into 33 Phyla. These include, among others, the Phylum PORIFERA (sponges), the Phylum CNIDARIA (cnidarians, i.e. hydroids, jellyfish, sea-anemones and corals) the Phylum ANNELIDA (annelids) the Phylum MOLLUSCA (molluscs) and the Phylum ECHINODERMATA (echinoderms, i.e. starfish, sea-urchins, brittle stars and sea-cucumbers).

One of the largest Phyla is ARTHROPODA, which groups animals with legs made up of jointed segments. This Phylum includes the Classes MYRIAPODA (myriapods, i.e. millipedes and centipedes), CRUSTACEA (crustaceans, i.e. woodlice, crabs and prawns), ARACHNIDA (arachnids, i.e. spiders, scorpions etc) and the very large and successful insect Class INSECTA.

Biologists often refer to 'vertebrates' and 'invertebrates'. Vertebrates refer to animals with a backbone, a Sub-Phylum of the Phylum CHORDATA. Vertebrates are subdivided into the Classes CHONDRYCHTHYES (cartilaginous fish), OSTEICHTHYES (bony fish), AMPHIBIA (amphibians), REPTILIA (reptiles), AVES (birds) and MAMMALIA (mammals). All other animals are collectively termed invertebrates, being animals without a backbone. The grouping of the Animal Kingdom as vertebrates and invertebrates is a simplistic classification: it is used only for convenience and has no scientific value.

SPONGES

Sponges (Phylum PORIFERA) are among the most primitive members of the Animal Kingdom. Their anatomy is unlike that of any other animal, in that they have neither organs nor tissues.

Each sponge functions as a number of cells living together rather than as integrated groups of cells forming a single organism. So much so that if a sponge is cut up into a number of fragments, each of these will regenerate to form another sponge. Furthermore, when two sponges grow in close proximity, they sometimes fuse to form a single entity. In spite of this, however, their component cells are unable to live in isolation, and this shows that sponges are in reality multicellular animals and not mere aggregations of individual cells.

Most sponges are marine: a few freshwater species are known, but none of them are found in Malta. Following the larval stage, sponges attach themselves to the seabed and become sessile. As larvae, however, they are free-living and can swim along with the current.

The internal anatomy of sponges is very simple. It is based on a system of **canals** which open to the exterior by means of minute incurrent **pores**. These canals connect together a large number of small chamber-like spaces, and these are in turn linked by other canals to a larger **cavity** opening to the outside through a large excurrent opening.

The body of a sponge is perforated all over, hence the scientific name for the Phylum: PORIFERA. The small internal chambers have a very important function as they are lined with collar cells bearing long **flagella** whose constant motion creates an internal current. The chambers act as pumps, drawing water into the sponge's body through the incurrent pores. This water then flows into the large chamber, from where it is expelled through the excurrent opening. This current of water carries both oxygen and food into the sponge, and also serves to remove waste products to the exterior.

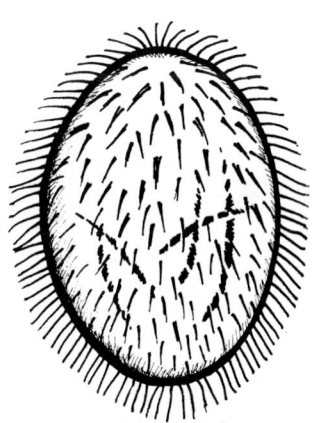

Larva of a sponge

The collar cells have another important function. Round the base of the flagellum is a delicate net-like structure. The water flows through these nets and any solid particles are filtered out. These particles constitute the food of the sponge, and they are digested inside other cells which are able to move from one part of the sponge to another, distributing the nutrients where they are required.

Apart from these cell-types, other important cells are found which form the **skeleton** of the sponge. Sponges can have two types of skeleton. One type is composed of mineral **spicules**, while another type is made up of organic **fibres**.

Different species have different types of skeleton. In some sponges the skeleton consists entirely of siliceous or calcareous spicules, while others have a fibrous skeleton. A third group has both mineral and fibrous elements.

The external appearance of sponges is also very variable. Some are spherical and others are either vase-shaped or resemble miniature trees. Certain species take the form of thin encrustations attached to the rocky substratum. Some do not live on rocks but on muddy bottoms. Specialised forms exist which bore into calcareous rocks or into mollusc shells. The body-form of a sponge is very dependent on the environment. Sponges which live in fast-moving currents tend to have a flattened shape, while sponges living in moderate currents tend to be spherical; in the absence of currents, sponges tend to have a tree-like or vasiform body.

Sponges which live on mud or fine sand usually have a stalk-like base, so that their body is raised from the bottom and can be kept free of sediment.

The most familiar sponges are of course those used as bath sponges. Two or three such species are found in the Mediterranean and in some countries, such as Greece and Tunisia, they are gathered on a commercial basis. Divers, sometimes using aqualungs, remove the sponges from the bottom. After thorough washing they are dried in the sun so that their body decomposes and only the fibrous skeleton is left (these species do not have any spicules). This is followed by chemical treatment to remove odours and any other remains. In the Mediterranean, this industry is presently suffering from a disease which attacks the skeletal fibres, causing them to decay.

Little is known about sponges which live in the sea around Malta, since this group has not yet been studied scientifically. What we know is that numerous species can be found growing on rocks, sea-grass rhizomes, in dark rock crevices, and even in deep undersea caves. Some shell and rock-boring forms are also known, as well as others which live on muddy bottoms.

Seasoned fishermen from the southern coasts of Malta maintain that bath sponges can be found around Filfla, and that these used to be collected by foreign sponge-divers. Recent studies conducted in shallow waters, however, failed to reveal the presence of these species, although this does not exclude their possible presence in deeper waters.

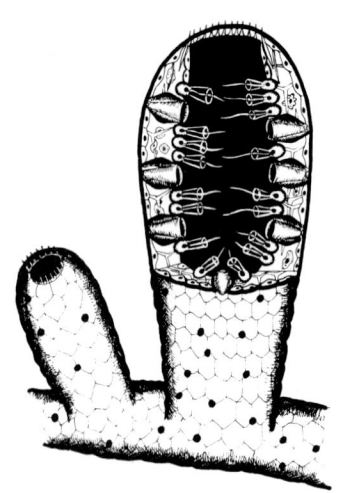

Internal structure of
a sponge

Order Dictyoceratida
Family Spongiidae

Black Sponge   p161

Ircinia spinosa   Sponża Sewda
6-20cm. Found on both deep and shallow rocky bottoms, in clear water where strong currents prevail. Very common.

Order Hadromerida
Family Chondrosiidae

Brown Sponge   p161
Chondrilla nucula   Sponża Kannella
3cm. Grows on shallow, rocky bottoms, especially in sheltered areas which are relatively free from currents. Very common.

Order Poecilosclerida
Family Myxillidae

Red Sponge   p161
Crambe crambe   Sponża Ħamra
10cm. Grows as thin layer on rocks in poorly illuminated places such as under ledges or inside the mouths of caves. Very delicate - disintegrates on handling. Common.

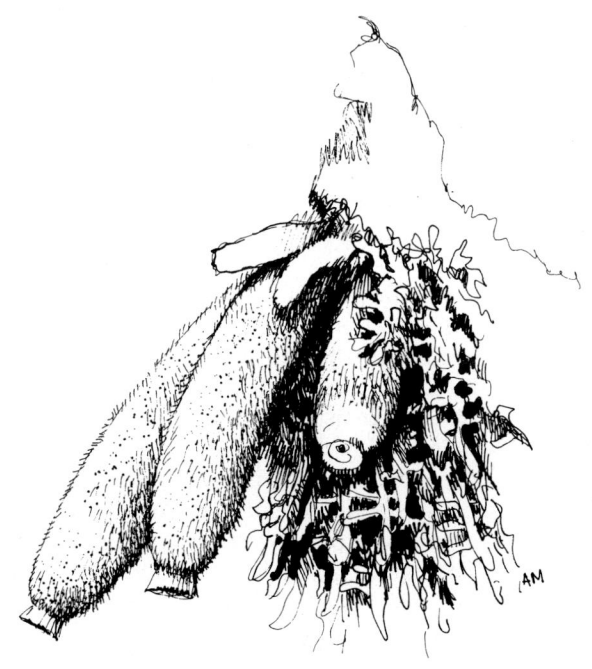

Different species of sponges

CNIDARIANS

The Phylum CNIDARIA is subdivided into three main Classes: HYDROZOA (hydroids), SCYPHOZOA (jellyfish) and ANTHOZOA (corals and sea-anemones).

The body of all these organisms consists of two **tissue-layers**: the external skin or **ectoderm**, and the internal **endoderm** which forms the wall of the animal's digestive system. These two layers are separated by a **gelatinous material**. The gut opens to the exterior through a single opening, the **mouth**. In most cnidarians, the mouth is surrounded by a number of **tentacles**. The body is usually bag-like.

Two types of organism are found in this Phylum: those attached to the bottom with the mouth uppermost, called **polyps**, and those which are not attached and swim freely in the water, with their mouth directed downwards. The latter are termed **medusae**. In many species there is an alternation between the polypoid and the medusoid forms. Many cnidarians also adopt a colonial habit, that is a number of individuals live together with their bodies connected to each other. Thus the basic bag-like body form can be diversified into various complex arrangements.

Jellyfish
Cotylorhiza tuberculata

Cnidarians are all carnivorous, feeding on other animals. Their prey ranges from small planktonic animals to larger animals like shrimps or fish. These are caught by means of the tentacles round the mouth, which contain hundreds of specialised cells, each bearing a fine trigger-like **hair**. When other animals make contact with this hair, the cell immediately ejects a long pointed thread. Various types of threads can be shot out: some are sticky, some entangle the prey, while others penetrate and inject a venom which paralyses and then kills the prey. It is this that causes the burning sensation on our skin whenever we come in contact with jellyfish or sea-anemones. The name CNIDARIA is in fact derived from the Greek word for nettles.

HYDROIDS

Class HYDROZOA

Most hydroids are marine, except members of one Family, the hydras, which are found in fresh water.

Most marine hydroids are colonial. The individual polyps are small and sometimes microscopic, but the colonies themselves may be quite extensive. There is sometimes variation in the structure of the polyps making up a colony, and in many species there is division of labour between the various types. Some individuals specialise in catching and ingesting prey, while others lack tentacles and have a reproductive function. The latter, however, do not starve because, since the members of the colony are linked, nutrients are distributed throughout the whole colony.

Many hydroid species are marine, but few people are aware of them, since most are small and inconspicuous, while the larger species look like seaweeds. Their presence is usually detected because of the burning sensation when brushing against them, or against the seaweeds on which they live.

Most hydroids pass through a medusoid as well as a polypoid phase in their life cycle. The medusae are sometimes short-lived, and the polyp predominates, while the opposite happens in other species. The hydras do not have a medusoid phase.

Order Hydroida
Family Hydridae
Freshwater polypoid hydras. At least 1 species.

Common Hydra   p161

Chlorohydra sp.   Hajdra Hadra

3mm. Lives attached to submerged plants in certain valleys with a good flow of water. Has long tentacles which are spread out in order to catch the many kinds of small organisms it feeds on. Reproduces by budding, a process in which small outgrowths are formed which later become detached to lead a separate existence. Sexual reproduction, involving the production of cyst-like eggs which fall to the bottom, also takes place. Eggs later hatch into larval hydras. Rare.

JELLYFISH

Class SCYPHOZOA

Jellyfish include both medusa and polyp forms in their life cycle. Here the medusa is much larger than the polyp, which only lives for a short time. Jellyfish spend most of their lives being carried about by ocean currents; although they can swim by opening and closing the umbrella-like body, they are not strong enough to overcome the force of the currents - at best they can rise or descend in the water. To help them maintain their position in the water, these organisms have a very thick layer of gelatinous material sandwiched between the two tissue-layers, hence the name jellyfish. They are generally much larger than the hydroids. Their tentacles carry thousands of stinging cells, and the larger species can therefore be quite dangerous. 10 species.

Order Semaestomae
Family Pelagiidae

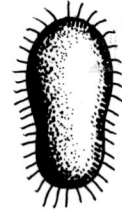

Larva of
Common Jellyfish

Common Jellyfish   p161

Pelagia noctiluca   Pelaġja

6cm. The most familiar of the species found in Maltese waters. One of the few species that do not have a polypoid phase. Very abundant in some years, tending to collect in large numbers in bays - a natural phenomenon which occurs from time to time in the Mediterranean. Common.

Cup Coral
Caryophyllia smithi

SEA-ANEMONES and CORALS
Class ANTHOZOA

This group includes many cnidarians whose external appearance varies greatly.

Sea-anemones are large polyps which live attached to rocks, to seaweeds or sea-grasses, or to the shells of other animals such as molluscs. Others burrow into sandy or muddy bottoms, leaving only their mouth, surrounded by rows of tentacles, exposed. Corals are quite different, their main feature being the calcareous skeleton they build. Each polyp secretes a calcareous material beneath and around its body. This serves a defensive function, and also provides a uniform, solid base for the polyps. The Class is divided into several Orders. Many species are known to occur, but no detail studies have yet been made.

Order Actiniaria
Family Actiniidae

Snakelocks Anemone   p161
Anemonia viridis   Artikla Ħadra
10cm. Lives in rock pools on the seashore. Green with tips of tentacles reddish. Has around 170 tentacles which can reach a length of 15cm. Very common.

Beadlet Anemone   p161
Actinia equina   Artikla Ħamra
4cm. Found in the splash zone, closer to surface than Snakelocks Anemone. Bright red with around 200 tentacles which are 2cm long. When exposed at low tide, tentacles are retracted and animal assumes spherical shape to minimise dehydration. Common.

Order Antipatharia
This Order includes the black corals. Black corals are colonial species, with a much-branched tree-like structure. This is in fact the skeleton on which the polyps grow. When dead, the skeleton has a shiny black appearance and is much sought after for the manufacture of jewellery. Black corals take years to grow, and their presence in the Mediterranean is endangered. The number of species in the Mediterranean is not firmly established.

Family Antipathidae

Black Coral   p161
Antipathes sp.   Qroll Iswed
10-100cm. Grows on muddy bottoms in very deep waters. Rare.

Order Scleractinia

Species with white skeletons. Many of the reef-forming corals of tropical seas belong to this Order. About 32 species occur in the Mediterranean.

Family Faviidae

White Coral   p161
Cladocora caespitosa   Qroll Abjad

12cm. Found in deep waters, also at shallow depths in some localities. The only reef-forming species in the Mediterranean. Reefs never wider than a few metres, in Maltese waters rarely thicker than 20cm. Collected for use in aquaria or for decoration. Declining. Frequent to rare.

Family Dendrophyllidae

Star-coral   p161
Astroides calycularis   Qroll tad-Dell

10cm. Forms colonies under shady rock ledges or in caves. Polyps bright orange. Frequent.

Order Gorgonacea

Colonial corals, where the skeleton assumes the shape of a long stalk with a few branches. The polyps grow around this skeleton. Number of species unknown.

Family Corallidae

Red Coral   p161
Corallium rubrum   Qroll Ahmar

6cm. Generally found in dark caves or in very deep water where illumination is poor. Skeleton red, sometimes pink. Some Mediterranean countries, such as Greece and Tunisia, harvest this coral for use in jewellery manufacture. Endangered in some parts of the Mediterranean. Rare.

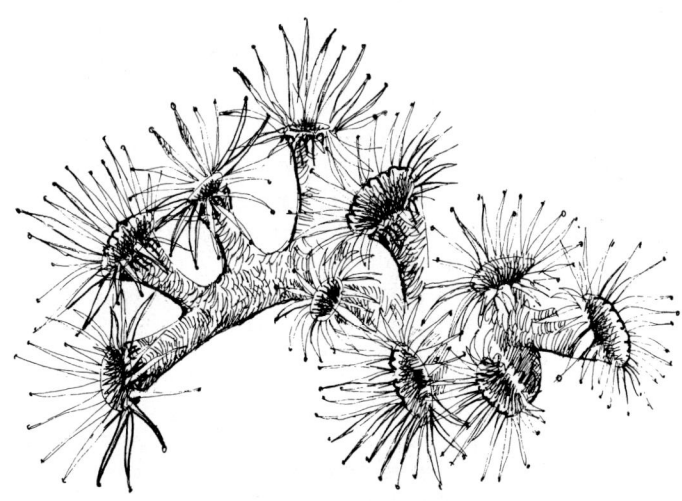

Detail of coral colony

ANNELIDS

Annelids are worms belonging to the Phylum ANNELIDA, a word derived from *annulus*, Latin for ring. This refers to one of the main characteristics of the Phylum: a body made up of a series of **rings** or segments attached to each other.

Annelids have an elongate, slender body with a **head** bearing a **mouth** at the front end. The body is composed of three layers of tissue: the external **skin**; a middle layer which includes the **muscles** and blood system; and an internal layer comprising the **lining** of the digestive system. The latter consists of a straight tube starting at the mouth and leading to a posterior **anus**. Annelids have a more complicated organisation than sea-anemones or jellyfish, and they are also more active.

The Phylum is subdivided into a number of Classes. The most important of these are the marine polychaetes (POLYCHAETA), the freshwater and terrestrial oligochaetes (OLIGOCHAETA) and the leeches (HIRUDINEA).

POLYCHAETES
Class POLYCHAETA

Polychaetes are found in all types of marine habitats. Some forms crawl over rocks, while others live in crevices or among seaweeds and sea-grasses. Bottom-living forms burrow in the sand or mud, while others secrete a tube in which they live. Certain species swim freely in open water; some of these are small or even microscopic and lead a planktonic existence.

The active, mobile species have a pair of lateral processes termed **parapodia** on each body segment; these bear fine **bristles** and are used to grip as they crawl on the bottom. These species are mostly carnivorous with a well-developed head bearing **tentacles** and **eyes**. Other marine polychaetes lead a more sedentary life buried in the bottom sand or mud, or in a **tube**. The parapodia here are much reduced and the head is not as well-developed as in the mobile forms.

The sand- and mud-burrowers feed on the surrounding sediment, either directly or else by drawing the particles towards their mouth by means of specialised tentacles. The organic matter is retained and digested, while the inorganic material is eliminated. The tentacles of the tube-dwelling forms are generally arranged around the head in a fan-like circle which can be opened and retracted. The finer branches of this fan are clothed with fine

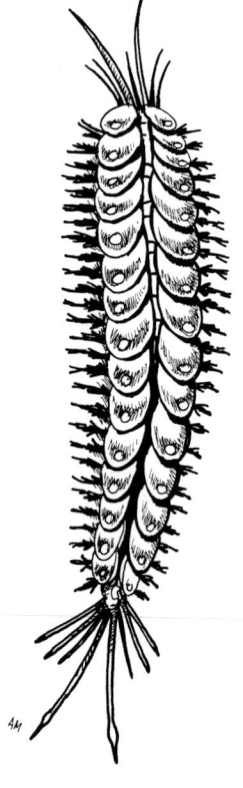

A marine annelid
Logisca extenuata

cilia. These hairs move in oar-like fashion and create currents which entrap microscopic organisms from the surrounding water: these they then propel towards the mouth.

The seas around Malta harbour over 100 species of polychaetes.

Order Eunicida
Family Eunicidae

Bristle Worm   p161

Eunice sp.   Hanex Imperjali
100cm. Lives under stones or among pebbles. A fierce predator which forages for prey during the night. Used by fishermen as bait for bream. Frequent.

Order Amphinomida
Family Amphinomidae

Dog Worm   p161

Hermodice carunculata   Busuf
30cm. Found among seaweeds on rocky substrates. Has two dense tufts of hairy bristles on each segment that are very irritating to the touch. When touched, worm erects bristles in defence. Feeds on remains of dead animals. Common.

Order Sabellida
Family Sabellidae

Fan Worm   p161

Spirographis spallanzani   Hanex tal-Fjuri
20-30cm. Tube-dwelling, using tentacles round head for filter-feeding. Fan has spiral arrangement with a diameter of about 15cm. Brightly coloured with orange, yellow and white streaks. Tube made of papery material secreted by worm itself. Any passing shadow or contact causes instant retraction of fan into tube. Frequent.

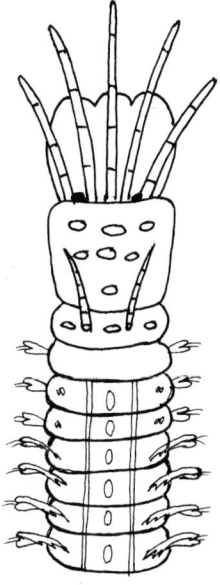

Head of Bristle Worm

OLIGOCHAETES

Class OLIGOCHAETA

Most oligochaetes live in fresh water, where they usually burrow in muddy bottoms or live among waterweeds. Many are microscopic or thread-like. One group is terrestrial, though still restricted to damp habitats. These worms live in moist soil, in decomposing leaf litter or in damp, rotting timber.

Oligochaetes do not have parapodia, and the head is poorly developed, with no tentacles or associated structures. This is because they spend their life burrowing through mud or soil, pushing the material with their head to form a small tunnel. Any head appendages would hamper such activity, and so the head is smooth and streamlined. Besides pushing through the surrounding medium, oligochaetes also ingest it and assimilate its organic components. Freshwater oligochaetes are generally small and poorly known. Many species are known to occur, but no detail studies have yet been made.

Order Haplotaxida
Family Tubificidae

Bloodworm   p161
Tubifex sp.   Hanex tal-Bjar
1cm. Lives in muddy sediment at the bottom of ponds, reservoirs or wells. Deep red, because blood is visible through transparent skin. Head usually buried in the mud, with only rear half of body exposed in the water. Common.

Family Lumbricidae
Various species of terrestrial oligochaetes are known. They play a significant role in maintaining soil fertility, because their activities increase aeration and water movement in the soil, and enrich its organic content.

Common Earthworm   p161
Allolobophora sp.   Hanex tal-Hamrija
20cm. Tunnels through soil. Comes to surface only at night in order to pull leaf litter into its hole. Also leaves burrow when soil is waterlogged. Common.

LEECHES
Class Hirudinea

Leeches evolved from the freshwater oligochaetes, and in fact few leeches live in the sea. They are generally found in fresh water or on adjoining land.

Leeches are oval in cross-section and they lack legs or a well-developed head. However, they have two structures that function as **suckers**: a small one placed at the front end near the mouth, and a larger one towards the rear end. These suckers are used for locomotion: the leech first grips the substratum with its posterior sucker, then elongates its body and attaches the anterior sucker; the rear sucker is then detached, the body shortened and the whole process repeated. In this way the animal moves about.

Leeches are notorious blood-suckers. However this habit is not common to all species: some are predatory, feeding on smaller organisms while others feed on dead animals. The blood-sucking species attach themselves to the body of larger animals, puncture the skin by means of specialised **teeth**, and suck up the blood of their host.

In the past, a leech species was used by the medical profession to draw blood from patients. This practice was also common in Malta, but since the species did not occur naturally, the leeches were imported from Sicily or mainland Italy.

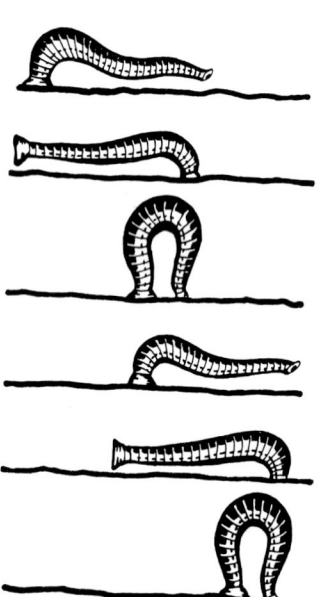

How a leech moves

Order Rhynchobdellidae
Family Piscicolidae

Fish Leech   p161

Pontobdella sp.   Sangisug tal-Bahar
3cm. Found attached to fish, generally round gills or eyes. Blood sucker.
Frequent.

Order Arhynchobdellae
Family Haemopidae

Horse Leech   p161

Haemopis sanguisuga   Sangisug Iswed
5cm. Found at Wied il-Lunzjata in Gozo, where fresh water flows all year
round. Not parasitic, but feeds on worms and small organisms. Rare.

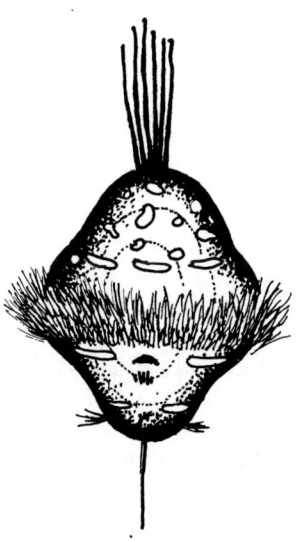

Larva of a polychaete
(Trochophore)

MOLLUSCS

The word mollusc is derived from the Latin *mollis*, meaning soft, since these are soft-bodied animals. There are around 100,000 species of molluscs in the world, found in all types of habitat, both aquatic and terrestrial. Their structure varies greatly. Apart from snails, bivalves, octopuses and cuttlefish, worm-like forms also exist; others are shaped like butterflies.

In the sea, molluscs can be found in very shallow water near the seashore; they also live in sea-grass meadows at depths of 2-40m and on rocky bottoms at depths of 60-120m. On muddy bottoms molluscs occur at depths of 10-600m; some even in waters 1000m deep. On land, molluscs occur in valleys, open countryside, on rubble walls, on plants and trees and even in cultivated ground. Others live in fresh water, but these (like their habitat) are scarce in Malta.

The body of a mollusc generally consists of five essential parts: the **foot**, the **head**, the **visceral mass**, the **mantle** and the **shell**. The shape of the foot depends on the animal's habitat, being used for locomotion, attachment or burrowing. At the front end of the foot is the head, usually bearing one or two pairs of **tentacles** with **eyes** at the top, on the side or near the base.

At the head end we also find the **mouth**, which often contains a tongue-like structure bearing a series of **teeth**. This is the rasp-like **radula**. The teeth are arranged in rows and vary in shape in different species. The radula is used to scrape off algae from rocks or seaweeds. Some predatory species use it to bore holes in the shells of other molluscs to reach at the soft tissue inside.

Molluscs known as chitons have some of the central teeth reinforced with iron minerals, so that they can withstand abrasion against the algal rocky surfaces off which they scrape algae. In advanced molluscs such as the turret shells and the cone shells, the radula is armed with venomous arrow-like teeth linked together by slender threads. These teeth can be shot out to catch other organisms, which may include small fish. Certain molluscs are parasites and have no radula: such species have developed a special type of mouth which they use to suck the body fluids of other animals. Bivalves lack a radula and ingest their food by means of small tentacles or else through special **siphons**.

The food passes into the stomach, where it is digested with the aid of a specialised rod-like crystalline **style**. Undigested particles are removed through an opening in the mantle.

Small periwinkle

The visceral mass is situated behind the foot. It is surrounded by the mantle, which also extends over the head and the foot and secretes the shell. The shell is an important feature of molluscs. It has several functions, including that of protecting the soft-bodied animal. Species have an internal shell, and in others the shell is absent. Some snails can retreat completely into their shell, and even close the shell's opening with a lid-like structure called the **operculum**. Some molluscs use the shell to swim.

The shape of the shell depends very much on the structure of the animal itself, and consists of several layers. In some molluscs, the outermost layer (the **periostracum**) is only a very thin, filmy membrane, while in others it can be robust and even hairy. Beneath the periostracum is a very hard layer of marble-like calcium carbonate. Internally, there is sometimes a third, very shiny layer: the mother-of-pearl. The shell grows through secretion and deposition by the mantle; this often follows a seasonal pattern.

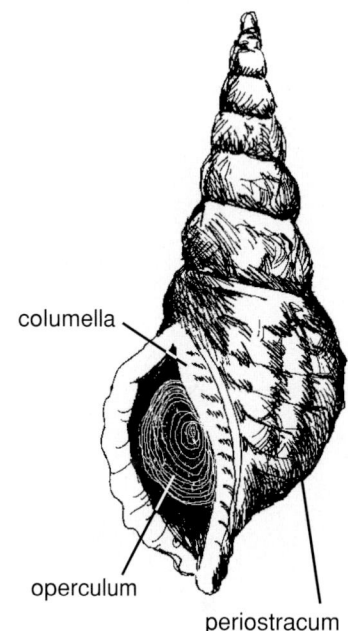

columella

operculum

periostracum

In molluscs of the Class GASTROPODA, this growth takes place around the aperture, where the mantle, which is very active, produces a substance which quickly hardens on exposure to air or water. First to be laid down is the outer periostracum, and this is followed by the inner layer. On reaching maturity, further growth only takes place round the aperture.

The shell of many snails takes the form of a spirally-coiled tube of constantly increasing diameter. In bivalves and chitons, shell growth takes place at the shell-margins. Bivalves have a shell made of two parts which are held together by means of a special muscle.

Terrestrial molluscs have a very primitive type of **lung**, which absorbs oxygen directly from the atmosphere. Bivalves obtain oxygen by drawing water through a siphon (an extension of the mantle), or through the mantle cavity, and passing it over the **gills**. The water is then ejected either through another siphon or through the same opening in the mantle.

Reproduction in molluscs differs from that of other animals, and differences also exist between different groups of molluscs. Some land snails shoot arrow-like, crystalline projectiles at each other to stimulate reproductive activity.

Certain mollusc groups are hermaphrodite, with both male and female sex organs found on the same individual. Sometimes these organs do not mature simultaneously, so that self-fertilisation is prevented. Species such as the bivalves release both sperm and ova into the seawater and these are brought together by currents. In certain advanced species, the male copulates with the female and the sperm is injected into the female's body.

Some molluscs hatch their eggs within their body, while others deposit the ova in packets, ribbons, or bag-like structures in sheltered places. Species such as the octopuses guard the eggs until hatching takes place.

In most marine molluscs, the larvae are carried away by currents. On reaching maturity, they sink to the bottom, where they will only survive if the right conditions are found.

The Phylum MOLLUSCA consists of eight Classes. One is not represented in the Maltese fauna; another two Classes consist of primitive, worm-like molluscs of which only a few species have been recorded from Malta.

CHITONS
Class POLYPLACOPHORA

Molluscs with a shell consisting of eight plates. They live in both shallow and deep waters, attached to rocks, stones and seaweeds. They feed on algae by scraping them off with their radula. About 17 species.

Family Chitonidae

Green Chiton   p161
Chiton olivaceus   Ħanżir il-Baħar
3.5cm. Lives attached to underside of stones in shallow water down to 20m. Colour very variable. Very common.

Tufted Chiton   p161
Acanthochitona fascicularis   Ħanżir Sufi
4.5cm. Lives in shallow waters, also down to 60m. Distinguished by hairy tufts at edges of plates. Common.

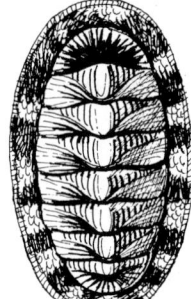

Green Chiton

SNAILS
Class GASTROPODA

The largest Class in the Phylum MOLLUSCA, with several Orders and Families. It includes marine, freshwater and even terrestrial forms. Some gastropods feed on algae and others on small animals, including other molluscs. Some lead a parasitic existence. The discarded shells of many marine snails are used by several species of crab and other animals for shelter.

The GASTROPODA is divided into three major groups: snails with gills anterior to the heart, those with gills posterior to the heart, and the terrestrial forms which have lungs instead of gills.

When a snail's aperture is on the left (with the shell viewed upright) it is said to be a 'left-handed' shell; if the aperture is on the right the shell is 'right-handed'. In Malta, only species of the Family Triphoridae are left-handed, although some left-handed terrestrial species also occur.

Maltese terrestrial and freshwater gastropods number about 60 species, while more than 600 marine species have been recorded.

Order Docoglossa
Family Patellidae

Blue Limpet   p161
Patella caerulea   Mħara
5cm. Lives attached to rocks at water's edge, also below surface. Shell yellowish inside, with bluish apex. Edible. Very common.

Brown Limpet   p161
Patella rustica   Mħara tas-Samma
3cm. Usually attached above waterline, in hollows which it excavates on exposed rocks. Very common.

Family Fissurellidae

Keyhole Limpet   p161
Fissurella nubecula   Mħara tat-Torok
3cm. Prefers sheltered habitats. Shell apex has keyhole-like opening surounded by purplish area. Frequent.

Family Haliotidae

Mediterranean Abalone   p161
Haliotis lamellosa   Mħara Imperjali
5cm. Feeds on algal growths on rock surfaces. Ear-shaped, with six or seven small openings along margin. Internally coated with mother-of-pearl. Common.

Mediterranean Abalone

Family Trochidae

Strawberry Topshell   p161
Clanculus corallinus   Frawla
1.5cm. Shell deep red, totally covered with rounded tubercles. Columella bears two large white teeth. Frequent.

Topshell   p161
Calliostoma conulus   Żugraga
3cm (larger specimens in deep waters). Feeds on algae. Frequent.

Granulated Topshell   p161
Calliostoma granulatum   Żgorra
4cm. Lives in fairly deep waters. Bears several granular growths around shell. Scarce.

Great Topshell   p161
Gibbula magus   Turban tas-Saħħar
3cm. Lives in Posidonia meadows at 30-40m. Very colourful striations on shell. Frequent.

Fabulous Topshell   p161
Gibbula fanulum   Fanal
2cm. Found in both deep and shallow waters, especially near Posidonia on sandy bottoms. Frequent.

Maltese Topshell p161
Gibbula nivosa — Gibbula ta' Malta
1cm. Lives on Lesser Neptune-grass *Cymodocea nodosa*. Ground colour is light brown with whitish patches. Empty shells very common, especially at San Tumas Bay and Birżebbuġa. Living specimens not seen for a long time. Endemic. Rare.

Toothed Topshell p161
Monodonta turbinata — Bebbuxu tal-Mazza
3cm. Prefers shallow water. Lives among stones and rocks, sometimes above waterline, also in rock pools. Very common.

Carinated Topshell p161
Jujubinus exasperatus — Lembut
1.5cm. Lives in shallow water on Posidonia leaves, also down to 80m. Deep-water form has beautiful red hue. Common.

Family Tricoliidae

Pheasant Shell p161
Tricolia speciosa — Faġjana
1.5cm. Lives in shallow water Posidonia meadows. Feeds on various algae. Shell coloration very variable. Common.

Family Turbinidae

Rough Star Shell p161
Bolma rugosa — Ghakrux ta' l-Ghajn
7cm. Calcareous operculum very thick and shaped like an eye. Frequent.

Order Neotaenioglossa
Family Cerithiidae

Common Cerith p161
Cerithium vulgatum — Brankutlu
7.5cm. Almost always buried lightly in sand or mud. Very common.

Needle Shell p161
Bittium latreillii — Taċċ
1.5cm. Found in all marine habitats. Extremely slender and elongate. Very common.

Family Turritellidae

Tower Shell p161
Turritella communis — Vit
4cm. Lives in mud, especially where dead Posidonia occurs, at depths of 40-80m. Very common.

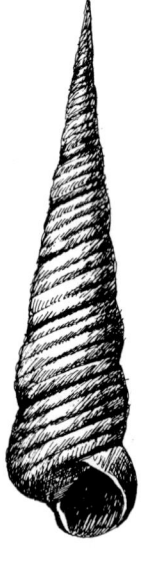
Tower Shell

Family Littorinidae

Small Periwinkle   p161
Melarhaphe neritoides   Żibġet il-Blat
7mm. Found above waterline, even on dry rocks, but approaches sea to lay eggs. Often found in groups numbering thousands of shells per square metre. Very common.

Family Aporrhaiidae

Pelican's Foot Shell   p161
Aporrhais pespelicani   Trikorni
5cm. Lives on deep, sandy or muddy bottoms. Frequent.

Family Capulidae

Bonnet Limpet   p161
Capulus ungaricus   Kapoċċ
5cm (up to 2cm in Maltese waters). Lives attached to living bivalves and sometimes on operculum of Tower Shell. Frequent.

Family Vermetidae

Giant Worm Snail   p161
Serpulorbis arenaria   Farrett tar-Ramel
30cm. Sessile, firmly attached to rocks or large boulders. Extends mucous 'net' to trap small animals which are then ingested when net is withdrawn. Common.

Giant Worm Snail
fishing with the mucous 'net'

Family Cypraeidae

Spotted Cowrie   p161
Erosaria spurca   Bahbuha Ttigrata
3cm. Lives on rocks and under stones. Mantle, which also covers shell externally, is dark pink and bears numerous lamellar filaments. Common.

Mediterranean Cowrie   p161
Luria lurida   Bahbuha ta' l-Ghajnejn
5cm. Found under stones or among rocks. Mantle, which also envelops shell externally, is dark brown or black. Frequent.

Ribbed Cowrie   p161
Trivia pulex   Bahbuha Żghira
7mm. Lives in very shallow water on rocks or seaweeds. Mantle light pink. Common.

Family Naticidae

Necklace Snail   p161
Natica stercusmuscarum   Ghakrux tar-Ramel
5cm. Lives buried in sand. Feeds mostly on other molluscs by boring a hole through their shell. Common.

Family Tonnidae

Giant Tun   p161
Tonna galea   Tina tal-Bahar

30cm. Lives buried in sand or mud. Lays large quantities of eggs on rocky bottoms or at edges of sea-grass meadows. Feeds on sea-cucumbers. Lacks protective operculum. Often falls prey to octopuses. Frequent.

Family Cassidae

Knobbed Helmet Shell   p163
Galeodea echinophora   Pum

7.5cm. Lives in fairly deep water on sandy or muddy bottoms. Common.

Ribbed Helmet Shell   p163
Phalium granulatum   Elmu

15cm. Lives on muddy or sandy bottoms. Lays eggs in Posidonia meadows and on rocky bottoms. Egg mass resembles large yellow sponge. Common.

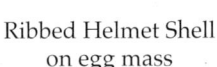

Ribbed Helmet Shell
on egg mass

Family Ranellidae

Hairy Triton   p163
Cymatium corrugatum   Bronja tas-Suf

10cm. Lives among rocks on underwater shoals at 60-100m. Periostracum thick and hairy. Frequent.

Triton Shell   p163
Charonia lampas   Bronja tal-Fond

50cm. Lives on deep sandy or muddy bottoms. Malta's largest snail. Feeds on starfish. Very rare.

Triton's Trumpet   p163
Charonia variegata   Bronja tal-Mithna

35cm. Lives at depths of 10-40m on rocky substrates. Preys on echinoderms. Has become rare owing to ease of collection. Very rare.

Family Triphoridae

Sinistral Horn   p163
Marshallora adversa   Bebbuxu Kuntrarju

2.5cm. Found on sponges on which it feeds. Long, slender left-handed shell. Common.

Family Janthinidae

Purple Sea Snail   p163
Janthina pallida   Bebbuxu Kahlani

2.5cm. Floats at surface in foamy mass of mucus and air bubbles. Feeds on surface zooplankton such as small jellyfish. Shell transparent violet. Scarce.

Family Epitoniidae

Wentletrap   p163
Gyroscala lamellosa   Garigor
3cm. Lives in shallow water among sea-anemones. Frequent.

Family Eulimidae

Parasite Shell   p163
Melanella polita   Labra
1.6cm. Parasitic on sea-cucumbers. Shell glossy white and slippery. Common.

Order Neogastropoda
Family Muricidae

Mediterranean Murex   p163
Bolinus brandaris   Sultan il-Bekkum
10cm. Lives on rocky bottoms at depths of 60-120m. Shell ornamented with spines which are easily entangled in fishing nets. Common.

Mediterranean Murex

Purple-dye Murex   p163
Hexaplex trunculus   Bekkum
10cm. Lives in both shallow and deep waters. Feeds on dead fish and sea-cucumbers. In breeding season, large numbers of females congregate and produce common egg mass which looks like large, yellow sponge. Snail secretes deep purple liquid, used since Phoenician times to dye material for nobility: this activity became an industry in the Mediterranean region. Edible. Common.

Horn Whelk   p163
Buccinulum corneum   Gharus
10cm. Lives in both shallow and deep waters. Produces small sponge-like egg mass, which it attaches to rocks or seaweeds. Common.

Tulip Shell   p163
Fasciolaria lignaria   Suffara
5cm. Animal is violet and feeds on snails and bivalves. Common.

Dog Whelk   p163
Nassarius mutabilis   Likk
2.5cm. Usually hidden in sand. Feeds on other molluscs and small animals. Common.

Rock Shell   p163
Stramonita haemastoma   Bronja Safra
12cm. Lives on shallow rocks where it feeds on limpets and other molluscs. Common.

Family Columbellidae

Rustic Dove Shell   p163
Columbella rustica   Bebbuxu tal-Ġiżirana.
2.5cm. Inhabits very shallow waters. Very common.

Family Marginellidae

Millet Grain Shell   p163
Volvarina mitrella   Qamha
1cm. Lives in both shallow and deep waters. Eggs laid singly on rocks or
seaweeds. On hatching, young snails are 2mm long and immediately crawl
off on the bottom. Common.

Family Mitridae

Fusiform Mitre   p163
Mitra zonata   Sigarru
10cm. Lives on fairly deep, sandy or muddy bottoms. Feeds on small marine
animals and other molluscs. Very rare.

Family Conidae

Mediterranean Coneshell   p163
Conus mediterraneus   Żgorru tal-Mediterran
5cm. Lives in shallow waters, generally on sandy bottoms. Catches small
creatures by shooting venomous darts, actually modified radular teeth. The
venom of this formidable weapon can cause fainting in humans! Common.

Family Turridae

Turret Shell   p163
Fusiturris similis   Torri
5cm. Lives at depths of around 200m. Preys on small animals as in
Mediterranean Coneshell, though venom not as powerful. Rare.

Family Omalogyridae

Atom Shell   p163
Omalogyra atomus   Tikka
1mm. Found in rock pools and shallow water, also at greater depths. One of
the smallest molluscs. Round and flat, rather like a disk. Common.

Order Cephalaspidea
Family Bullidae

Bubble Shell   p163
Bulla striata   Żebbuġa
3cm. Lives on seaweed near sand. Animal is brown with black spots.
Common.

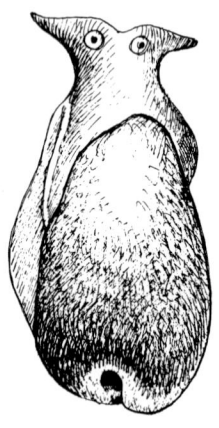

Bubble Shell

Family Haminoeidae

Green Bubble Shell   **p163**
Haminoea hydatis   Bajda tas-Serduq
2.5cm. Lives on seaweeds in shallow as well as in deep waters. Common.

Family Cylichnidae

Canoe Bubble   **p163**
Scaphander lignarius   Sassla
5cm. Lives on deep, muddy bottoms. Animal larger than shell. Gizzard
contains scaly structures (gizzard stones) which break up food to aid
digestion. Rare.

Order Anaspidea
Family Aplysiidae

Sea Hare   **p163**
Aplysia fasciata   Serduq il-Bahar
30cm. Found in shallow water, especially in bays and sheltered inlets, where
it feeds on algae. Has thin shell under mantle. Can swim. If threatened,
releases violet liquid from special glands. Common.

Order Nudibranchia
Family Discodoridae

Patched Dorid   **p163**
Discodoris atromaculata   Serduq tat-Tbajja'
7.5cm. Carnivorous. Lives and feeds on the sponge *Petrosia fuciformis*.
Shell absent. Very common.

Order Stylommatophora
Family Helicidae

Edible Snail   **p163**
Cantareus aspersus   Ghakrux Ragel
4cm. Found everywhere, especially among rocks and stones of rubble walls.
Considered an agricultural pest because it feeds on crops such as cabbages.
Edible. Very common.

Goat Snail   **p163**
Cantareus apertus   Moghza
3cm. Generally found in garigue and steppic habitats, where it feeds on
vegetation, especially leaves of Squill. Flesh blackish. Common.

Red-banded Snail   **p163**
Eobania vermiculata   Ghakrux Mara
2.5cm. Found everywhere, mostly in garigue habitats. Feeds on vegetation.
Spiral band variable in colour, not always distinct. Considered edible in
certain countries. Very common.

Red-banded Snail

Maltese Marmorana   p163
Marmorana melitensis   Bebbuxu tal-Bejt
2cm. Lives in rubble walls and shady habitats. Endemic. Common.

Family Subulinidae

Decollated Shell   p163
Rumina decollata   Trajbu
3cm. Found under stones on soil. Shell cylindrical, with top missing in adult snails. Top rounded in immature forms. Common.

Family Ancylidae

Freshwater Limpet   p163
Ancylus fluviatilis   Mhara ta' l-Ilma Helu
8mm. Found in water reservoirs and springs, especially among freshwater algae. Common.

Family Hygromiidae

Despott's Top-snail   p163
Trochoidea spratti form *despotti*   Żugraga ta' Filfla
1.5cm. Endemic to Malta, form *despotti* specifically to Filfla. Rare.

Family Clausiliidae

Mamo's Door-snail   p163
Muticaria macrostoma form *mamotica*   Dussies ta' Ghawdex
1.5cm. Form endemic to Gozo, restricted to Wied ix-Xlendi area. Threatened. Rare.

Family Limacidae
Slugs in this Family all have an internal shell underneath the mantle.

Common Slug   p163
Limacus flavus   Bugharwien tal-Bjar
12.5cm. Found everywhere, round mouths of wells, in houses, gardens and roads in rural and urban areas. Eats everything, including paper. Generally very pale yellowish. Very common.

Maltese Lehmannia   p163
Lehmannia melitensis   Bugharwien ta' Malta
4cm. Found in countryside, especially valley sides. Feeds on leaf litter and vegetation. Not easily distinguished from Common Slug, although smaller. Often bears dark stripe along back. Endemic to Malta and Sicily. Scarce.

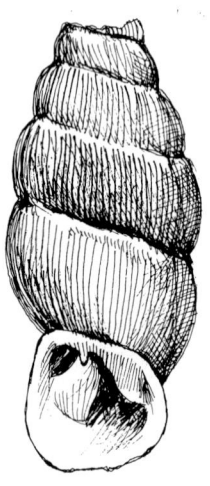

Mamo's Door-snail

TUSK SHELLS
Class SCAPHOPODA

Scaphopod molluscs have a shell shaped like an elephant's tusk. They live buried in sand or mud. About 10 species.

Family Dentaliidae

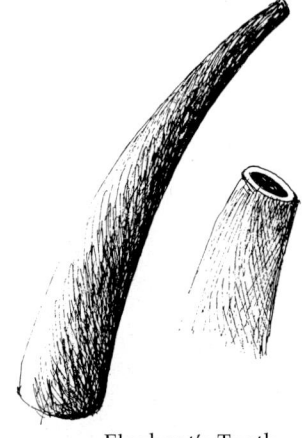
Elephant's Tooth

Elephant's Tooth   p163
Dentalium vulgare   Xifa Lixxa
5cm. Lives almost completely buried in sand, with pointed end protruding. Anchored by means of foot at other end of shell. Feeds on minute animals and particles gathered from sand by specialised tentacles. Common.

BIVALVES
Class BIVALVIA

The second largest Class of molluscs found in Malta, with about 200 species. The shell is made of two equal or unequal parts or 'valves' which articulate by means of a hinge-like device based on interlocking tooth-like projections and an elastic ligament. The valves are closed by means of a powerful muscle, and are opened automatically by the ligament when the muscle is relaxed. Some bivalves have developed a specialised burrowing foot, which they use to reach depths of up to 50cm in mud or sand. Others have adapted the foot for different functions. Some can bore into wood and even hard rock by rotation of the shell and secretion of corrosive chemicals. Certain species have a mass of hair-like fibres called the **byssus** which is used to anchor them to the bottom or some other substratum. Swimming bivalves also occur.

Some bivalves feed by drawing in water through an often elongate siphon and filtering it through gills where both food and oxygen are extracted. Others gather food from the bottom. Predatory species also exist.

Order Nuculoidea
Family Nuculidae

Nutshell   p163
Nucula nitidosa   Fażola
1.5cm. Usually stays buried under a thin layer of sand. Common.

Order Arcoida
Family Arcidae

Noah's Ark Shell   p163
Arca noae   Pedipork
8cm. Generally attached by byssus to rocks or other objects. Common.

Family Glycymerididae

Dog Cockle p163
Glycymeris glycymeris Arzella tal-Bellus
10cm. Lives half-buried in sand, especially near Posidonia at depths of 20-60m. Shell entirely covered with felt-like fur. Frequent.

Order Mytiloidea
Family Mytilidae

Bunch of
Mediterranean Mussels

Mediterranean Mussel p163
Mytilus galloprovincialis Masklu
7.5cm. Often found attached bunch-like to each other in large numbers. Anchor themselves by byssus to ropes and seacraft. Commercially farmed (not in Malta). Common.

Date Mussel p163
Lithophaga lithophaga Tamla
7cm. Lives in burrows which it excavates, even in hard rock, by shell-rotation and corrosive secretions. Edible. Sold at fishmarkets. Common.

Family Pinnidae

Fan Mussel p163
Pinna nobilis Nakkra tal-Ħarira
80cm. Anchors itself by long byssus to stones buried in sand or mud near Posidonia beds. Largest bivalve in the Mediterranean. Up to the 19th century, the byssus was dried and woven into gloves, shawls, stockings and similar articles and sold to upper classes. Endangered because of excessive collecting. Frequent.

Order Pteroida
Family Pteridae

Butterfly Mussel p163
Pteria hirundo Farfett
8cm. Lives in deep waters attached to algae, gorgonians and ropes. A predominantly Atlantic species, well-established in Maltese waters. Frequent.

Family Pectinidae

St. James' Scallop p163
Pecten jacobeus Pellegrina
15cm. Lives at depths of 40-60m on sandy bottoms. Left valve flattened, right valve convex. During the Crusades, scallop symbol was worn by pilgrims travelling to the Holy Land. Frequent.

Queen Scallop p163
Aequipecten opercularis Mrewha
5cm. Lives at depths of 60-160m, attached to rocks by the byssus. Valves equal in size and almost identical. Common.

Mediterranean Scallop   p163
Chlamys glabra   Taġen
5cm. Found on muddy bottoms, especially in harbours, where it attaches itself to stones or other objects. Rare.

Family Spondylidae

Thorny Oyster   p163
Spondylus gaederopus   Gajdra
10cm. Found in exposed places where currents prevail. Right valve cemented to rock, left valve serves as movable cover. Edible, formerly sold in fishmarkets. Formerly frequent. Scarce.

Family Limidae

File Shell   p163
Lima lima   Żbiba Ħakkieka
10cm. Can swim. Mantle extends beyond valves in the form of long sticky tentacles. Frequent.

Order Ostreoida
Family Ostreidae

Oyster   p165
Ostreola stentina   Koċċla
10cm. Lives in shallow waters. Many individuals often attached to each other. Right valve cemented to rock (sessile), left valve serves as a movable lid. Common.

Order Veneroida
Family Sphaeriidae

Caserta Pea-mussel   p163
Pisidium casertanum   Arzella ta' l-Ilma Ħelu
6mm. Very small. Freshwater mud-living species. Formerly thought extinct, recently rediscovered at Xlendi Valley. Eggs hatch within valves, where young are retained until old enough to be released. Endangered because of pollution and scarcity of perennial flowing water. Rare.

Family Lucinidae

Lucine Shell   p165
Loripes lacteus   Arzella tal-Fjuri
2cm. Lives underneath sand or mud in very shallow waters. Occurs in all main beaches. Common.

Family Carditidae

Old Cardita   p165
Venericardia antiquata   Lewża tal-Baħar
2cm. Lives on rocky bottoms and Posidonia meadows. Attached by the byssus to stones and algae. Common.

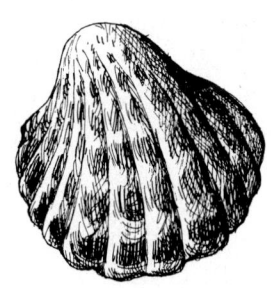

Old Cardita

Family Cardiidae

Cockle Shell
p165

Acanthocardia tuberculata
Xedaq
5cm. Lives buried in shallow sandy bottoms. Common.

Edible Cockle
p165

Cerastoderma glaucum
Arzella tal-Marsa
3cm. Occurs in brackish water. Lives buried in mud. Common.

Family Mactridae

Rayed Trough Shell
p165

Mactra stultorum
Arzella tar-Ramel
5cm. Found in all sandy bays, generally in shallow waters. Common.

Family Solenidae

Razor Shell
p165

Solen marginatus
Stoċċ
12cm. Lives entirely buried in sand, except two siphon openings which form a figure-of-eight pattern on sand surface. Frequent.

Family Tellinidae

Smooth Tellin
p165

Tellina planata
Moxt
6cm. Buried in sand, often in large numbers. Common.

Family Donacidae

Common Wedge Shell
p165

Donax trunculus
Feles
3cm. Can burrow rapidly in sand. Very common.

Family Solecurtidae

Pod Razor
p165

Solecurtus strigilatus
Ċuqlajta
10cm. Entirely buried in sand. One of the most attractive Maltese bivalves. Frequent.

Family Glossidae

Heart Cockle
p165

Glossus humanus
Hawha
7cm. Lives among small algae in sand and gravel patches on rocky bottoms at depths of around 80m. Rare.

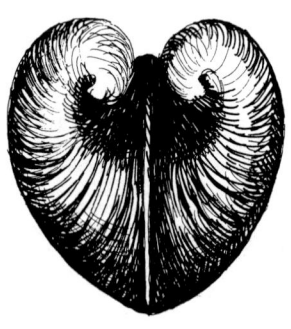

Heart Cockle

Family Veneridae

Warty Venus Shell   **p165**
Venus verrucosa   Gandoffla
5cm. Lives in sand and mud. Sold for food. Common.

Brown Venus   **p165**
Callista chione   Kannellina
10cm. Lives in fine, clean sand at depths of around 40m. Very popular
seafood in restaurants. Common.

Cross-cut Carpet Shell   **p165**
Tapes decussatus   Arzella nigra
5cm. Lives in shallow, muddy, brackish waters as at Salina and Il-Maghluq
ta' Marsascala. Common.

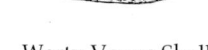

Warty Venus Shell

Family Petricolidae

Rock-eating Petricola   **p165**
Petricola lithophaga   Tamla Bajda
2cm. Lives in soft rock in shallow waters, where it excavates close-fitting
burrow. Common.

Family Teredinidae

Common Shipworm   **p165**
Teredo navalis   Qerd ix-Xwieni
10cm. Shell very small, covering only small part of worm-like mollusc. Shell
valves function as drill. Burrows into wood, generally in large numbers,
producing very long tunnels. Forms thin calcareous tube up to 20cm long.
Burrow sealed by two pallets. Wood eventually reduced to dry, spongy
consistency. Frequent.

CEPHALOPODS
Class CEPHALOPODA

The cephalopods are among the most advanced of molluscs. They have
developed a foot which is divided into ten tentacles (only eight in octopuses)
directly attached to the head. Each tentacle is armed with a number of
suckers. When threatened, they release an inky smoke screen. Cephalopods
are excellent predators and very fast swimmers thanks to a powerful jet of
water which is ejected from a siphon in the mantle. Unlike many other
molluscs, cephalopods have separate sexes. They are also important
commercially. 10 species.

Order Sepioidea
Family Sepiidae

Common Cuttlefish p165

Sepia officinalis Siċċa

30cm. Lives in sandy, muddy or rocky habitats. Feeds on fish and crustaceans, which it catches with great swiftness. Lays large, round, blackish eggs which it attaches to seaweeds or Posidonia in shallow water round about March. Eggs hatch in April-May. Shell (cuttlebone) often washed ashore. Common.

Family Sepiolidae

Little Cuttle p165

Sepiola rondeletti Dakkru

6cm. Lives on sandy or muddy bottoms, at depths of 40-200m. Young have shell which disappears on reaching adulthood. Common.

Order Teuthoidea
Family Loliginidae

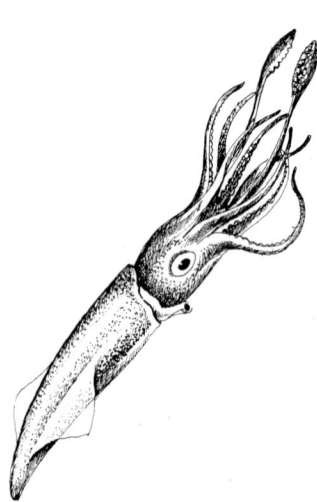

Common Squid

Common Squid p165

Loligo vulgaris Klamar

50cm. Found in both shallow and deep waters. Lays numerous eggs in clusters attached to rocks or seaweeds. Eggs hatch in June-July. Preys on fish. Releases deep black ink when threatened. Shell is like long, transparent quill. Common.

Family Ommastrephidae

Sagittal Squid p165

Todarodes sagittatus Totlu

100cm. Generally found at great depths, where it is constantly on the move. Towards end of summer, large numbers often come close to shore in shallow waters; they sometimes jump out of water in protracted leaps. Catches large fish from both surface and bottom. Shell is like long, reddish straw ending in small quill. Common.

Order Octopoda
Family Octopodidae

Octopus p165

Octopus vulgaris Qarnita

150cm. Lives in all types of marine habitats, usually hiding in holes. Feeds on crabs, fish, bivalves and gastropods. Lacks shell. Tentacles armed with two rows of suckers. Releases cloud of black ink when threatened. Has excellent camouflage. Female lays numerous eggs, which it tends until they hatch. Common.

Long-armed Octopus   **p165**
Eledone moschata   Qarnita tal-Misk
40cm. Like Octopus, but smaller. Tentacles have only one row of suckers, and joined by thin membrane extending from base to a good part of their length. Common.

Family Argonautidae

Paper Nautilus   **p165**
Argonauta argo   Dakar
Female 20cm, male 1cm. Pelagic species which sometimes ventures close to shore. Female almost completely enveloped in papery shell or sac. Ten tentacles, two of which are specialised to grasp sac, in which eggs are deposited. Male very small and lacks shell. Rare.

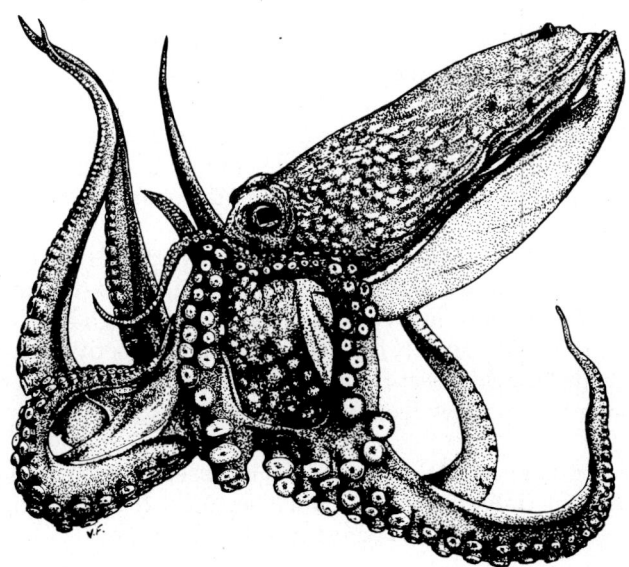

Octopus

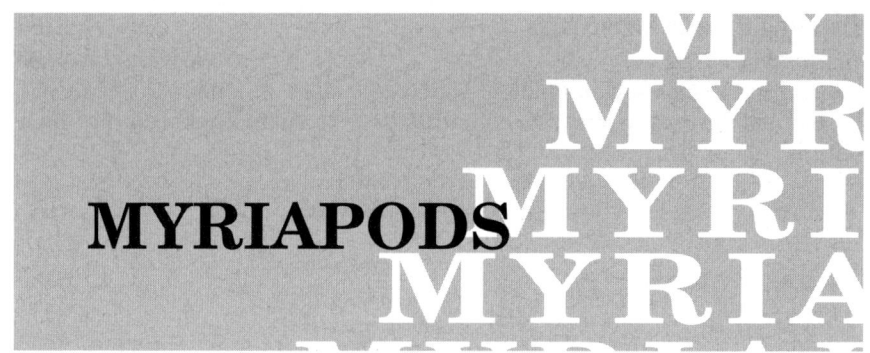

MYRIAPODS

Myriapods form part of the Phylum ARTHROPODA, and are generally slender, elongated animals with many legs. Formerly grouped in a single Class MYRIAPODA (meaning 'many-legged'), they are now classified in four separate Classes which are morphologically similar but not closely related.

Two of these Classes consist of very small, little-known animals. The other two include larger and more familiar forms, namely the millipedes (Class DIPLOPODA) and the centipedes (Class CHILOPODA).

Common Millipede

MILLIPEDES
Class DIPLOPODA

Millipedes have a body covered with a hard **exoskeleton** in the form of a number of **rings**. Each ring has two pairs of **legs**, except the head and tail rings. Some species are short and only have five rings, others are very long with more than 85 rings. These have about 170 pairs of legs, but none come anywhere near 1000 legs, as the name millipede suggests! The largest species, which live in the tropics, reach lengths of about 28cm.

Millipedes are not worms, although there is a superficial resemblance. They live in dark, damp places: under stones, in the soil, under rotting logs, in leaf litter, under flower pots or in cellars. They require a high level of humidity because in dry air they rapidly lose water through the body surface and soon die. During the day they retreat into their hiding place and only venture out during damp nights. They feed on rotting vegetation.

Millipedes are not very active. To defend themselves from predators many species have specialised **glands** which secrete a foul-smelling liquid. In some cases this liquid is also corrosive to human skin.

15 species of millipede occur in Malta, many of them small and inconspicuous.

Order Julida
Family Julidae

Common Millipede   p167
Pachyiulus flavipes   Ħanex ta' l-Indewwa tad-Djar
9cm. The largest millipede in Malta. Found in houses, especially in damp

places such as cellars, garden sheds, on humid limestone or in leaf litter. Glands arranged in a row on either side of body secrete a pungent liquid with a very persistent smell. Very common.

Order Callipodida
Family Schizopetalidae

Cave Millipede   p167
Acanthopetalum sicanum   Dudu ta' l-Intiena
5cm. Found mainly in the countryside, especially in caves, sometimes also in cellars. The only carnivorous millipede in Malta, and can survive in very dark places, where no plants grow. Produces very evil-smelling secretion. Common.

Order Glomerida
Family Glomeridae

Pill Millipede   p167
Glomeris distichella   Żibġa ta' l-Indewwa
1cm. Lives in damp leaf litter under trees or shrubs in the countryside. Not elongate, but stocky, rather like a woodlouse. Can roll up into ball in woodlouse fashion. This is done as a defence against predators, but also to minimise dehydration. Distinguished from woodlice because of colours: black and yellow or black and orange. It also has more legs than woodlice. Endemic to Sicily and Malta. Frequent.

Pill Millipede rolled up

CENTIPEDES
Class CHILOPODA

Like millipedes, centipedes have a body made up of a number of rings or segments, covered with a hard exoskeleton. They differ from millipedes, amongst other things, in having only one pair of legs on each ring, and in the legs being longer in relation to the body. The number of rings varies from species to species. Short centipedes may have about 15 segments, longer ones anything up to 181. The latter have about 362 legs, indeed far more than the hundred implied by the word 'centipede'!

Unlike millipedes, centipedes also are very active creatures. A centipede walks by smooth oar-like co-ordination of its legs, reminiscent of the oar-movements that propelled galleys in the past. Hence the word *xini* (meaning galley), the Maltese name for these animals. A centipede's first pair of legs are not used for walking, but are modified into a pair of strong, pointed claws which are used to catch and bite the prey, mainly insects, annelids and similar animals. These claws can also inject a venom which first paralyses and then kills the prey.

Centipedes live under stones, in crevices, soil and leaf litter, but are usually found in drier conditions than millipedes. This is due to the fact that their body-wall can better resist dehydration.

About 16 species of centipede occur in Malta.

Order Scolopendromorpha
Family Scolopendridae

Yellow Centipede   p167

Scolopendra cingulata   Xini Isfar

10cm. Lives in countryside under stones. Longish, yellow body with blue stripes on back. Claws large and strong. Has painful bite, although not dangerous to humans. Frequent.

Order Scutigeromorpha
Family Scutigeridae

House Centipede   p167

Scutigera coleoptrata   Xini ta' l-Indewwa

2cm. Found in houses. Emerges at night to hunt insects. Has 15 pairs of legs which reach a length of 2cm, equal to the body-length. Legs are adapted for swift running: this species is in fact one of the fastest invertebrates known. Eyes well-developed and able to detect prey at a considerable distance. Feeds on domestic insects such as house-flies. Common.

Order Geophilomorpha
Family Geophilidae

Soil Centipede   p167

Himantharium gabrielis   Xini tal-Ħamrija

15cm. Lives in soil. Unique appearance, being long, thin and rather string-like. Yellowish. Burrows in soil in search of worms and insect larvae. Frequent.

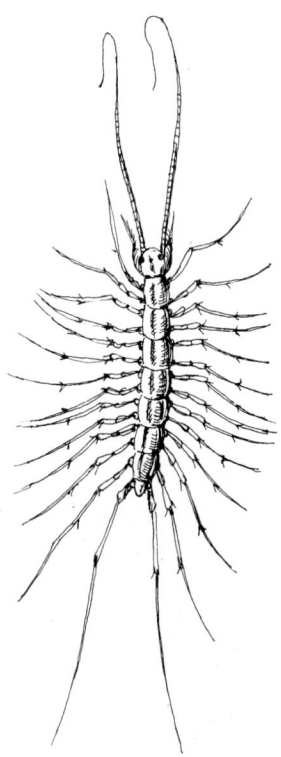

House Centipede

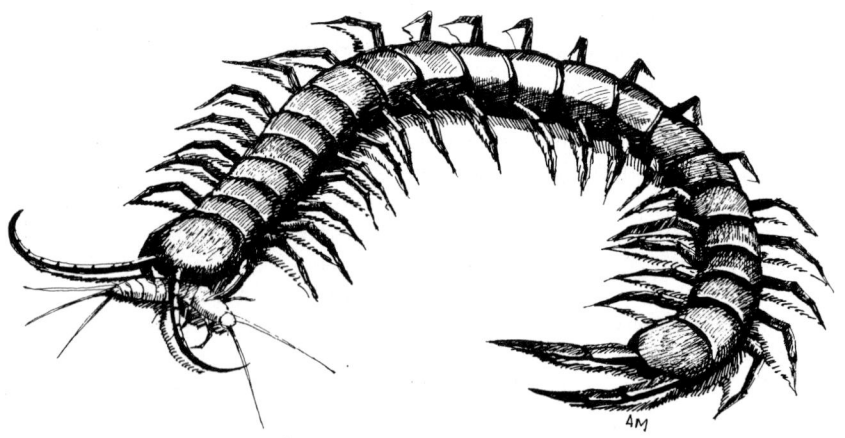

Yellow Centipede feeding on a silverfish

INSECTS

The Class INSECTA comprises hundreds of thousands of species world-wide, indeed three times the number of all other species in the Animal Kingdom put together! Insects are found in all kinds of habitats, both on land and in freshwater, although very few species live in the sea.

Insects belong to the Phylum ARTHROPODA, animals with a hard exoskeleton and jointed legs. Many insects are winged and capable of flight, a feature which distinguishes them from all other invertebrates.

An insect's body generally consists of three main sections: the **head**, the **thorax** and the **abdomen**. The thorax carries three pairs of **legs**, and frequently also two pairs of **wings**, (although some have one pair, others none at all).

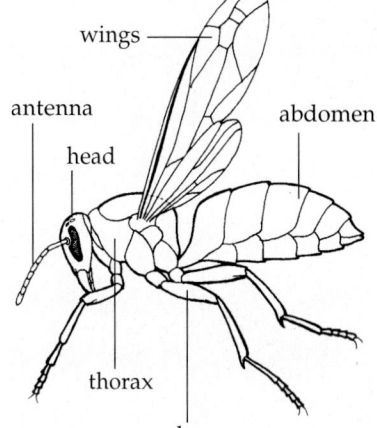

Insects play an important role in ecosystems. Their activities affect the life of other organisms, including humans. Some insects provide humans with useful materials, such as honey, wax and silk. They are important plant pollinators, which is vital for many food and other crops. Many insects are themselves the food of numerous animals, including fish, reptiles, birds and mammals. Others feed on leaves, dead wood, animal corpses and waste products, in this way contributing to the natural recycling of these remains. Several insect species are considered pests because they transmit diseases, damage stored food, and attack crops.

At least 4200 species of insect have been recorded from Malta, but it is thought that the actual figure is closer to 5000.

SILVERFISH
Order Zygentoma (= Thysanura)

Small to medium-sized, elongate insects, which are flattened and bear three filaments at the tip of the abdomen. The body is covered with scales. Their life cycle is not metamorphic. The Order is still being studied, and so far about 10 species have been found in Malta, including one endemic.

Family Lepismatidae
Insects that live in houses and also in humid habitats such as cave mouths, under stones, in ants' nests and in leaf litter. They are active insects, capable of rapid movements.

House Silverfish

House Silverfish p167

Ctenolepisma longicaudata Kamla tad-Djar

20mm. Found in human habitations. Lives among books and papers in libraries, behind hanging pictures and similar situations, where it feeds on starchy materials, fabrics, wallpaper etc. Not found in open country. Common.

MAYFLIES
Order Ephemeroptera

Fairly large, slender, soft-bodied insects, with two to three long, erect filamentous tails. Commonly found near pools and water reservoirs. The wing veins are numerous. Most species have two pairs of wings, some have only one pair. The adults are mostly nocturnal. The immature stages live in various freshwater habitats, respiring by means of gills arranged in rows along the abdomen. They feed on algae and dissolved nutrients. The life cycle is simple and when they are ready to become adult, the immatures leave the water and turn into a winged form which is, however, not yet the true adult. Another moult soon follows, and the true adult stage is reached. Adults only live for one or two days, during which time they do not feed. In Malta, mayflies are still being studied and so far 1 species has been recorded.

Family Baetidae

Mayfly p167

Cloeon sp. Ninfa

15-20mm. Found near water pools. Often enters houses, attracted by lights. Immature stages live in freshwater pools. Common.

DRAGONFLIES and DAMSELFLIES
Order Odonata

Large, colourful insects. They spend most of their life in flight, usually in the vicinity of some water cistern, pond, open reservoir or freshwater pool. They have two pairs of large, many-veined wings. The eyes are prominent and well-developed, occupying most of the head. Acute vision is necessary as these insects are swift and active predators, chasing and catching mosquitoes and other small insects in flight. The Emperor Dragonfly manages larger insects like butterflies, moths and even smaller dragonflies.

These insects lay small eggs which hatch into aquatic nymphs that breathe by means of gills. In damselflies, the external gills are flattened, leaf-like and are attached to the tip of the abdomen. They are also used for swimming. In dragonfly nymphs, the gills are internal.

Nymphs live on the bottom among weeds and can dart through the water by expelling a jet of water from the hind end. They feed on aquatic animals such as tadpoles and mosquito larvae, which they catch with a special extension of their mouth, kept folded under the head when not in use.

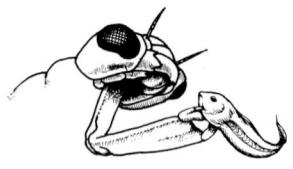

Larva of dragonfly gripping tadpole

When the nymph is mature, it leaves the water and climbs up a stalk, rock, or the side of a cistern, where it settles. After undergoing internal changes, the skin splits and the winged adult emerges. At first it is soft and moist, but it soon dries out, stiffens and flies off.

All Maltese species occur near water, laying their eggs in water cisterns, open reservoirs, ponds and pools. Some species often fly far from water, and some are migratory.

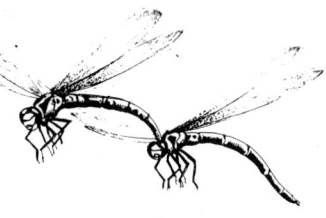

Adult dragonflies
in tandem

Family Aeshnidae
Large dragonflies. Their wings are held straight out and not folded over the body when at rest. 2 species occur all year round; 2 others are rare migrants.

Emperor Dragonfly   p167
Anax imperator   Mazzarell Sultan
75mm. One of the largest species in Europe. Territorial. Prefers still water. Male distinguished by blue abdomen with black band; female has greenish abdomen. Very strong flier, often flying far from water. Frequent.

Family Libellulidae
Relatively short dragonflies. Wings held out from the body and not folded when at rest. They have a rapid, wayward flight. Generally reddish, bluish or brownish. 7 species.

Black-lined Skimmer   p167
Orthetrum cancellatum   Mazzarell ta' l-Istrixxi
44-49mm. Largest Libellulid dragonfly. Adult often flies far from water and settles on ground. Nymph usually lives in mud and covers itself with bottom detritus. Frequent.

Scarlet Darter   p167
Crocothemis erythraea   Mazzarell Skarlat
38-40mm. Adult remains near freshwater habitat, especially during breeding period. Conspicuous red colour. Often migratory. Male is territorial. Common.

Red-veined Darter   p167
Sympetrum fonscolombei   Mazzarell Ahmar
38-40mm. Abdomen long and slender. Nymph lives among vegetation or in mud. Adult often flies long distances. Very common.

Family Coenagrionidae
Weak-flying insects with a slender abdomen. When at rest, the wings are kept slightly parted or folded vertically over the abdomen. 1 species.

Damselfly   p167
Ischnura genei   Damiġella
27-32mm. Found near running water in valleys, also near water reservoirs, ponds and large pools, where populations are fairly large. Adults remain near water. Widespread. Frequent.

GRASSHOPPERS and CRICKETS
Order Orthoptera

A diverse Order with many species, including locusts and crickets, which are stocky, large or medium-sized. The hind legs are well-developed and adapted for jumping.

Locusts and grasshoppers feed on vegetation and some can cause serious damage to crops. Some species are predators; others are scavengers or omnivorous. Both winged and wingless species occur. The winged species have a weak flight, though some are strong fliers and are capable of long migrations. There are generally two pairs of wings. The forewings are rather thick and strap-like, with many veins. The hindwings also have a copious venation, but they are membranous and are kept folded under the forewings. In some species one or both pairs are much reduced or absent. The males of many species attract females by making chirping or squeaking sounds produced by rubbing one part of their body against another. The life cycle is simple.

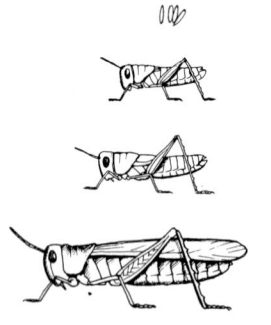

Development stages of
a grasshopper
from egg to adult

Family Acrididae

Grasshoppers which are mostly very common in the countryside. The antennae look like short horns. The hearing organs are situated at the sides of the abdomen, and the females have a short ovipositor. Coloration is usually grey or brown, but some species have brightly-coloured hindwings which are very conspicuous in flight.

Many species overwinter as eggs which are laid in the soil, others as nymphs and some as adults. Some males produce sounds during the day by rubbing their hind legs, which bear rows of peg-like projections, against the lower edges of the forewings.

About 25 species.

Brown Field Grasshopper   p167
Chorthippus brunneus   Ġurat tal-Faxxina
15-20mm. Lives among vegetation, especially in sheltered areas which are not too dry, and in valleys. Frequent.

White-banded Grasshopper   p167
Eyprepocnemis plorans   Ġurat tad-Dlil
20-40mm. Lives mostly along damp valley-bottoms, where it is often very numerous. Very common.

Field Grasshopper   p167
Aiolopus strepens   Kaħlani tal-Widien
22-32mm. Found everywhere in the countryside, but prefers damp situations. Very common.

Blue-winged Grasshopper   p167
Sphingonotus coerulans   Kaħlani tax-Xaghri
20-32mm. Found in dry situations, especially near the coast on stones and sand. Very common.

Pink-winged Grasshopper   p167
Calliptamus barbarus   Ġurat tal-Furketta
Male 15-18mm, female 30mm. Found everywhere in the countryside, often
in large numbers, in cultivated fields and arid land. Very common.

Mediterranean Slant-faced Grasshopper   p167
Acrida ungarica ssp. *mediterranea*   Ġurat ta' Rasu Twila
Male 47-52mm, female 65-77mm. Found in steppic habitats, in dry as well as
in humid areas, generally along valleys. Basks on grass on which it also
feeds. Large with flattened antennae and an elongated head. Twig-like in
appearance. Common.

Slender Red-winged Grasshopper   p167
Acrotylus patruelis   Ruxxan Irqiq
23-30mm. Found on open ground in the country. Very common.

Black-banded Grasshopper   p167
Oedipoda miniata   Ruxxan Oħxon
25-30mm. Found in open country, on sand and rocks in dry coastal areas or
on barren ground. Very common.

Egyptian Grasshopper   p167
Anacridium aegyptium   Ġurat tar-Raba'
Male 50mm, female 70mm. One of the largest grasshoppers. Found
everywhere in the countryside, especially near cultivated land, where it is
often seen on trees and shrubs. Despite large size, it causes little damage to
crops. Common.

Nymph of
Egyptian Grasshopper

Family Tettigoniidae
Species with long, slender, hair-like antennae. The auditory organs, which
are missing in some species, are located on the forelegs. The flattened
ovipositor is very conspicuous. Many species produce sounds which vary
from one species to another. Most overwinter as eggs, which females lay in
the stems of plants. About 10 species, some very common, others extremely
rare.

Common Green Bush-cricket   p167
Phaneroptera nana   Buqrun Aħdar
35mm. Delicately structured. Found among greenery in the countryside and
in gardens. Rather inconspicuous. Frequent.

Common Grey Bush-cricket   p167
Platycleis intermedia   Buqrun ta' l-Ghelieqi
33-36mm. Found mostly in fields on drying grass. Common.

Family Gryllidae
Insects with long, slender antennae. The auditory organs are on the forelegs,
while sounds are produced by special areas on the forewings. The ovipositor
is needle-like. The forewings are angled downwards along the sides of the
abdomen. Known for the sounds they produce, each species having a
distinctive tune. Nocturnal. 13 species

House Cricket   p167
Acheta domesticus   Werżieq tad-Djar
20-30mm. Found mostly in houses, bakeries and gardens, also in open countryside. A native of Southeast Asia and North Africa, but common in temperate Europe. Frequent.

Two-spotted Field Cricket   p167
Gryllus bimaculatus   Grillu
33-41mm. Found in houses and on irrigated land. More easily heard than seen. Stops singing on being approached. Formerly kept as a pet for its song! Common.

Common Ground Cricket   p167
Gryllomorpha dalmatina   Werżieq tad-Dlil
20-30mm. Found in humid places in gardens and in open countryside. Generally nocturnal. Wingless. Frequent.

Mole Cricket   p167
Gryllotalpa quindecim   Buharrât
40-45mm. Lives undergound in wetlands such as Is-Simar and Ghadira. Burrows into soil with shovel-like forelegs. Causes damage to potatoes and other crops by feeding on roots. Adult occurs all year round, but usually dormant in winter. Frequent.

Cricket in 'singing' position

EARWIGS
Order Dermaptera

Medium-sized insects, long and slightly flattened, armed with pincers at the tip of the abdomen. They may be winged or wingless, the winged forms with rounded hindwings folded under the thicker forewings. Mostly nocturnal. During the day they retreat under stones, in crevices, leaf litter and generally humid places. Feed on rotting vegetation. The female lays a batch of eggs in a hole in the soil and guards them till some time after they hatch. 5 species.

Family Forficulidae

Common Earwig   p167
Forficula decipiens   Mqass
15-20mm. Found in various habitats: under loose bark, in rotting vegetation, under stones, hollow logs and in abandoned nests of many species of bees and wasps. Widespread. Common.

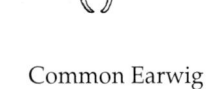

Common Earwig
with wings unfolded

MANTIDS and COCKROACHES
Order Dictyoptera

This Order comprises mantids and roaches, which are mostly tropical species. Mantids are predators with a long and slender body. Cockroaches are scavengers, and are generally ill-regarded by humans.

Family Mantidae

The mantids are large or medium-sized insects. They have a slender body and are generally slow-moving. They have excellent vision, aided by a free-revolving head. They lie immobile waiting for their prey, which they catch with a swift movement of their front legs. They overwinter as eggs, which are laid in a characteristic papery case under stones or logs. 3 species.

Praying Mantis   p167

Mantis religiosa   Debba tax-Xitan Kbira

50-70mm. Found in two colour-forms: green or brown. Eggs usually laid under or on sides of stones. Adults live in low vegetation and are difficult to spot. Frequent.

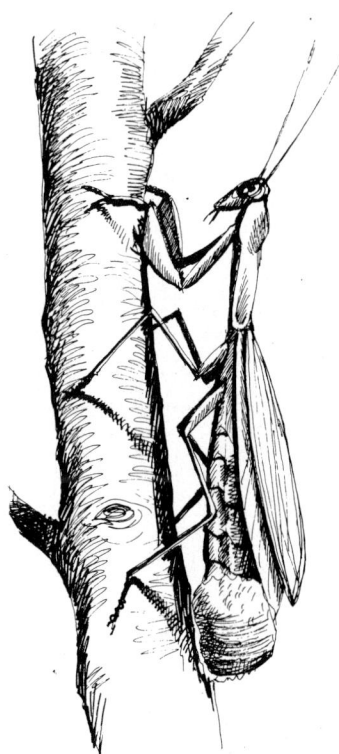

Praying Mantis
laying egg mass

Family Blattidae

Oval insects, with the head hidden underneath the thorax. The antennae are long. The wings can be well-developed, small or absent. The female often carries the eggs in an egg case until they hatch. Some species of tropical origin are now found all over the world, and are well-known pests. Native European species are all of small size. The most familiar are those living in human habitations. They are scavengers and eat any food they can find. Most have an unpleasant smell and can contaminate food. Their presence in houses is unwelcome. About 7 species.

Common Cockroach   p167

Blatta orientalis   Wirdiena tad-Djar

22mm. Relatively large, with very spiny hind legs. Often seeks warmth of houses. Wings non-functional in male, and absent in female. Adults usually appear in summer. Common.

American Cockroach   p167

Periplaneta americana   Wirdiena Ħamra

30-35mm. Relatively large, with spiny hind legs. Despite name, introduced from Africa rather than America. Found mostly in warehouses, bakeries, houses and sewers, often in large numbers, especially in harbour areas. Adults occur all year round, mostly in summer. Good fliers. Very common.

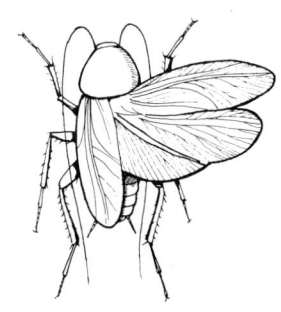

American Cockroach
with right set of wings open

Egyptian Cockroach   p167

Polyphaga aegyptiaca   Wirdiena Sewda

Male 30mm, female 27mm. Found in damp places, especially in or near houses, in gardens or roadsides. Sexes very different: male known in Maltese as *patri* (monk) and female as *soru* (nun). Frequent.

Brown-banded Cockroach   p167

Supella supellectilium   Kokroċ Isfar

Male 14mm, female 12mm. Found in houses, especially kitchens, often in large populations. Very common.

Field Cockroach   p167

Loboptera decipiens   Wirdiena ta' l-Ghelieqi

10mm. Does not occur in inhabited areas, but widespread in the countryside. Lives under stones, rubble and leaf litter, generally singly or in pairs. Frequent.

TERMITES
Order Isoptera

Small, white, soft-bodied insects with rather transparent skin. They have an ant-like appearance, even in the way they move, although they are in no way related to ants. They can be winged or wingless. The winged forms have two pairs of wings which are profusely veined and elongate.

These insects have a complex colonial organisation. A nest contains both males and females in considerable numbers. The sexual forms are all winged, but do not leave the nest except for mating or for establishing a new colony, which only takes place at a specific time of the year. A typical colony will contain an egg-laying queen and a king. The queen has a grossly distended abdomen full of eggs, of which she lays a large number throughout her life. The workers are smaller, wingless and more numerous. They look after the queen, the king and the developing termites, fetch food, and enlarge and maintain the nest. The colony also includes soldiers with well-developed heads; their function is to defend the colony. In some species, the head and mandibles are so enlarged that they have to be fed by the workers.

Many termite species are wood-borers, feeding on the wood itself. They frequently establish colonies in gardens, and when the colonies grow they often cause extensive damage to wooden structures. Although more than 2000 species of termites are known, only two are native to southern Europe. Both species occur in Malta.

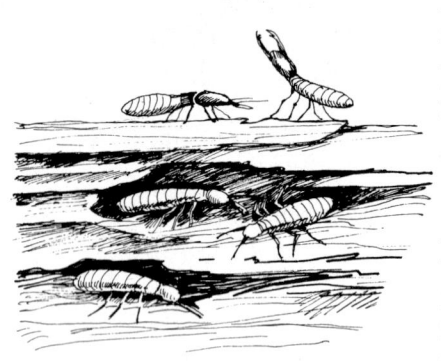

Section of a
termite colony

Family Rhinotermitidae

Damp-wood Termite   p167
Reticulitermes lucifugus   Nemla Bajda
Male and female 5mm, worker 3.5mm, soldier 5mm. Found in many localities. Burrows into wood where colonies are formed, but can also live on the ground or under the soil. Colonies often divide, and capable of rapid multiplication and dispersal. Common.

BUGS
Order Heteroptera

A large Order with a variety of generally terrestrial insects, but also including several aquatic forms. Most feed by sucking nutrients from plants. Some of these insects are found on crops and cause some damage, while others are predators and hence beneficial. A number of species suck blood from humans and livestock, and some of them can transmit diseases.

They are very variable in size and form but are generally flat, with wings folded smoothly along the body, and beak-like mouthparts. They have two pairs of wings, the front pair being thicker. When threatened, many emit an unpleasant odour. The newly-hatched young are rather different from the adults, but they change gradually to the adult form through a process of simple metamorphosis.

In Malta, over 200 species from 23 Families have been recorded. Their colour is generally brownish, although some brightly-coloured species also occur.

Family Veliidae

Common predators which live on the surface of pondwater. They have specialised hairs which enable them to move over the water surface without getting wet. They feed on organisms which fall into the water and also on mosquito larvae which rise to the surface. They pierce and hold their prey with their pointed mouthparts which are placed below the head. 2 species.

Water Cricket   p169
Velia mulleri   Żgiċċ
7mm. Found in rainwater pools in the countryside, near springs, open reservoirs and water tanks. The adult can be either winged or wingless. Common.

Family Corixidae

Insects which resemble backswimmers but have a flatter back. They swim with their back uppermost, 'rowing' with the hind legs which are clothed with specialised hairs. They feed on weeds, algae and rotting bottom vegetation. They lift the food with spoon-like forelegs and suck the liquids from it through tubular mouthparts. They only rise to the surface for air. Some species are very good swimmers. 3 species.

Lesser Water Boatman   p169
Corixa affinis   Qaddief ta' l-Ghadajjar
10mm. Found in pools among water weeds, especially Water Crowfoot. Common.

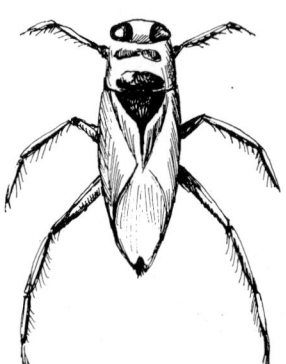

Backswimmer

Family Notonectidae

Aquatic insects which swim on their backs using their long hind legs, which are covered with long hairs. They rise to the surface for air. They feed on other creatures, such as other insects and tadpoles. They can leave the water and are good fliers. 2 species.

Greater Backswimmer   p169
Notonecta maculata   Mqass ta' l-Ilma
15mm. Found in rainwater pools; not partial to stagnant water. Often found in appreciable numbers in open reservoirs. Common.

Smaller Backswimmer   p169
Anisops sardea   Mqass ta' l-Ilma Żgħir
7-9mm. Found in rainwater pools, open reservoirs and other bodies of water, often in large groups. Common.

Family Pentatomidae

A large Family of generally colourful insects. When threatened, some species release strong, unpleasant smells. Many live and feed on plants. 30 species.

Green Vegetable Bug   p169
Nezara viridula   Spallut Ahdar
14-17mm. Found on wild and cultivated plants. Occasionally damages potato and pea crops. Common.

Underside of shield bug

Striped Shield Bug   **p169**
Graphosoma lineatum ssp. *italicum*   Spallut Irrigat
10mm. Found mostly on Fennel and Giant Fennel. Very conspicuous striped pattern. Very common.

Ornamental Shield Bug   **p169**
Eurydema ornatum   Spallut ta' l-Orjent
9mm. Found on White Mustard. Colour variable. Very common.

Bishop's Mitre   **p169**
Aelia acuminata   Spallut Qamhi
9mm. Lives on grass and other plants such as Pennyroyal and Squirting Cucumber. Occasionally harms cultivated cereals. Common.

Rufous Shield Bug   **p169**
Codophila varia   Spallut tal-Porpra
12mm. Found principally on Fennel, Golden Samphire and Bear's Breeches. Common.

Samphire Shield Bug   **p169**
Eysarcoris inconspicuus   Spallut tax-Xorbett
6mm. Lives in leaf litter under Golden Samphire plants. Common.

Family Cydnidae
Resemble bugs of the Family Pentatomidae, but have a more oval body and spiny legs. Generally live in leaf litter or sand, usually near roots. Some are good fliers and are attracted to lights. About 10 species, all blackish.

Black Burrower Bug   **p169**
Cydnus aterrimus   Seffud tat-Terrapien
11mm. Found in the countryside under stones among exposed roots. Common.

Shiny Burrower Bug   **p169**
Macroscytus brunneus   Leqqien tat-Trab
8mm. Often burrows in topsoil, leaf litter and under stones. Frequent.

Family Stenocephalidae
Very restless, strong flying insects. 5 species.

Common Stenocephalid Bug   **p169**
Dicranocephalus agilis ssp. *moralesi*   Żeġġieni
11-14mm. Widespread, living on various plant species. Common.

Family Lygaeidae
Generally drab-coloured insects. Many eat seeds, some are predators. Almost all ground dwellers, especially in sandy areas. About 50 species.

Common Ground Bug   **p169**
Apterola kunckeli   Seffud ta' l-Art
6.5 mm. Found mostly in coastal areas. Wingless and often seen running on the ground. Very common.

Soldier Bug   p169
Spilostethus pandurus   Suldat
14mm. Scurries about on the ground, but also found at the base of many plants. Common.

Samphire Lygaeid Bug   p169
Nysius graminicola   Seffud tax-Xorbett
4-5mm. Found on many plants, especially on Samphire and Fleabane flowers. Very active and flies readily. Common.

Two-spotted Ground Bug   p169
Beosus maritimus   Seffud taż-Żewġ Tikki
5.5-7.5mm. Found among leaf litter, under loose bark and under stones. Common.

Diamond-backed Ground Bug   p169
Rhyparochromus saturnius   Djamantin
7-8 mm. Same habitat as that of Two-spotted Ground Bug. Common.

Common Brown Seed Bug   p169
Emblethis denticollis   Seffud taż-Żerriegha
6mm. Prefers leaf litter, but also occurs on open ground and under stones. Common.

Red-spotted Ground Bug   p169
Aphanus rolandri   Seffud tat-Tebgha Hamra
8mm. Same habitat as that of Brown Ground Bug. Common.

Family Pyrrhocoridae
Mostly colourful insects in bright shades of red, brown and black. 1 species.

Fire Bug   p169
Scantius aegyptius   Seffud tal-Ġamar
8-9mm. Found mostly in the open on bare ground, occasionally under stones. Common.

Family Reduviidae
Generally predatory on other insects, which they pierce with beak-like mouthparts situated below the head. Some species mimic their prey, while others suck the blood of mammals. 12 species.

Red Assassin Bug   p169
Rhinocoris erythropus   Seffud ta' l-Assalt
13-14mm. Lives among vegetation, especially underneath flowers of Fennel and on branches of Samphire and Fleabane. Preys on many different insects, particularly Honey Bees. Flies for short distances when threatened. Common.

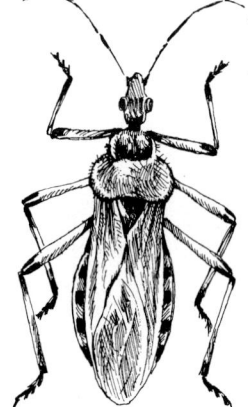

Red Assassin Bug

Family Nabidae
Delicate, long-legged, brown insects which resemble the Reduviids and like them are predators of other small insects and larvae. All morphologically similar. 8 species.

PLATE
1

ALGAE

1 **Stonewort** (p31)
2 **Grass-kelp** (p31)
3 **Sea Lettuce** (p31)
4 **Sponge Seaweed** (p32)
5 **Halimeda** (p32)
6 **Udotea** (p32)
7 **Caulerpa** (p32)
8 **Mermaid's Cup** (p32)
9 **Balloons** (p33)
10 **Pinched Seaweed** (p33)
11 **Sea-fern** (p33) and detail
12 **Dictyopteris** (p33)
13 **Peacock's Tail** (p33)
14 **Common Sargasso-weed** (p33)
15 **Rainbow Bladder-weed** (p34) and detail
16 **Flat Bladder-weed** (p34) and detail
17 **Laurencia** (p35)
18 **Pterocladia** (p34)
19 **Coral Weed** (p34)
20 **Jania** (p34) and detail
21 **Lithophyllum** (p34)
22 **Vidalia** (p35)

PLATE

2

FUNGI

1   **Cramp Balls** (p36)
2   **Early Cup Fungus** (p36)
3   **Morel** (p37)
4   **Bracket Fungus** (p37)
5   **Pine Boletus** (p37)
6   **Red-cracked Boletus** (p37)
7   **Scallop Fungus** (p37)
8   **Field Mushroom** (p37)
9   **Rose-gilled Grisette** (p38)
10 **Edible Amanita** (p38)
11 **Wood Blewits** (p38)
12 **Pied Mushroom** (p38)
13 **Pine Clitocybe** (p38)
14 **Oyster Mushroom** (p38)
15 **Stropharia** (p38)
16 **Shaggy Ink-cap** (p39)
17 **Blood Milk-cap** (p39)
18 **Pretty Russula** (p39)
19 **Stinkhorn** (p39)
20 **Colus** (p39)
21 **Earthball** (p39)

LICHENS

22 **Wall Xanthoria** (p40)
23 **Ramalina** (p40)
24 **Karst Cladonia** (p40)

PLATE
3

VASCULAR PLANTS

1 **Branched Horsetail** (p42)
2 **Tooth-leaved Clubmoss** (p42)
3 **Maidenhair Fern** (p42)
4 **Aleppo Pine** (p43) (a) female cone (b) male cone
5 **Sandarac** (p43)
6 **White Poplar** (p43) and catkin
7 **Evergreen Oak** (p43)
8 **Fig** (p44)
9 **Pellitory-of-the-wall** (p44)
10 **Large-leaved Stinging Nettle** (p44)
11 **Malta Fungus** (p44)
12 **Willow-leaved Knotgrass** (p45)
13 **Red Dock** (p45)
14 **Clustered Dock** (p45)
15 **Fat Hen** (p45)
16 **Shrubby Orache** (p45)
17 **Maltese Cliff-orache** (p46)
18 **Twiggy Glasswort** (p46)
19 **Maltese Salt-tree** (p46)
20 **Smooth-leaved Saltwort** (p46)
21 **Lesser Crystal-plant** (p46)
22 **Red Campion** (p47)

PLATE 4

VASCULAR PLANTS

1 **Love-in-a-mist** (p47)
2 **Winged Larkspur** (p47)
3 **Crown Anemone** (p47)
4 **Evergreen Traveller's Joy** (p47)
5 **Pheasant's Eye** (p47)
6 **Lesser Celandine** (p48)
7 **Autumn Buttercup** (p48)
8 **Sanicle-leaved Water Crowfoot** (p48)
9 **Bay Laurel** (p48)
10 **Opium Poppy** (p48) and fruit
11 **Common Poppy** (p48) and fruit
12 **Yellow Horned-poppy** (p49) and fruit
13 **Italian Fumitory** (p49)
14 **Caper** (p49)
15 **London Rocket** (p49)
16 **Maltese Stocks** (p49)
17 **Sweet Alison** (p50)
18 **Shepherd's Purse** (p50)
19 **Mediterranean Buckler Seed** (p50)
20 **White Mustard** (p50)
21 **Perennial Wall-rocket** (p50)
22 **Bargeman's Cabbage** (p50)
23 **Mediterranean Stocks** (p50)
24 **Sea Rocket** (p51)
25 **Wild Radish** (p51)

PLATE 5

VASCULAR PLANTS

1 **White Mignonette** (p51)
2 **Narrow Navelwort** (p51)
3 **Mediterranean Stonecrop** (p51)
4 **Blue Stonecrop** (p51)
5 **Bramble** (p52) and fruit
6 **Evergreen Rose** (p52) and fruit
7 **Salad Burnet** (p52)
8 **Creeping Cinquefoil** (p52)
9 **Hawthorn** (p52) and fruit
10 **Carob** (p52) and habit
   (a) male flower (b) female flower
11 **Milk-vetch** (p53)
12 **Pitch Clover** (p53)
13 **Common Vetch** (p53) and seed pod
14 **Crimson Pea** (p53) and seed pod
15 **Bushy Restharrow** (p53)
16 **Mediterranean Melilot** (p53)
17 **Toothed Medick** (p54)
18 **Sea Medick** (p54)
19 **Star Clover** (p54)
20 **Hop Trefoil** (p54)
21 **Lesser White Clover** (p54)
22 **Edible Birdsfoot Trefoil** (p54)
23 **Common Birdsfoot Trefoil** (p54)
24 **Grey Birdsfoot Trefoil** (p54) and seed pod

PLATE
6

VASCULAR PLANTS

1   **Winged Pea** (p55) and seed pod
2   **Common Kidney Vetch** (p55)
3   **Bladder Kidney Vetch** (p55)
4   **Shruby Kidney Vetch** (p55)
5   **Shrubby Crown Vetch** (p55)
6   **Common Horseshoe Vetch** (p55)
7   **Scorpion-tail Vetch** (p55)
8   **Sulla** (p56)
9   **Cape Sorrel** (p56)
10   **Dovesfoot Cranesbill** (p56)
11   **Glandular Storksbill** (p56)
12   **Musk Storksbill** (p56)
13   **Fagonia** (p57)
14   **Maltese Cross** (p57)
15   **Upright Yellow Flax** (p57)
16   **Annual Mercury** (p57)
17   **Castor Oil Tree** (p57) and dry fruit
18   **Pine Spurge** (p58)
19   **Tree Spurge** (p58) and habit
20   **Maltese Spurge** (p58)
21   **Sun Spurge** (p58)
22   **Fringed Rue** (p58)

PLATE

7

VASCULAR PLANTS

1   **Lentisk** (p58) and fruit
2   **Mediterranean Buckthorn** (p59) and fruit
3   **Olive-leaved Buckthorn** (p59) and fruit
4   **Common Mallow** (p59)
5   **Tree Mallow** (p59)
6   **Large-flowered Mallow** (p59)
7   **Egyptian St. John's-wort** (p59)
8   **Crisped St. John's-wort** (p60)
9   **Hoary Rock-rose** (p60)
10 **Narrow-leaved Rock-rose** (p60)
11 **Mediterranean Sun-rose** (p60)
12 **African Tamarisk** (p60) and habit
13 **Squirting Cucumber** (p60)
14 **Prickly Pear** (p61) and habit
15 **Creeping Loosestrife** (p61)
16 **Myrtle** (p61) and fruit
17 **Ivy** (p61)
18 **Sea Holly** (p61)
19 **Alexanders** (p61)
20 **Sea Samphire** (p62)
21 **Fennel** (p62)
22 **Giant Fennel** (p62)
23 **Mediterranean Hartwort** (p62) and fruit
24 **Wild Carrot** (p62)

PLATE
8

VASCULAR PLANTS

1   **Mediterranean Heath** (p62)
2   **Blue/Scarlet Pimpernel** (p62)
3   **Maltese Sea-lavender** (p63)
4   **Olive** (p63) with fruit and habit
5   **Common Centaury** (p63)
6   **Yellow-wort** (p63)
7   **Wolfbane** (p63) and fruit
8   **Field Madder** (p63)
9   **Rock Crosswort** (p64)
10 **Common Goosegrass** (p64)
11 **Wild Madder** (p64) and fruit
12 **Mallow Bindweed** (p64)
13 **Field Bindweed** (p64)
14 **Olive-leaved Bindweed** (p64)
15 **Dodder** (p64) and habit
16 **Common Heliotrope** (p65)
17 **Honeywort** (p65)
18 **Small-flowered Bugloss** (p65)
19 **Pale Bugloss** (p65) and habit
20 **Large Blue Alkanet** (p65)
21 **Borage** (p65)
22 **Vervain** (p65)
23 **Chaste Tree** (p66)

PLATE
9

VASCULAR PLANTS

1 **Olive-leaved Germander** (p66)
2 **Yellow Germander** (p66)
3 **Great Sage** (p66)
4 **White Hedge-nettle** (p66)
5 **Henbit Dead-nettle** (p66)
6 **Lesser Calamint** (p66)
7 **Maltese Savory** (p66)
8 **Mediterranean Thyme** (p67) and habit
9 **Pennyroyal** (p67)
10 **Rosemary** (p67)
11 **Wild Clary** (p67)
12 **White Henbane** (p67)
13 **Black Nightshade** (p67) and fruit
14 **Greater Thorn-apple** (p67)
15 **Shrub Tobacco** (p68)
16 **Wavy-leaved Mullein** (p68)
17 **Greater Snapdragon** (p68)
18 **Sicilian Snapdragon** (p68)
19 **Round-leaved Fluellen** (p68)
20 **Maltese Toadflax** (p68)
21 **Three-leaved Toadflax** (p69)
22 **Water Speedwell** (p69)
23 **Bellardia** (p69)

1

2

3

4

5

6

7

8

9

10

11

12

13

14

15

16

17

18

19

20

21

22

23

PLATE 10

VASCULAR PLANTS

1 **Bear's Breeches** (p69)
2 **Dwarf Broomrape** (p69)
3 **Bean Broomrape** (p69)
4 **Hare's-foot Plantain** (p70)
5 **Dwarf Elder** (p70) and fruit
6 **Evergreen Honeysuckle** (p70)
7 **Horn-of-plenty** (p70) and fruit
8 **Southern Scabious** (p70) and fruit
9 **Annual Daisy** (p71)
10 **Southern Daisy** (p71)
11 **Narrow-leaved Aster** (p71)
12 **South American Fleabane** (p71)
13 **Pygmy Cudweed** (p71)
14 **Eastern Phagnalon** (p71)
15 **Maltese Everlasting** (p71) and habit
16 **Golden Samphire** (p72)
17 **Sticky Fleabane** (p72)
18 **Maltese Fleabane** (p72)
19 **Spiny Ox-eye Daisy** (p72)
20 **Maltese Sea Chamomile** (p72)
21 **Chamomile** (p72)

PLATE 11

VASCULAR PLANTS

1   **Crown Daisy** (p73)
2   **Silvery Ragwort** (p73)
3   **Groundsel** (p73)
4   **Field Marigold** (p73)
5   **Shrubby Marigold** (p73)
6   **Boar Thistle** (p73)
7   **Horse Thistle** (p73)
8   **Wild Artichoke** (p73)
9   **Milk Thistle** (p74)
10 **Southern Star Thistle** (p74)
11 **Maltese Star Thistle** (p74)
12 **Maltese Rock-centaury** (p74)
13 **Woolly Safflower** (p74)
14 **Clustered Carline-thistle** (p74)
15 **Ground Thistle** (p74)
16 **Spiny Chicory** (p75)
17 **Perennial Hyoseris** (p75)
18 **Gozo Hyoseris** (p75) and habit
19 **Smooth Goatsbeard** (p75) with dry seed-ball
20 **Smooth Sow-thistle** (p75)
21 **Great Lettuce** (p76) with seed
22 **Maltese Hawksbeard** (p76)

PLATE
12

VASCULAR PLANTS

1 **Water Plantain** (p76)
2 **Mediterranean Starfruit** (p76)
3 **Posidonia** (p76) and balls
4 **Branched Asphodel** (p77)
5 **Mediterranean Meadow Saffron** (p77)
6 **Wild Tulip** (p77)
7 **Autumn Squill** (p77)
8 **Sicilian Squill** (p77)
9 **Southern Star of Bethlehem** (p77)
10 **Large Star of Bethlehem** (p78)
11 **Sea Squill** (p78) and habit
12 **Tassel Hyacinth** (p78)
13 **Maltese Dwarf Garlic** (p78)
14 **Wild Leek** (p78)
15 **Hairy Garlic** (p79)
16 **Rosy Garlic** (p79)
17 **Spiny Asparagus** (p79)
18 **Common Smilax** (p79) and fruit
19 **Sea Daffodil** (p79) and habit
20 **French Daffodil** (p79)

PLATE
13

VASCULAR PLANTS

1 **Barbary Nut Iris** (p80)
2 **Southern Dwarf Iris** (p80) (a) violet form (b) yellow form
3 **Sicilian Iris** (p80)
4 **Field Gladiolus** (p80)
5 **Yellow-throated Crocus** (p80)
6 **Sand-crocus** (p80)
7 **Sharp Rush** (p80) and habit
8 **Small-flowered Tongue Orchid** (p81)
9 **Mirror Orchid** (p81)
10 **Yellow Bee Orchid** (p81)
11 **Brown Orchid** (p81)
12 **Maltese Spider Orchid** (p81)
13 **Bumble Bee Orchid** (p81)
14 **Fan-lipped Orchid** (p82)
15 **Scented Bug Orchid** (p82)
16 **Milky Orchid** (p82)
17 **Common Pyramidal Orchid** (p82)
18 **Maltese Pyramidal Orchid** (p82)
19 **Italian Lords-and-Ladies** (p82) and fruit
20 **Friar's Cowl** (p82)

PLATE
14

VASCULAR PLANTS

1	**Southern Reed-mace** (p82)
2	**Round-headed Club-rush** (p83)
3	**Round Galingale** (p83)
4	**Large Quaking Grass** (p83)
5	**Stiff Rye-grass** (p83)
6	**Golden Dog's-tail** (p83)
7	**Great Brome** (p83)
8	**Goat Grass** (p84)
9	**Hare's-tail Barley** (p84)
10	**Hare's-tail Grass** (p84)
11	**Annual Beard-grass** (p84)
12	**Animated Oat** (p84)
13	**Purple Canary Seed** (p84)
14	**Great Reed** (p84) and habit
15	**Bermuda Grass** (p85)
16	**Sticky Bristle-grass** (p85)
17	**Mediterranean Steppe-grass** (p85)
18	**Rice-grass** (p85)
19	**Hispid Beard-grass** (p85)
20	**Purple Beard-grass** (p85)
21	**Esparto Grass** (p85) and habit

PLATE
15

SPONGES · CNIDARIANS

1 **Black Sponge** (p90)
2 **Brown Sponge** (p91)
3 **Red Sponge** (p91)
4 **Common Jellyfish** (p93)
5 **Common Hydra** (p93)
6 **Snakelocks Anemone** (p94)
7 **Beadlet Anemone** (p94)

8 **Black Coral** (p94)
9 **White Coral** (p95)
10 **Star-coral** (p95)
11 **Red Coral** (p95)

ANNELIDS

12 **Bristle Worm** (p97)
13 **Dog Worm** (p97)
14 **Fan Worm** (p97)
15 **Bloodworm** (p98)

16 **Common Earthworm** (p98)
17 **Fish Leech** (p99)
18 **Horse Leech** (p99)

MOLLUSCS

19 **Green Chiton** (p102)
20 **Tufted Chiton** (p102)
21 **Blue Limpet** (p103)
22 **Brown Limpet** (p103)
23 **Keyhole Limpet** (p103)
24 **Mediterranean Abalone** (p103)
25 **Strawberry Topshell** (p103)
26 **Topshell** (p103)
27 **Granulated Topshell** (p103)
28 **Great Topshell** (p103)
29 **Fabulous Topshell** (p103)
30 **Maltese Topshell** (p104)
31 **Toothed Topshell** (p104)
32 **Carinated Topshell** (p104)
33 **Pheasant Shell** (p104)
34 **Rough Star Shell** (p104)
35 **Common Cerith** (p104)
36 **Needle Shell** (p104)
37 **Tower Shell** (p104)
38 **Small Periwinkle** (p105)
39 **Pelican's Foot Shell** (p105)
40 **Bonnet Limpet** (p105) on oyster
41 **Giant Worm Shell** (p105)
42 **Necklace Shell** (p105)
43 **Spotted Cowrie** (p105)
44 **Ribbed Cowrie** (p105)
45 **Mediterranean Cowrie** (p105)
46 **Giant Tun** (p106) and feeding on sea-cucumber

PLATE
16

MOLLUSCS

1 **Knobbed Helmet Shell** (p106)
2 **Ribbed Helmet Shell** (p106)
3 **Hairy Triton** (p106)
4 **Purple Sea Snail** (p106)
5 **Triton Shell** (p106)
6 **Sinistral Horn** (p106) at left with animal
7 **Triton's Trumpet** (p106)
8 **Mediterranean Murex** (p107)
9 **Parasite Shell** (p107)
10 **Wentletrap** (p107)
11 **Dog Whelk** (p107)
12 **Atom Shell** (p108)
13 **Tulip Shell** (p107)
14 **Horn Whelk** (p107)
15 **Purple-dye Murex** (p107)
16 **Canoe Bubble** (p109)
17 **Rustic Dove Shell** (p108)
18 **Fusiform Mitre** (p108)
19 **Freshwater Limpet** (p110)
20 **Green Bubble Shell** (p109)
21 **Bubble Shell** (p108)
22 **Sea Hare** (p109)
23 **Patched Dorid** (p109) with young on sponge
24 **Rock Shell** (p107)
25 **Millet Grain Shell** (p108)
26 **Mediterranean Coneshell** (p108)
27 **Turret Shell** (p108)
28 **Edible Snail** (p109)
29 **Goat Snail** (p109)
30 **Red-banded Snail** (p109)
31 **Maltese Marmorana** (p110)
32 **Decollated Shell** (p110)
33 **Mamo's Door-snail** (p110)
34 **Despott's Top-snail** (p110)
35 **Elephant's Tooth** (p111)
36 **Nutshell** (p111) smooth (left) and with periostracum (right)
37 **Maltese Lehmannia** (p110)
38 **Common Slug** (p110)
39 **Noah's Ark Shell** (p111)
40 **Mediterranean Mussel** (p112)
41 **Date Mussel** (p112)
42 **Dog Cockle** (p112)
43 **Fan Mussel** (p112)
44 **Butterfly Mussel** (p112)
45 **Thorny Oyster** (p113)
46 **St. James' Scallop** (p112)
47 **Queen Scallop** (p112)
48 **Mediterranean Scallop** (p113)
49 **File Shell** (p113)
50 **Caserta Pea-mussel** (p113)

MOLLUSCS

1   **Oyster** (p113) three specimens stuck together
2   **Lucine Shell** (p113)
3   **Old Cardita** (p113)
4   **Cockle Shell** (p114)
5   **Edible Cockle** (p114)
6   **Rayed Trough Shell** (p114)
7   **Razor Shell** (p114) with siphon openings in sand
8   **Smooth Tellin** (p114)
9   **Common Wedge Shell** (p114)
10   **Pod Razor** (p114)
11   **Heart Cockle** (p114)
12   **Warty Venus Shell** (p115)
13   **Brown Venus** (p115)
14   **Cross-cut Carpet Shell** (p115)
15   **Rock-eating Petricola** (p115) with specimen stuck to rock
16   **Common Shipworm** (p115) two live specimens in wood
17   **Common Cuttlefish** (p116) (a) adult (b) egg mass (c) cuttlebone
18   **Little Cuttle** (p116)
19   **Common Squid** (p116) (a) adult (b) quill
20   **Sagittal Squid** (p116) (a) adult (b) quill
21   **Octopus** (p116)
22   **Long-armed Octopus** (p117)
23   **Paper Nautilus** (p117) (a) female (b) male

PLATE
18

MYRIAPODS

1 **Common Millipede** (p118) moving and dormant
2 **Cave Millipede** (p119) moving and dormant
3 **Pill Millipede** (p119)
4 **Yellow Centipede** (p120)
5 **Soil Centipede** (p120)
6 **House Centipede** (p120)

INSECTS

7 **House Silverfish** (p122)
8 **Damselfly** (p123) two forms
9 **Mayfly** (p122)
10 **Black-lined Skimmer** (p123) (a) male (b) female
11 **Red-veined Darter** (p123) (a) male (b) female
12 **Scarlet Darter** (p123) (a) male (b) female
13 **Emperor Dragonfly** (p123) (a) male (b) female (c) larva
14 **Common Earwig** (p126) (a) male (b) female
15 **Brown Field Grasshopper** (p124)
16 **White-banded Grasshopper** (p124)
17 **Field Grasshopper** (p124)
18 **Pink-winged Grasshopper** (p125) (a) male (b) female
19 **Slender Red-winged Grasshopper** (p125)
20 **Black-banded Grasshopper** (p125)
21 **Blue-winged Grasshopper** (p124)
22 **Mediterranean Slant-faced Grasshopper** (p125)
23 **Egyptian Grasshopper** (p125)
24 **Common Green Bush-cricket** (p125)
     (a) male (b) female ovipositor
25 **Common Grey Bush-cricket** (p125) male
26 **Mole Cricket** (p126) (a) dorsal view with wings extended (b) side view
27 **House Cricket** (p126) male
28 **Two-spotted Field Cricket** (p126) male
29 **Common Ground Cricket** (p126) male
30 **Praying Mantis** (p127) green form
31 **Field Cockroach** (p127)
32 **Common Cockroach** (p127) (a) male (b) female
33 **American Cockroach** (p127)
34 **Egyptian Cockroach** (p127) (a) male (b) female
35 **Brown-banded Cockroach** (p127) (a) male (b) female hind end
36 **Damp-wood Termite** (p128)
     (a) colony (b) male (c) queen (d) worker (e) soldier

PLATE
19

INSECTS

1 **Water Cricket** (p129) wingless adult
2 **Lesser Water Boatman** (p129)
3 **Greater Backswimmer** (p129)
4 **Smaller Backswimmer** (p129)
5 **Green Vegetable Bug** (p129) (a) adult (b) nymph
6 **Striped Shield Bug** (p130)
7 **Ornamental Shield Bug** (p130) two forms
8 **Bishop's Mitre** (p130)
9 **Rufous Shield Bug** (p130)
10 **Samphire Shield Bug** (p130)
11 **Black Burrower Bug** (p130)
12 **Shiny Burrower Bug** (p130)
13 **Common Stenocephalid Bug** (p130)
14 **Common Ground Bug** (p130)
15 **Soldier Bug** (p131)
16 **Samphire Lygaeid Bug** (p131)
17 **Two-spotted Ground Bug** (p131)
18 **Diamond-backed Ground Bug** (p131)
19 **Common Brown Seed Bug** (p131)
20 **Red-spotted Ground Bug** (p131)
21 **Red Assassin Bug** (p131)
22 **Fire Bug** (p131) three types
23 **Common Damsel Bug** (p216)
24 **Chrysanthemum Bug** (p216)
25 **Asphodel Bug** (p216)
26 **Cicada** (p216) (a) adult (b) empty nymphal case
27 **Common Froghopper** (p217) (a) adult (b) larva (c) froth mass
28 **Greenhouse Whitefly** (p217)
29 **Cottony-cushion Scale** (p217) females
30 **Citrus Mealybug** (p217) females
31 **Black Bean Aphid** (p218) wingless female
32 **Green Lacewing** (p218)
33 **Ant-lion** (p218)
34 **Soft-winged Flower Beetle** (p221)
35 **Terricolous Ground Beetle** (p219)
36 **Shore Ground Beetle** (p219)
37 **Soft-backed Ground Beetle** (p219)
38 **Great Ground Beetle** (p219)
39 **Emerald Ground Beetle** (p219)
40 **Devil's Coach-horse** (p220)
41 **Large Hister Beetle** (p220)
42 **Drilid Beetle** (p221) (a) male (b) female
43 **Carrion Beetle** (p222)
44 **Common Click Beetle** (p221)
45 **Glow-worm** (p221) (a) male (b) female (c) larva feeding on snail
46 **Large Predacious Diving Beetle** (p220)
47 **Black Predacious Diving Beetle** (p220)
48 **White-haired Rove Beetle** (p220)
49 **Peach Buprestid** (p222)
50 **Varied Carpet Beetle** (p222)
51 **Dried-fruit Beetle** (p222)

PLATE
20

INSECTS

1 **Seven-spot Ladybird** (p222)
   (a) adult (b) larva (c) pupa
2 **Vedalia Beetle** (p222)
3 **Heather Ladybird** (p223)
4 **Gourd Ladybird** (p223)
   (a) adult (b) larva
5 **Furniture Beetle** (p223)
6 **Yellow False Blister Beetle** (p223)
7 **Green False Blister Beetle** (p223)
8 **Common Oil Beetle** (p223)
9 **Churchyard Beetle** (p224)
10 **Leach's Darkling Beetle** (p224)
11 **Maltese Field Beetle** (p224)
12 **Tortoise Darkling Beetle** (p224)
13 **Striated Darkling Beetle** (p224)
14 **Schembri's Darkling Beetle** (p224)
15 **Black Flower Scarab** (p224)
16 **Rhinoceros Beetle** (p224)
17 **White-spotted Barbary Bug** (p225) two specimens
18 **Yellow-haired Barbary Bug** (p225)
19 **Emerald Chafer** (p225)
20 **Dung Roller** (p225) pushing dungball
21 **Horned Dung Beetle** (p225) male
22 **Pear Tree Borer** (p225)
23 **Red Leaf Beetle** (p225)
24 **Rosemary Leaf Beetle** (p225)
25 **Pea Beetle** (p226)
26 **Onion Weevil** (p226)
27 **Elongated Bean Weevil** (p226)
28 **Rice Weevil** (p226)
29 **Pea Weevil** (p226)
30 **Mottled-wing Crane-fly** (p227)
31 **Common Moth-fly** (p227)
32 **Mosquito** (p227) female
33 **March-fly** (p227)
34 **Long-horned Soldier-fly** (p228)
35 **Yellow Horse-fly** (p228)
36 **Common Robber-fly** (p228)
37 **Schembri's Spider Fly** (p228)
38 **Silvery Bee-fly** (p229)
39 **Common Yellow Bee-fly** (p229)
40 **Red-backed Bee-fly** (p229)
41 **Drone-fly** (p229) (a) adult (b) larva with extended breathing tube
42 **Lesser Drone-fly** (p229)
43 **Common Yellow-banded Hover-fly** (p229)
44 **Slender Hover-fly** (p229)

45 **Heleomyzid Fly** (p229)
46 **Black Scavenger-fly** (p230)
47 **Mediterranean Fruit-fly** (p230)
48 **Fruit-fly** (p230)
49 **Red-tailed Tachinid Fly** (p230)
50 **Fertoni's Flesh-fly** (p231)
51 **Common House-fly** (p231)
52 **Bluebottle** (p231)
53 **Greenbottle** (p231)
54 **Stable-fly** (p231)
55 **Lesser House-fly** (p231)
56 **Pigeon Louse-fly** (p232)

PLATE

21

INSECTS (MOTHS)

1 **Death's Head Hawkmoth** (p233)
   (a) adult (b,c) larva, two forms
2 **Convolvulus Hawkmoth** (p234) (a) adult (b) pupa
3 **Hummingbird Hawkmoth** (p234) on *Lantana* flower
4 **Spurge Hawkmoth** (p234) (a) adult (b) larva
5 **Striped Hawkmoth** (p234) (a) adult (b) pupa
6 **Leopard Moth** (p232) (a) adult (b) larva in wood fissure
7 **Maltese Ruby Tiger Moth** (p234) (a) adult (b) larva
8 **Tiger Moth** (p234) (a) adult (b) larva
9 **Indian Meal Moth** (p232)
10 **Meal Moth** (p232)
11 **Bordered Straw Moth** (p234)
12 **De Lucca's Moth** (p235)
13 **Silver Y Moth** (p235)
14 **Bloxworth Snout Moth** (p235)
15 **Large Yellow Underwing** (p235)
16 **Almond Tree Moth** (p235)
17 **Plume Moth** (p233)
18 **Oak Eggar** (p233) (a) male (b) female (c) larva (d) pupa
19 **Lappet Moth** (p233)
20 **Vapourer** (p234) (a) male (b) female (c) larva
21 **Vestal** (p233)

PLATE

22

INSECTS (BUTTERFLIES)

1 Pygmy Skipper (p235)
(a) male (b) female (c) egg (d) larva (e) pupa

2 Swallowtail (p235)
(a) adult (b) egg (c) larva (d) pupa

3 Large White (p236)
(a) male (b) female (c) larva (d) pupa

4 Small White (p236)
(a) male (b) female (c) egg (d) larva

5 Bath White (p236)
(a) male (b) female (c) underside (d) egg (e) larva (f) pupa

6 Clouded Yellow (p236)
(a) male (b) female (c) female - pale form (d) underside (e) egg (f) larva (g) pupa

7 Cleopatra (p236)
(a) male (b) female (c) underside (d) egg (e) larva (f) pupa

8 Small Copper (p236)
(a) adult - winter (b) adult - summer (c) underside (d) larva - two forms

9 Lang's Short-tailed Blue (p236)
(a) male (b) female (c) underside (d) larva (e) pupa

10 Long-tailed Blue (p237)
(a) male (b) female (c) underside (d) larva (e) pupa

11 African Grass Blue (p237)
(a) male (b) female (c) underside (d) egg (e) larva

12 Holly Blue (p237)
(a) male (b) female (c) underside (d) larva

13 Brown Argus (p237)
(a) male (b) female (c) underside

14 Common Blue (p237)
(a) male (b) female - summer (c) female - winter (d) underside (e) egg (f) larva

15 Plain Tiger (p237)
(a) adult (b) underside (c) egg (d) larva (e) pupa - two forms

16 Red Admiral (p237)
(a) adult (b) underside (c) larva (d) pupa

17 Painted Lady (p237)
(a) adult (b) underside (c) larva (d) pupa

18 Meadow Brown (p238)
(a) male (b) female (c) male - underside (d) female - underside (e) larva (f) pupa

19 Small Heath (p238)
(a) male (b) female (c) winter - underside (d) summer - underside (e) egg

20 Speckled Wood (p238)
(a) male (b) female (c) underside (d) egg (e) larva (f) pupa

21 Wall Brown (p238)
(a) male (b) female (c) underside (d) egg (e) larva (f) pupa

PLATE
23

INSECTS

1   **Common Sawfly** (p238)
2   **Large Red-legged Ichneumon Fly** (p239) (a) male (b) female
3   **Black Ensign Wasp** (p239)
4   **Ruby-tailed Wasp** (p239)
5   **Red Harvester Ant** (p240)
     (a) queen (b) worker (c) large-headed worker
6   **Cocktail Ant** (p240) (a) worker (b) workers on branch
7   **Carpenter Ant** (p240) (a) queen (b) small worker (c) large worker
8   **Black Harvester Ant** (p240) (a) worker (b) male (c) queen
9   **Acantholepis Ant** (p240) queen
10   **Maltese Slave-keeping Ant** (p240)
11   **Velvet Ant** (p240) (a) male (b) female
12   **Large Yellow-banded Scolid Wasp** (p241) (a) female (b) male
13   **Black Spider-hunting Wasp** (p241) female about to sting spider
14   **Common Potter Wasp** (p241) and two nests
15   **Digger Wasp** (p242) with prey (caterpillar)
16   **Mud-dauber** (p242) (a) adult (b) gathering mud
17   **Weevil Wasp** (p242)
18   **Bee-killer** (p242) (a) female about to transport bee
19   **Common Paper Wasp** (p242) (a)adult (b) comb
20   **Large Paper Wasp** (p242) (a) on plum (b) comb
21   **German Wasp** (p242)
22   **Yellow Halictid Bee** (p243) (a) male (b) female
23   **Common Halictid Bee** (p243)
     (a) two colour varieties (b) nest entrances
24   **Yellow-striped Megachilid Bee** (p243)
25   **Black Mining Bee** (p243)
26   **Kohli's Megachilid Bee** (p243)
27   **Long-horned Digger Bee** (p244) (a) male (b) female
28   **White-banded Digger Bee** (p244)
29   **Honey Bee** (p244) (a) male (b,c) workers of different colours
30   **Common Leaf-cutting Bee** (p243) (a) adult (b) carrying leaf
     (c) Judas Tree leaf showing semi-circular cut-marks; nest in wood fissure
31   **Mason Bee** (p243) near nest
32   **Bumble Bee** (p244)
33   **Large Carpenter Bee** (p244)
     (a) near nest entrance in dry Giant Reed stalk
     (b) feeding from Great Snapdragon flower

PLATE
24

CRUSTACEANS

1 **Fairy Shrimp** (p247)
2 **Clam Shrimp** (p248)
3 **Pool Flea** (p248)
4 **Chydorid Water Flea** (p248)
5 **Water Flea** (p248)
6 **Tadpole Shrimp** (p247)
7 **Seed-shrimp** (p248)
8 **Golden Seed-shrimp** (p249)
9 **Common Copepod** (p249)
10 **Maquis Woodlouse** (p250)
11 **Garigue Woodlouse** (p250)
12 **Common Maltese Woodlouse** (p250)
13 **Common Woodlouse** (p250) and rolled into ball
14 **Sandhopper** (p251)
15 **Common Amphipod** (p251)
16 **Shore Louse** (p250)
17 **Sea-slater** (p250)
18 **Goose Barnacle** (p249)
19 **Flattened Barnacle** (p249)
20 **Star Barnacle** (p249)
21 **Nut Crab** (p253) light phase (see also Plate 25)

CRUSTACEANS

1 **Spot-tailed Mantis Shrimp** (p251)
2 **Monaco Shrimp** (p252)
3 **Caramote Prawn** (p251)
4 **Glass Prawn** (p252)
5 **Common Shrimp** (p251)
6 **Processa Shrimp** (p252)
7 **Common Spiny Lobster** (p252)
   (a) adult (b) typical multiple-lensed crustacean eye
8 **European Paddle-nosed Lobster** (p252)
9 **Nut Crab** (p253) (a) dark phase (see also Plate 24)
10 **European Lobster** (p252)
11 **Deep-water Hermit Crab** (p253)
   (a) outside shell (b) in Purple-dye Murex shell
12 **Shore Hermit Crab** (p253) outside shell

1

2

3

4

5

6

7a

8

9

10

7b

11a

11b

12

GUIDO LANDRANCO

PLATE
26

CRUSTACEANS

1 **Sponge Crab** (p253)
  (a) without sponge (b) with sponge on back
2 **Shame-faced Crab** (p253)
3 **Toothed Crab** (p254)
4 **Stone Crab** (p254)
5 **Angular Crab** (p254)
6 **Arched Swimming Crab** (p254)
7 **Green Crab** (p254)
8 **Velvet Swimming Crab** (p254)
9 **Mediterranean Shore Crab** (p255)
10 **Long-armed Crab** (p255)
11 **Four-horned Spider Crab** (p255)
12 **Clinging Crab** (p255)
13 **Round-jointed Spider Crab** (p255)
14 **Spiny Spider Crab** (p255)
15 **Spiny Crab** (p254)
16 **Long-legged Spider Crab** (p255)
17 **Maltese Freshwater Crab** (p256)

PLATE
27

ARACHNIDS

1 **Scorpion** (p257)
2 **Green Pseudoscorpion** (p258)
3 **Red Pseudoscorpion** (p258)
4 **Common Tick** (p259) (a) starved (b) gorged
5 **Red Spider Mite** (p259) on cucumber leaf
6 **Trapdoor Spider** (p260) (a) adult (b) at nest entrance
7 **Red-headed Spider** (p260)
8 **Daddy-long-legs Spider** (p260) with egg mass
9 **Schembri's Jumping Spider** (p260)
10 **Jumping Spider** (p261)
11 **Crab Spider** (p261) (a,b) two females (c) male
12 **Humped Crab Spider** (p261) (a) male (b) female
13 **Funnel-web Spider** (p261) near nest
14 **Lobed Argiope** (p261) (a) male (b) female
15 **Cathedral Spider** (p261)
16 **Beady Spider** (p261)
17 **Wolf Spider** (p262) carrying young
18 **Maltese Palpigrade** (p262)
19 **False Spider** (p262)
20 **Harvestman** (p262)

ECHINODERMS

21 **Common Starfish** (p264)
22 **Cushion-star** (p264)
23 **Red Starfish** (p264)
24 **Violet Starfish** (p264)
25 **Red Comb-star** (p265)
26 **Blue Starfish** (p265)
27 **Spiny Starfish** (p265)
28 **Brown Brittle-star** (p265)
29 **Rock-urchin** (p266)
30 **Black Sea-urchin** (p266)
31 **Violet Sea-urchin** (p266)
32 **Red Lance-urchin** (p266)
33 **Pea-urchin** (p267) (a) animal (b) test
34 **Black Sea-cucumber** (p267)

PLATE
28

FISH

1 **Short-fin Mako Shark** (p270)
2 **Thresher Shark** (p270)
3 **Blackmouth Cat-shark** (p270)
4 **Nursehound** (p270) (a) adult (b) mermaid's purse
5 **Blue Shark** (p270)
6 **Starry Smooth Hound** (p271)
7 **Smooth Hammerhead Shark** (p271)
8 **Angular Rough Shark** (p271)
9 **Gulper Shark** (p271)
10 **Longnose Spurdog** (p271)
11 **Angel Shark** (p271)
12 **Common Guitar Fish** (p272)
13 **Common Torpedo** (p272)
14 **Longnose Skate** (p272) (a) adult (b) mermaid's purse
15 **Maltese Brown Ray** (p272)
16 **Brown Ray** (p272)
17 **Common Stingray** (p272)
18 **Common Eagle Ray** (p273)

PLATE
29

FISH

1 **Twaite Shad** (p273)
2 **European Pilchard** (p273)
3 **Atlantic Lizardfish** (p273)
4 **Mediterranean Conger** (p274)
5 **Mediterranean Moray** (p274)
6 **Eel** (p274)
7 **Garfish** (p274) (a) adult (b) two stages in mouth development
8 **Flying Fish** (p274)
9 **Killifish** (p275) (a) male (b) female
10 **Snipefish** (p275) (a) adult (b) two young specimens
11 **Short-nosed Seahorse** (p275)
12 **John Dory** (p276)
13 **Hake** (p276)
14 **Ribbonfish** (p276)
15 **Boarfish** (p277) (a) normal colour (b) deep-water colour
16 **Deep-nosed Pipefish** (p275) (a) female (b) male with egg sac
17 **Scalloped Ribbonfish** (p276)
18 **Three-bearded Rockling** (p276)
19 **Dusky Grouper** (p277)

FISH

1   **Comber** (p277)
2   **Painted Comber** (p277)
3   **Brown Comber** (p277)
4   **European Sea Bass** (p277)
5   **Vadigo** (p278)
6   **Cardinal Fish** (p277)
7   **Blue Runner** (p278)
8   **False Scad** (p278)
9   **Mediterraneran Horse Mackerel** (p278)
10 **Pilotfish** (p278)
11 **Common Dolphin-fish** (p278)
      (a) adult (b) immature (c) head of old male
12 **Greater Amberjack** (p278)
13 **Bogue** (p279)
14 **Striped Red Mullet** (p278)
15 **Annular Sea Bream** (p279)
16 **Common Dentex** (p279)
17 **Zebra Sea Bream** (p279)
18 **Common Two-banded Sea Bream** (p279)
19 **Sharpsnout Sea Bream** (p279)

PLATE
31

FISH

1 **Saddled Bream** (p279)
2 **Pandora** (p279)
3 **Red-banded Sea Bream** (p280)
4 **Common Sea Bream** (p280)
5 **Salema** (p280)
6 **Gilthead Sea Bream** (p280)
7 **Small-spot Picarel** (p280)
8 **Damsel Fish** (p280) (a) adult (b,c) two immature stages
9 **Green Wrasse** (p281)
10 **Rainbow Wrasse** (p280) (a) male (b) female
11 **Black-tailed Wrasse** (p281) (a) male (b) female
12 **Cuckoo Wrasse** (p281) (a) male (b) female
13 **Peacock Wrasse** (p281) (a) male (b) female

1

2

3

4

5

6

7

8a

8b

8c

9

10a

10b

11a

11b

12a

12b

13a

13b

PLATE
32

FISH

1 **Ornate Wrasse** (p281) (a) male (b) female
2 **Parrotfish** (p281) (a) male (b) female
3 **Greater Weever** (p281)
4 **Stargazer** (p281)
5 **Large-eyed Hairtail** (p282)
6 **Atlantic Bonito** (p282)
7 **Chub Mackerel** (p282)
8 **Atlantic Bluefin Tuna** (p282)
9 **Mediterranean Spearfish** (p282)
10 **Swordfish** (p282)
11 **Rock Goby** (p283)
12 **Black-spotted Dragonet** (p283) (a) male (b) female
13 **Butterfly Blenny** (p283)
14 **Bearded Ophidion** (p283)

1a

1b

2c

2b

2a

3

5

4

6

7

8

9

10

11

12a

12b

13

14

PLATE
33

FISH

1 **Red Scorpionfish** (p284)
2 **Thick-lipped Grey Mullet** (p284)
3 **Barracuda** (p283)
4 **Rockfish** (p284)
5 **Red Gurnard** (p284)
6 **Piper Gurnard** (p284)
7 **Black Scorpionfish** (p284)
8 **Armed Gurnard** (p284)
9 **Flying Gurnard** (p285)
10 **Four-eyed Sole** (p285)
11 **Turbot** (p285)
12 **Common Sole** (p285)
13 **Common Remora** (p286)
14 **Ocean Sunfish** (p286)
15 **Grey Triggerfish** (p286)
16 **Connemara Suckerfish** (p286)
17 **Greater Angler Fish** (p287)

GUIDO LANFRANCO -94

PLATE

34

AMPHIBIANS • REPTILES

1 **Painted Frog** (p288)
2 **Leathery Turtle** (p289)
3 **Loggerhead Turtle** (p290)
4 **Green Turtle** (p290)
5 **Moorish Gecko** (p290)
6 **Turkish Gecko** (p290)
7 **Ocellated Skink** (p292)
8 **Mediterranean Chamaeleon** (p291)

   (a,b) two shades of camouflage

9 **Maltese Wall Lizard** (p291)

   (a) male - Filfla ssp.
   (b) male - Selmunett ssp.
   (c) male - Fungus Rock ssp.
   (d,e) male - Malta/Gozo/Comino ssp. (two varieties)
   (f) female - Malta/Gozo/Comino ssp.
   (g) male - Filfla ssp. (underside)
   (h) male - Selmunett ssp. (underside)
   (i) male - Fungus Rock ssp. (underside)
   (j,k) male - Malta/Gozo/Comino ssp. (underside - two varieties)

10 **Algerian Whip Snake** (p292)
11 **Cat Snake** (p292)
12 **Western Whip Snake** (p292)
13 **Leopard Snake** (p292)

PLATE

35

BIRDS

1   **Black-necked Grebe (p294)** winter
2   **Cory's Shearwater (p294)**
3   **Mediterranean Shearwater (p294)**
4   **Storm Petrel (p295)**
5   **Cormorant (p295)**
6   **Little Bittern w(p295)** (a) adult male (b) immature
7   **Night Heron (p295)**
8   **Little Egret (p295)**
9   **Grey Heron (p296)**
10 **Purple Heron (p296)**
11 **Glossy Ibis (p296)**
12 **Mallard (p296)** (a) male (b) female
13 **Teal (p296)** (a) male (b) female
14 **Garganey (p296)** (a) male (b) female
15 **Pintail (p296)** (a) male (b) female

PLATE

36

BIRDS

1   **Honey Buzzard** (p297)
2   **Black Kite** (p297)
3   **Marsh Harrier** (p297) (a) male (b) female
4   **Montagu's Harrier** (p297) (a) male (b) female
5   **Kestrel** (p297) (a) male (b) female (c) male, hovering
6   **Osprey** (p297)
7   **Red-footed Falcon** (p298) (a) male (b) female
8   **Hobby** (p298)
9   **Peregrine** (p298) (a) adult (b) juvenile
10   **Quail** (p298) (a) male (b) female
11   **Water Rail** (p298)
12   **Spotted Crake** (p299)
13   **Moorhen** (p299) (a) adult (b) juvenile
14   **Coot** (p299)
15   **Scops Owl** (p303)
16   **Short-eared Owl** (p303)
17   **Barn Owl** (p303)

37

BIRDS

1 **Stone Curlew** (p299)
2 **Little Ringed Plover** (p299) (a) adult (b) juvenile
3 **Lapwing** (p300)
4 **Dotterel** (p300) winter
5 **Golden Plover** (p300) winter
6 **Snipe** (p300)
7 **Dunlin** (p300) (a) summer (b) winter
8 **Ruff** (p300) winter
9 **Little Stint** (p300) winter
10 **Curlew Sandpiper** (p300) (a) summer (b) winter
11 **Woodcock** (p301)
12 **Redshank** (p301)
13 **Spotted Redshank** (p301) (a) winter (b) summer
14 **Black-winged Stilt** (p299) (a) male or female (b) male - summer
15 **Greenshank** (p301)
16 **Wood Sandpiper** (p301)
17 **Green Sandpiper** (p301)
18 **Common Sandpiper** (p301)

BIRDS

1 **Black-headed Gull** (p302)
   (a) adult - winter (b) immature (c) head - summer
2 **Mediterranean Gull** (p301)
   (a) adult - winter (b) immature (c) head - summer
3 **Yellow-legged Gull (p302)** (a) adult (b) immature
4 **Sandwich Tern** (p302)
5 **Swift** (p304)
6 **Nightjar** (p303)
7 **Kingfisher** (p304)
8 **Bee-eater** (p304)
9 **Hoopoe** (p304)
10 **Roller** (p304)
11 **Turtle Dove** (p302)
12 **Cuckoo** (p303) (a) male (b) female - rufous phase
13 **Sand Martin** (p305)
14 **House Martin** (p306)
15 **Swallow** (p306)
16 **Wryneck** (p305)
17 **Short-toed Lark** (p305)
18 **Skylark** (p305)

PLATE
39

BIRDS

1   **Meadow Pipit** (p306)
2   **Tree Pipit** (p306)
3   **White Wagtail** (p306)

(a) male - winter (b) male - summer (c) juvenile

4   **Yellow Wagtail** (p306)

(a) male - blue-headed ssp. (b) male - grey-headed ssp.

(c) male - black-headed ssp. (d) female

5   **Grey Wagtail** (p306) (a) male - winter (b) male - summer
6   **Robin** (p307)
7   **Nightingale** (p307)
8   **Dunnock** (p307)
9   **Bluethroat** (p307) (a) white-spotted ssp. (b) red-spotted ssp.
10 **Black Redstart** (p307) (a) male (b) female
11 **Redstart** (p307) (a) male (b) female
12 **Stonechat** (p307) (a) male (b) female
13 **Whinchat** (p307) (a) male (b) female
14 **Wheatear** (p308) (a) male (b) female
15 **Black-eared Wheater** (p308) (a) male - western ssp.

(b) male - eastern ssp. (c) western black-throated form

(d) eastern black-throated form (e) female

16 **Redwing** (p308)
17 **Song Thrush** (p308)
18 **Blackbird** (p308) (a) male (b) female
19 **Fieldfare** (p308)
20 **Blue Rock Thrush** (p308) (a) male (b) female
21 **Rock Thrush** (p308) (a) male (b) female

PLATE
40

BIRDS

1 **Fan-tailed Warbler** (p309)
2 **Sedge Warbler** (p309)
3 **Reed Warbler** (p309)
4 **Great Reed Warbler** (p309)
5 **Cetti's Warbler** (p308)
6 **Spectacled Warbler** (p309) (a) male (b) female
7 **Subalpine Warbler** (p309) (a) male - spring (b) female
8 **Sardinian Warbler** (p309) (a) male (b) female
9 **Whitethroat** (p309) (a) male (b) female
10 **Blackcap** (p310) (a) male (b) female
11 **Garden Warbler** (p310)
12 **Icterine Warbler** (p309)
13 **Firecrest** (p310) (a) male (b) female
14 **Goldcrest** (p310) (a) male (b) female
15 **Willow Warbler** (p310)
16 **Chiffchaff** (p310)
17 **Wood Warbler** (p310)
18 **Pied Flycatcher** (p311) (a) male (b) female
19 **Collared Flycatcher** (p310) male
20 **Spotted Flycatcher** (p310)

PLATE
41

BIRDS

1 **Golden Oriole** (p311) (a) male (b) female
2 **Woodchat Shrike** (p311)
3 **Starling** (p311) (a) winter (b) summer
4 **Spanish Sparrow** (p311)
   (a) male - summer (b) male - winter (c) female
5 **Tree Sparrow** (p311)
6 **Siskin** (p312) (a) male (b) female
7 **Serin** (p312) (a) male (b) female
8 **Chaffinch** (p312)
   (a) male - summer (b) female (c) male - autumn/winter
9 **Greenfinch** (p312) (a) male (b) female
10 **Goldfinch** (p312)
11 **Hawfinch** (p312) (a) male (b) female
12 **Linnet** (p312) (a) male - spring (b) female
13 **Crossbill** (p312) (a) male (b) female or juvenile
14 **Ortolan** (p313) (a) male - spring (b) juvenile
15 **Corn Bunting** (p313)

1b 1a 2 3a 3b 6b 6a 4b 4a 4c 7b 7a 8a 8b 8c 5 9b 9a 10 11b 11a 12a 12b 13b 13a 14b 14a 15

MAMMALS

1   **Lesser Horseshoe Bat (p316)**
       (a) in flight (b) head (c) at rest

2   **Grey Long-eared Bat (p316)**

3   **Lesser Mouse-eared Bat (p316)** (a) in flight (b) at rest

4   **Pipistrelle (p316)** (a) in flight (b) head

5   **Wood Mouse (p318)**

6   **House Mouse (p318)**

7   **Brown Rat (p318)**

8   **Black Rat (p318)**

9   **Wild Rabbit (p319)** two varieties

10   **Weasel (p317)**

11   **Vagrant Hedgehog (p315)**

12   **Pygmy White-toothed Shrew (p315)**

13   **Sicilian Shrew (p315)**

14   **Common Dolphin (p317)** (a) adult (b) skull

15   **Bottle-nosed Dolphin (p317)** (a) adult (b) skull

Common Damsel Bug   p169
Nabis capsiformis   Assaltin
9mm. Often found on dry vegetation. Common.

Family Miridae

Small to medium-sized insects with a rather soft body. They live in a variety of habitats, feeding on many different plants. Some are predatory on other insects; certain species are ant-mimics. Coloration variable, but the plant-living forms are generally green or brown. These feed on fruits and seeds, some of them being agricultural pests. At least 40 species.

Chrysanthemum Bug   p169
Calocoris nemoralis   Seffud tal-Lellux
9-10mm. Found mostly on flowers of Crown Daisy. Colour very variable. Common.

Asphodel Bug   p169
Capsodes lineolatus   Seffud tal-Berwieq
8mm. Found mostly on Sage and Asphodel. Common.

CICADAS, APHIDS, SCALE INSECTS etc
Order Homoptera

A large, diverse Order. All are rather small, with the exception of the cicadas. They are plant-feeders, some of which cause damage to crops. The mouthparts are adapted for piercing plant tissue and sucking sap. Some have no mouth and do not feed. The winged forms have two pairs of veined wings, which are held in a tent-like position over the abdomen when not in flight. In some species one or both sexes are wingless. Certain species have both wingless and winged forms in the same sex. Metamorphosis is generally simple, although that of whiteflies and of male scale insects is almost of the complete type. This Order has been little studied in Malta.

Family Cicadidae

Large insects with transparent wings. They live on trees and shrubs, but will frequently settle on walls. To attract the female, the male produces a shrill song by vibrating membranes in ventral stridulatory organs at the base of the abdomen. The eggs are laid in cracks on tree trunks. On hatching, the nymphs fall to the ground and burrow into the soil, feeding on roots. They have strong forelegs adapted for digging. In some species, metamorphosis takes years. 1 species.

Cicada   p169
Cicada orni   Werżieq ta' Bi Nhar
Body 25mm, 44mm up to the tips of the folded wings. Found everywhere in summer. Male sings incessantly during the day, changing tone of song or stopping altogether when threatened. When fully-developed nymph emerges from soil, it climbs a stem, undergoes internal changes and moults into adult phase. Empty nymphal skin often seen attached to stems in early summer. Very common.

Underside of
Cicada showing
sound organs

Family Cercopidae

Generally brown or greenish insects with spiny hind legs. Good jumpers. The nymphs of many species live in the shelter of a mass of foam which they produce themselves around plant stems. This enables them to escape predators while keeping their body moist. This Family has not been studied in Malta, but many species are found, some of them extremely common. Several specires.

Common Froghopper   p169

Philaenus spumarius   Pulċinell
6mm. Very variable in colour, but usually light brown. Found on many shrubs and herbaceous plants. Very common.

Common Froghopper
with cuckoo spit
and nymph

Family Pseudococcidae

This Family belongs to the Superfamily Coccoidea. It includes many small insects which do not resemble other Homopterans due to the way in which they have evolved. The wingless and often legless females do not change their position. Most males have only one pair of wings, lack mouthparts and do not feed; they resemble small mosquitoes. The life-cycle is complex and varies in different species. Number of species unknown.

Citrus Mealybug   p169

Planococcus citri   Miskta Qotnija
2.5mm. Found attached to all plant parts. Female is oval and segmented and covered with sticky liquid (honeydew) secreted by body. A pest of citrus trees, also damaging greenhouse crops. Very common.

Family Margarodidae

Females are often covered with a waxy substance. Males are usually winged. They live on a variety of plants, causing damage. 1 species.

Cottony-cushion Scale   p169

Icerya purchasi   Miskta Bajda
3mm. Has the same habits as Citrus Mealybug, and likewise a pest of citrus and other trees and plants, including decorative and indoor plants. Very common.

Family Aleyrodidae

Small insects. The wings are covered with a white dust. The adults are active and feed on leaves. Metamorphosis differs from that of other Homopterans. They attack various plants and are pests of fruit trees and greenhouse crops. 9 species.

Greenhouse Whitefly   p169

Trialeurodes vaporariorum   Nemusa Bajda tas-Serer
2mm. Attacks several greenhouse crops, causing serious damage especially in cucumbers and tomatoes. Sucks sap from lower surface of leaves. Common.

Family Aphididae

Small, soft-bodied insects, known as plantlice or greenfly. They are pear-shaped, with two dorsal pipe-like tubercles at the hind end, from which exudes a liquid used for defensive purposes. Some species are enveloped in a waxy substance. Others secrete honeydew which is very attractive to ants.

The winged forms have a specialised type of venation, with the forewings larger than the hindwings. Some species are serious pests and are often vectors of plant diseases. They are generally found in large numbers, sucking sap from the tissues of plants and trees. Large groups often include individuals at all stages of the life cycle, which differs from that of other insects. Several species.

Black Bean Aphid p169

Aphis fabae   Berghud tal-Ful
2mm. Black or olive-green body. Found on herbaceous plants, especially peas and beans. Common.

LACEWINGS and ANT-LIONS
Order Neuroptera

Soft-bodied insects with two pairs of usually profusely veined wings which are held erect when not in use. Metamorphosis is complete. The larvae are generally predatory, as are many of the adult insects. Some adults only attack weakened prey while a few probably do not feed at all. They are found in many different habitats, and are generally weak fliers.

In Malta the most frequent are the members of the Family Myrmeleontidae, which are still being studied. About 30 species in various Families.

Family Chrysopidae
Common insects which are frequently found on vegetation. Generally greenish, with golden or rust-coloured eyes. The larvae feed on aphids. Some species camouflage themselves with pieces of leaf and other plant debris. The eggs are usually laid on leaves. The pupa is formed in a silken cocoon attached to the lower leaf surface. About 10 species.

Green Lacewing p169

Chrysoperla carnea   Insett tal-Bizzilla
18mm (from head to tip of folded wings). Lives among vegetation in the countryside. Mostly nocturnal and often attracted to domestic lights. Larva rather inconspicuous as it camouflages itself with the empty skins of its prey. Common.

Family Myrmeleontidae
The largest Family in this Order, the adults showing a superficial resemblance to damselflies. They have long wings with many veins, a long slender abdomen and a rather soft body-wall. Their flight is weak and they are often attracted to lights. The larvae have pointed mandibles for the capture of other insects. The larvae of some species lie in wait for their prey in funnel-shaped pits dug in sand or dust; they remain hidden until some insect (usually an ant) falls into the trap, and slips down the sloping sides into the open jaws of the larva. About 12 species.

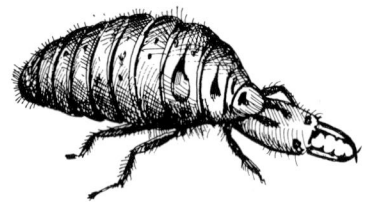
Larva of Ant-lion

Ant-lion p169

Macronemurus appendiculatus   Qerd in-Nemel
40-45mm. Widespread in the countryside, especially among vegetation of sandy localities near the coast. Common.

BEETLES
Order Coleoptera

The largest Order of insects, both in number of species as well as number of individuals. Very variable in size. Found in virtually all habitats. They have two pairs of wings. The forewings (known as elytra) are tough and thick and meet along the dorsal midline of the abdomen. The hindwings are longer, delicate and are kept folded under the elytra when the insect is not flying. Some species are wingless. The mouthparts are generally of the biting type. Some feed on plant tissue, including a number of wood-borers. The Order also includes scavengers as well as predatory and parasitic forms.

Many species cause damage to crops, furniture, seeds and grain, carpets and textiles. On the other hand, several beetles are beneficial because they prey on harmful pests such as aphids, or because they help to decompose organic matter. The larvae are totally different from the adults. They usually have well-developed mouthparts and their feeding habits resemble those of the adults. In Malta many Families still await detailed study, but it is estimated that 1200-2000 species probably occur.

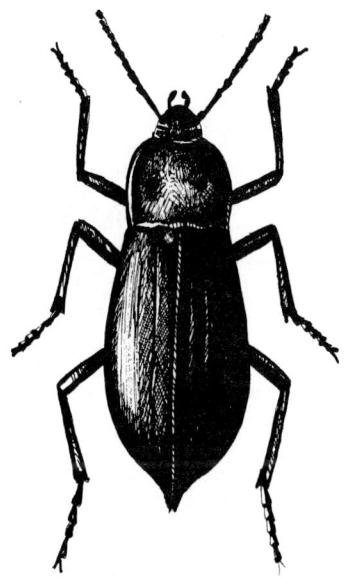

Churchyard Beetle

Family Carabidae
Beetles which are variable in size and morphology. Most are shiny black, of medium size and rather flattened, with striated elytra. They are found under stones, leaf litter, loose bark and the like, or else wandering on the ground. When threatened they run off rapidly, but rarely take to flight. Many are active by night, and are attracted to light. They are almost all predators of other insects. The larvae are also predatory. More than 130 species, mostly small to medium-sized.

Terricolous Ground Beetle   p169
Amara eurynota   Busewdien tat-Terriċċju
11mm. Lives among leaf litter, often in large numbers. Very fast-moving. Common.

Soft-backed Ground Beetle   p169
Calathus erythroderus   Busewdien Artab
7-9mm. Same habits as Ground Beetle and lives in similar situations. Common.

Shore Ground Beetle   p169
Acinopus ambiguus   Busewdien tax-Xatt
12-16mm. Found under stones in many coastal localities. Frequent.

Great Ground Beetle   p169
Carabus morbillosus ssp. *alternans*   Bunittien
27-32mm. One of our largest beetles. Emits a foul smell when threatened. Frequent.

Emerald Ground Beetle   p169
Chlaenus velutinus   Żmeralda ta' l-Ilma
14-17mm. Shiny beetle which lives near fresh water among or beneath partly-submerged stones. Frequent.

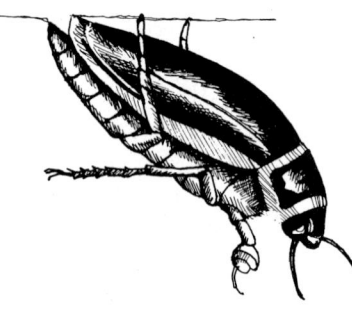

Diving beetle
taking air from
water surface

Family Dytiscidae
Aquatic beetles with a hard exoskeleton, smooth and streamlined to move easily through the water. Hind legs are hairy to aid swimming. Very good swimmers, taking air at the surface through the tip of their abdomen. They can remain submerged for extended periods. Adults and larvae are predatory on other aquatic creatures. Adults have pointed mouthparts which they use to absorb the body fluids of their prey. Males of certain species have swollen tarsi on the forelegs to help clasp the female during mating. They can leave the water and are good fliers. About 20 species.

Large Predacious Diving Beetle   **p169**
Dytiscus circumflexus   Wirdiena ta' l-Ilma
30mm. Found in open reservoirs and in small or large, rather deep, pools. Larva lives among water weeds. Common.

Black Predacious Diving Beetle   **p169**
Meladema coriacea   Hanfusa Sewda ta' l-Ghadajjar
21mm. Same habitat as Large Predacious Diving Beetle, but prefers deeper water. Similar habits. Frequent.

Family Histeridae
Small, shiny, black beetles with a rounded body. Generally associated with rotting organic matter, such as animal carcasses and excrement; they feed on other insects which live in these habitats. Some species are flattened, an adaptation to living under bark; others live in ants' or termites' nests. Certain species have cylindrical bodies and inhabit the galleries of wood-boring insects. When threatened they close up and adopt a bead-like appearance. About 25 species, mostly small.

Large Hister Beetle   **p169**
Macrolister major   Boċni Kbir
9-12mm. Usually found near or under animal carcasses, but sometimes also in leaf litter. Common.

Family Staphylinidae
One of the largest Families of beetles. Long and slender. A good part of their abdomen is exposed dorsally as the elytra are foreshortened. The hindwings are well-developed, and are kept folded beneath the elytra when not in use. They live in diverse habitats, but mostly among rotting organic matter, especially animal remains and excrement. They can also be found under stones or logs in humid places or near the shore, in leaf litter, fungi, and in the nests of birds, ants and termites. Many are predators or scavengers, as are their larvae, which live in the same habitat as the adults. About 170 species.

Devil's Coach-horse   **p169**
Staphylinus olens   Katarina-Gholli-Denbek
22-30mm. Largest staphylinid species. Nocturnal, hiding under stones by day, emerging at night to feed on invertebrates such as slugs. When threatened, raises tip of abdomen and opens mandibles. Common.

White-haired Rove Beetle   **p169**
Creophilus maxillosus   Kappillan
15-22mm. Feeds on other insects which live in dung or other decomposing organic matter. Frequent.

Family Lampyridae

Beetles, most of which emit a weak greenish light. The body is soft and elongated. The females of many species are wingless. Lampyrids glow to attract mates. Nocturnal. During the day, they keep mostly to the grass. Larvae prey on small snails and insects. The larvae of several species also glow. 1 species.

Glow-worm   p169

Lampyris sp.   Musbieh il-Lejl

Male 12mm, female 20mm. Male flies by night and is attracted to the glowing female, which takes up a prominent position on rubble walls, roadsides or country paths. Female is wingless and does not look like a beetle; emits light ventrally from tip of abdomen. Formerly common. Scarce.

Family Melyridae

Medium-sized beetles with an elongate, soft body. Mostly black, red or brown. The larvae of many species are predators and live in rotting timber. The adults are often seen on flowers. About 10 species.

Soft-winged Flower Beetle   p169

Psilothrix viridicoeruleus   Ħadranija tal-Ward

6-8mm. Found on many flowers, especially yellow ones like those of Cape Sorrel. Very common.

Family Drilidae

A small Family of medium-sized beetles. Only the males are winged. The females resemble the larvae and live in damp places, such as beneath stones. Males live on flowers. The larvae prey on slugs and snails. 1 species.

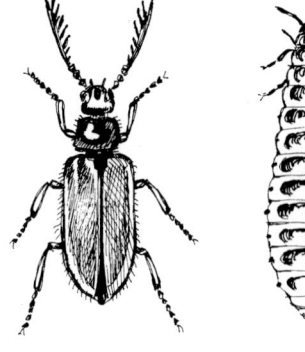

Male   Female

Drilid Beetle

Drilid Beetle   p169

Drilus flavescens   Ħanfusa Ċerv

Male 6-8.5mm, female 13-15mm. Male flies about among vegetation. Female not very visible, hiding on the ground amongst vegetation. Frequent.

Family Elateridae

Medium-sized beetles. When upturned, they spring back to an upright position with an audible click. The adults are found on flowers, under bark or on vegetation. They are plant-feeders. The larvae, known as 'wireworms', are long and slender, with a rather hard, shiny skin. They cause damage by feeding on sown seed and on the roots of many crop plants. About 8 species, including one endemic.

Common Click Beetle   p169

Harminius spiniger   Ħanfusa tas-Salt

8-11.5mm. Found in the countryside among grass. Nocturnal. Frequent.

Family Buprestidae

Medium to large wood-boring beetles. Many are green, red, blue, black or bronze with a metallic sheen. The exoskeleton is hard and pointed posteriorly. They attack dead or dying trees or logs. They are sometimes found among foliage of trees and shrubs. They are good fliers, escaping quickly when threatened. They frequently bask in the sun. The eggs are laid in crevices on tree trunks. On hatching, the larvae bore into the wood or beneath the bark. Many species are timber pests. About 15 species.

Peach Buprestid   p169

Capnodis tenebrionis   Susa ta' l-Gheruq
20-24mm. Found in gardens, fruit orchards and near wild *Prunus* trees. Frequent.

Family Dermestidae

Small beetles, some of which are pests. They feed on a large variety of natural products such as leather, woollen and silken materials, carpets, stored food and meat. Most damage is caused by the larvae. The adults are quite small with an oval, sometimes elongate, appearance; they are often covered with hairs or scales. In Malta, this Family has not been well studied. So far about 10 species are known to occur.

Varied Carpet Beetle   p169

Anthrenus verbasci   Hanfusa tat-Tessuti
2mm. Often found in houses, and on flowers in the countryside. Adult feeds on nectar and pollen, while larva feeds on dry materials in houses, causing damage to woollen clothes, carpets and similar goods. Very common.

Carrion Beetle   p169

Dermestes undulatus   Hanfusa ta' l-Iġsma
6-10mm. Found mostly on carcasses and animal remains. Causes damage to stored dried meats. Common.

Family Nitidulidae

Variable in size and shape. Many are small, oval or elongate, with short forewings. They are often found near fermenting vegetable matter, especially rotten fruit. Some species live in fungi, under bark, on logs and on decomposed animal remains. About 20 species.

Dried-fruit Beetle   p169

Carpophilus hemipterus   Hanfusa ta' l-Gheneb
3-3.5mm. Feeds on fermenting fruit. Often found in vineyards, on grapes which are beginning to rot. Very common.

Family Coccinellidae

Predators on other insects, such as aphids. They have an oval, hemispherical shape and are generally brightly coloured. Larvae and adults are usually found on trees and shrubs infested with aphids.   About 30 species.

Ladybird laying eggs

Seven-spot Ladybird   p171

Coccinella septempunctata   Nannakola tas-Seba' Tikki
7-8mm. Found on plants virtually all year round. In cold weather seeks shelter individually or in sizeable groups, usually under bark. Common.

Vedalia Beetle   p171

Rodolia cardinalis   Nannakola tas-Salib
4mm. Introduced in 1911 for the control of aphid infestations which had broken out in some gardens at St. Julians. Frequent.

Heather Ladybird
p171

Chilocorus bipustulatus   Nannakola tal-Faxx

3-4.5mm. Found on various plants and trees. Common.

Gourd Ladybird
p171

Henosepilachna elaterii   Nannakola tal-Faqqus il-Ħmir

8mm. Lives and feeds on Squirting Cucumber. Common.

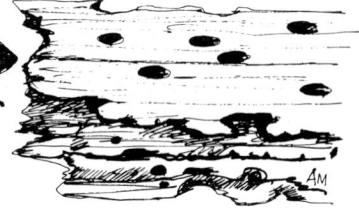

Furniture Beetle
and its effect on wood

Family Anobiidae

Small, hairy beetles, cylindrical to oval. The head is generally twisted downwards and is not visible from above. They live on dry vegetable matter such as twigs, wood and dead trees. Some larvae live in fungi, in seeds or in the stems of various plants. Many are pests, especially those attacking cereals, tobacco, preserved goods and household products such as spices. Others bore into furniture and timber. About 7 species.

Furniture Beetle
p171

Anobium punctatum   Susa ta' l-Għamara

2.5-5mm. Damages furniture and other wooden items in houses. Common.

Family Oedemeridae

Slender, medium-sized beetles with a soft body-wall and pale coloration, mostly yellow, pink or orange. Often found on flowers and grasses. The larvae live in damp or rotting timber. About 6 species, including one endemic to Malta and Pantelleria.

Yellow False Blister Beetle
p171

Oedemera brevicollis   Dliela Safra

10mm. Widespread in the countryside on many different flowers. Common.

Green False Blister Beetle
p171

Oedemera caudata   Dliela Ħadra

6-9mm. Same habits and habitat as Yellow False Blister Beetle. Common.

Family Meloidae

Medium-sized to large, stout beetles, with a soft, generally shiny surface. Species of the genus *Meloe* lack hind wings, and the forewings overlap. They are usually black or blue-black. When threatened, they emit an oily liquid which causes blistering on human skin. At one stage of their life history they are parasites of solitary bees or grasshoppers. About 10 species.

Common Oil Beetle
p171

Meloe tuccius   Dliela Żejtnija

Male 16-21mm, female 25-30mm. Found near vegetation in rather humid places. Crawls about on grasses, on which it also feeds. Common.

Family Tenebrionidae

Beetles of variable form and size, generally with a hard, blackish body. Most are flightless. They live in arid conditions, usually beneath stones and among refuse. They feed on plants and plant products. A few species often cause serious damage to flour and other cereal products in storage. About 50 species, including several endemics.

Churchyard Beetle p171

Blaps gigas   Ħanfusa tal-Kantina

27-37mm. The largest beetle in this Family. Occurs in damp places such as cellars and basements. Also found in the open in rubble walls and under stones in the mouths of caves. Frequent.

Leach's Darkling Beetle p171

Tentyria laevigata ssp. *leachi*   Ħanfusa Mogħża

13-15mm. Found in gardens and in the countryside. Endemic. Very common.

Maltese Field Beetle p171

Pimelia rugulosa ssp. *melitana*   Ħanfusa tar-Raba'

16-20mm. Found in the countryside, especially in coastal areas, where it gnaws bases of plants. Endemic. Very common.

Tortoise Darkling Beetle p171

Alphasida grossa ssp. *melitana*   Ħanfusa tal-Fekruna

13-16mm. Found under stones in gardens and open country. Endemic. Very common.

Striated Darkling Beetle p171

Scaurus striatus   Ħanfusa tal-Ġanċ

12-18mm. Generally found under stones in damp places, sometimes in small groups. Common.

Schembri's Darkling Beetle p171

Stenosis schembrii   Ħanfusa ta' Schembri

6mm. Usually lives under large stones, often with another endemic species, *Stenosis melitana*, which it resembles. Described in 1979 by an Italian coleopterologist who named it after Maltese entomologist Stephen Schembri. Endemic. Scarce.

Antenna of Chafer

Family Scarabaeidae

Rather stout oval or elongate beetles which are very variable in size, colour and habitat. The terminal segments of the clubbed antennae are flattened plates. Good fliers. Many are scavengers, feeding on animal remains and rotting vegetation. Some feed on leaves, flowers and fruit, and a number are considered pests. Certain species live in the nests of vertebrates, ants or termites, while a few live on fungi. About 33 species.

Rhinoceros Beetle p171

Oryctes nasicornis ssp. *grypus*   Buqarn Kbir

37-40mm. Relatively massive. Male has long horn on head. Female has small projection. Larva lives in rotting logs or wood. Scarce.

Black Flower Scarab p171

Pentodon bidens ssp. *punctatus*   Bugħawwâr Botni

18-26mm. Usually found among fallen leaves or leaf litter, or wandering about on the ground. Sexes slightly different. Common.

White-spotted Barbary Bug   p171
Oxythyrea funesta   Busuf tat-Tikki Bojod
12-13mm. Usually found feeding on blossoms of ornamental plants and fruit trees. Hairy. Very common.

Yellow-haired Barbary Bug   p171
Tropinota squalida   Busuf tal-Pil Isfar
12-13mm. Hairy, with same habits and habitat as White-spotted Barbary Bug. Very common.

Emerald Chafer   p171
Protaetia cuprea ssp. *incerta*   Ghawwâr Dehbi
17-22mm. Found mainly in habitats with trees, usually on blossoms. Large and attractive. Scarce.

Dung Roller   p171
Scarabaeus variolosus   Ħanfusa tad-Demel
13-21mm. Forms a ball of dung and rolls it on the ground using its hind legs. It places it in a hole in the ground where it lives, feeding on the dung. Scarce.

Horned Dung Beetle   p171
Onthophagus taurus   Ħanfusa Barri tad-Demel
8-11mm. Lives in animal dung. Smaller than Dung Roller, and does not form dungballs. Male has pair of long horns on head. Frequent.

Family Cerambycidae

Beetles of variable size, generally medium to large, with a long, cylindrical body and very long antennae. Many are nocturnal and are found on tree trunks and branches. They feed on plants and timber. The larvae of many species bore into wood and are harmful to forest trees, fruit trees and sawn timber. In spite of the local scarcity of trees, about 32 species have been recorded.

Pear Tree Borer   p171
Cerambyx nodulosus   Susa tal-Langas
25-40mm. One of the largest beetles. A pest, especially harmful to pear trees. Frequent.

Larva of a
long-horned beetle

Family Chrysomelidae

Medium-sized beetles, many with vivid colours. They feed on vegetable matter, especially leaves and flowers. The larvae of many species are pests of crops, and include forms which eat leaves and others which bore into them, while some feed on roots or bore into stems. About 60 species.

Red Leaf Beetle   p171
Chrysolina grossa   Żabbella Ħamra
9-11mm. Found on vegetation in the countryside, but not in large numbers. Common.

Rosemary Leaf Beetle   p171
Chrysolina americana   Żabbella tal-Klin
7.5mm. Infests Rosemary, often in large numbers. Common.

Family Bruchidae

Small beetles which are short and stout, with the elytra not reaching the tip of the abdomen. Colours usually pale grey or brown. The larvae of many species live in and feed on various seeds. About 35 species so far recorded, but more probably occur.

Pea Beetle   p171

Bruchus pisorum   Hanfusa tal-Piżelli

5mm. Larva develops inside peas or broad beans. On reaching adulthood, emerges through a round hole bored in the seed. Often causes serious damage. Very common.

Family Curculionidae

A large Family of beetles with an elongated head with a beak-like projection. Variable in size and colour. The vast majority feed on plants or plant products. Many of their larvae infest grain, rice and other seeds or bore into stems. They can cause damage to field crops, fruit trees and stored foodstuffs. They are mostly small, although a few are of medium size. Over 120 species, including some endemics.

Onion Weevil   p171

Brachycerus undatus   Bumunqar tal-Basal

9-17mm. Has a very hard and gnarled integument. Larva is more familiar as it is sometimes encountered inside onions. Common.

Elongated Bean Weevil   p171

Lixus algirus   Qirda tal-Ful

13-19mm. Found on various plants. Often covered with fine red or yellow dust, depending on flowers visited. Larva develops inside stems. Common.

Rice Weevil   p171

Sitophilus oryzae   Bumunqar tar-Ross

4mm. Winged. Infests all sorts of seeds, including rice. Especially harmful in granaries. Common.

Pea Weevil   p171

Sitona lineatus   Bumunqar tal-Miżwed

5.5mm. Nocturnal. Feeds on various plant products such as peas and beans. Larva lives among roots of these plants. Very common.

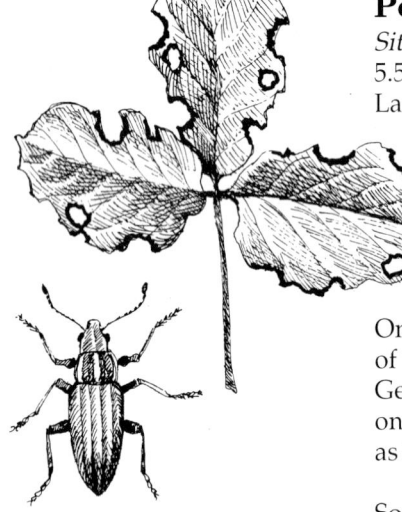

Pea Weevil
and its effect on leaves

FLIES
Order Diptera

One of the largest insect Orders, both in number of species and in number of individuals. Flies are usually small or very small, soft-bodied insects. Generally distinguishable from other winged insects because they only have one pair of functional wings. The hind wings are much reduced and function as balance organs during flight.

Some blood-sucking forms are harmful to humans and to livestock because they can transmit serious diseases such as malaria and dysentery. Other species are pests of crops. On the other hand, many species of flies are beneficial to humans because they act as scavengers or because they are predators or parasites of harmful insects; they are also important pollinators.

Family Tipulidae

Insects which resemble large mosquitoes; generally brown or grey, with very long legs. The larvae live in water or damp soil and feed on rotting vegetable matter. They do not bite. About 8 species.

Mottled-wing Crane-fly   p171
Limonia nubeculosa   Nemusun tad-Djar
8mm. Generally occurs in humid conditions among vegetation and in caves, where it often congregates in large numbers. Occasionally enters houses. Common.

Family Psychodidae

Very small flies, less than 5mm, which can be separated into two groups: the moth-flies and the sand-flies. The wings are wide and pointed. Moth-flies keep them closed in a tent-like fashion similar to moths, while sand-flies keep them together over their abdomen. Sand-flies live near water and even in houses, and in spite of their small size, have a very painful bite. They can act as vectors of certain diseases. Moth-flies do not bite and live in damp, shady places, often gathering in considerable numbers. About 20 species.

Common Moth-fly   p171
Psychoda sp.   Nemusa Muswafa
2mm. Restricted to damp places, especially in the vicinity of drains. Larva lives on decaying organic matter. Common.

Family Culicidae

A large family of blood-sucking mosquitoes. They are slender and long-legged. The males often have feathery antennae. The females have needle-like piercing mouthparts which are used to puncture the skin and suck blood. Many are nocturnal. The larvae live in freshwater in a variety of habitats. About 10 species.

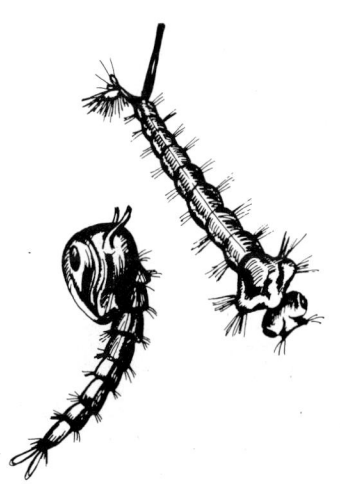

Mosquito
larva (above) and
pupa (below)

Mosquito   p171
Culex pipiens   Nemusa
4.5mm. Found practically everywhere, even in houses, where it spends a lot of time during cool weather. Very common.

Family Bibionidae

Medium-sized or small but rather robust flies. Generally black or yellow. The adults are commonly seen on flowers. The larval stages live on rotting grass and roots. About 3 species.

March-fly   p171
Bibio siculus   Dubbiena Bikrija
7-8mm. Appears during the first months of the year, especially on flower-heads of Alexanders in damp, shady places. Common.

Family Stratiomyidae

Flies of variable form; generally dark, although some species are brightly coloured and resemble wasps. The larvae live in various habitats, including fresh water, and rotting organic matter. About 4 species.

Long-horned Soldier-fly   **p171**

Stratiomys longicornis   Dubbiena Moqrana
12mm. Lives near fresh water, especially stagnant pools, where it rests on damp banks and on vegetation. Common.

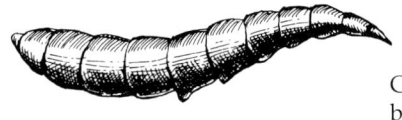

Larva of a horse-fly

Family Tabanidae

Corpulent flies of medium to large size, with coloured, often shiny, eyes. The blood-sucking females can be harmful to humans and livestock. The males generally live on flowers, feeding on nectar and pollen. The larvae of most species live in water and are predatory. 3 species.

Yellow Horse-fly   **p171**

Atylotus sp.   Xidja
12mm. Strong flier. Lives near fresh water, mostly in coastal areas, especially sandy bays, where it often settles on bathers. Bite is painful. Occasionally common.

Family Asilidae

Flies which can be hairy or quite smooth. Predatory, often attacking insects such as bees, wasps, other flies and grasshoppers, even if larger than they are. The adults live in various habitats. The larvae are generally found in the soil or in rotting wood; they often attack other insect larvae. About 8 species.

Common Robber-fly   **p171**

Serdistus sp.   Dubbiena ta' l-Assalt
9mm. Occurs on vegetation and open ground in dry localities. Lies in wait for its prey, which it takes on the wing. Frequent.

Family Acroceridae

Flies with a humped appearance. Head very small, seemingly consisting only of a pair of eyes. Adults are mostly found on flowers, although in some species they do not feed. The larvae are parasites of spiders. 2 species so far recorded.

Schembri's Spider Fly   **p171**

Ogcodes schembrii   Dubbiena tal-Brimb ta' Schembri
5mm. Found mainly on vegetation. Often settles on rocks, and even on people. Described in 1980 by a Czech dipterist, who named it after Maltese entomologist Stephen Schembri. Endemic. Scarce.

Family Bombyliidae

A large Family of flies which usually frequent arid localities. Many are of medium to large size, with a robust, hairy body. Others are small, slender and less hairy. A good number have elongated mouthparts. The adults are found on flowers or flying close to the ground; they often bask in the sun. They are frequently encountered near pools in otherwise dry localities. Many species are good fliers. The larvae are parasitic on caterpillars, beetle grubs, bees, wasps and grasshopper eggs. Over 20 species.

Common Yellow Bee-fly
Bombylius medius

p171

Nahhalija Muswafa

8mm. Found on flowers. Flies off at the slightest disturbance. Frequent.

Silvery Bee-fly
Exoprosopa jacchus

p171

Nahhalija Fiddiena

10mm. Found in dry areas and in valleys, where it basks in the sun on bare ground and on footpaths. Very common.

Red-backed Bee-fly
Usia versicolor

p171

Nahhalija tat-Tebgha Hamra

4-5mm. Found mostly on flat, open flowers such as marigolds. Sexes different. One of the smaller bombylid species. Frequent.

Family Syrphidae

A large Family with many common species. Found practically everywhere, but certain species live in specific habitats. They are particularly frequent on or near flowers. They vary greatly in size and appearance, but they are generally small to medium-sized with vivid colours. Many resemble bees and wasps. The larval stages are variable in appearance and habitat. Many are predators of aphids; others live in the nests of social insects, in grass, rotting timber or in stagnant water. A few live on plants. About 30 species recorded, but others almost certainly occur.

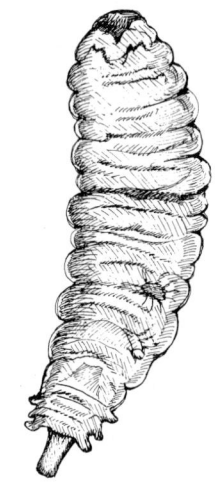

Larva of a Syrphid fly

Drone-fly
Eristalis tenax

p171

Dubbiena Dakar

14mm. Found on various flowers, or basking on sunny walls. Very similar to Honey Bee in appearance, but lacks a sting. Larva found in stagnant, even polluted, water. Very common.

Lesser Drone-fly
Eristalinus taeniops

p171

Dubbiena ta' l-Ghajnejn Irrigati

13mm. Resembles Drone-fly in habits and appearance, but slightly smaller. Very common.

Common Yellow-banded Hover-fly
Metasyrphus corollae

p171

Dubbiena Żunżanija

9mm. Found in countryside and gardens. Wasp-like. Larva found on trees and shrubs, where it feeds on aphids. Common.

Slender Hover-fly
Syritta pipiens

p171

Dubbiena tal-Fjuri

7-9mm. Found everywhere, frequently entering houses. Larva lives in decomposing organic matter. Common.

Family Heleomyzidae

Small to medium-sized flies, generally brownish. Prefer damp, dark places. The larvae of many species live on rotting vegetation or animal remains, or in fungi. 1 species.

Heleomyzid Fly
Suillia variegata

p171

Dubbiena tal-Faqqiegh

5.5mm. Frequently seen in large numbers in the shade of trees, especially in rather damp localities, such as Buskett. Very common.

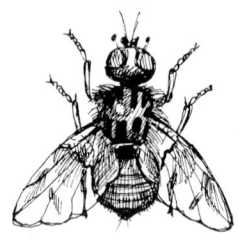

Mediterranean Fruit-fly
adult (above) and
larvae in peach (below)

Family Sepsidae

Small, shiny, black flies, with a round head and a superficial resemblance to ants. The larvae live in rotting organic matter, as do the adults of most species. Often numerous in humid localities with lush vegetation. 3 species.

Black Scavenger-fly   p171

Sepsis punctum   Rewwieha

3-4mm. Found among vegetation, especially in damp, shady spots, e.g. under trees. Very common.

Family Tephritidae

Small to medium-sized flies with striped or spotted wings. Found on flowers and other plants. Some species fan their wings slowly while resting on vegetation. The larvae develop in fruit and other parts of plants. Some are agricultural pests. About 12 species.

Mediterranean Fruit-fly   p171

Ceratitis capitata   Dubbiena tal-Frott

4mm. Found on many different fruit trees and causes considerable damage, especially to oranges. Very common.

Family Drosophilidae

Small flies, including many common species, generally yellowish. Attracted strongly to rotting fruit and vegetation. The larvae usually live in the rotting fruit, probably feeding on the fermenting yeast found therein. Some species are parasites or predators of bugs. At least 1 species.

Fruit-fly   p171

Drosophila melanogaster   Ferminella

2mm. Usually seen in summer. Often enters houses where ripening fruit is found. Attracted by wine, frequently settling on glasses and open bottles. Common.

Family Tachinidae

A large Family of flies which are found practically everywhere. The larvae are parasites of a large variety of other insects. They all look similar, but they vary in size, and their body is often clothed with bristles. The hosts of many species are caterpillars of butterflies and moths or the larvae of wasps and beetles. Some also attack other arthropods. About 30 species recorded, but others certainly occur.

Red-tailed Tachinid Fly   p171

Cylindromyia intermedia   Dubbiena Romblija

10mm. Found on flowers, in holes in walls, and in mouths of caves. Frequent.

Family Sarcophagidae

Common flies, blackish with paler stripes. The adults feed on sugary substances. The larvae live in various habitats, but all feed on one form or another of animal matter. Many are scavengers and feed on animal carcasses. Some are parasitic on other insects, especially beetles and grasshoppers. Others feed on the stored food in bee-hives and wasps' nests. Over 30 species.

Fertoni's Flesh-fly   p171
Sarcophaga fertoni   Dubbiena tal-Laham
12mm. Found on flowers, also on decomposing organic matter. Species in this genus generally similar in appearance. Common.

Family Calliphoridae
Medium-sized or large flies found practically everywhere. They have metallic green or blue coloration. Many species are scavengers. The larvae live in animal carcasses, or in organic refuse. They are carriers of various diseases. About 6 species.

Bluebottle   p171
Calliphora vicina   Żarżura
8-12mm. Stout and robust. Often enters houses, flying about haphazardly towards windows, emitting strong buzzing. Very common.

Bluebottle
larva (above) and
pupa (below)

Greenbottle   p171
Lucilia sericata   Dehbija tal-Ħmieġ
8mm. Found mainly near refuse and animal remains. Also seen on flowers. Very common.

Family Muscidae
A large Family of ubiquitous flies. Some species are pests. The larvae generally live in organic waste. About 20 species.

Common House-fly   p171
Musca domestica   Dubbiena tad-Djar
6.5mm. Lives on all kinds of refuse and found everywhere, especially in summer. Can transmit various diseases. Very common.

Stable-fly   p171
Stomoxys calcitrans   Niggiżija
6.5mm. Found mainly near livestock farms. Bites and sucks blood. Larva lives in manure and other organic matter. Common.

Common House-fly

Family Fanniidae
Strongly resemble the Muscidae. In certain localities, they are more common than the house-fly. The larvae live in various types of decomposing organic matter. 2 species.

Lesser House-fly   p171
Fannia canicularis   Dubbiena Żghira tad-Djar
4-5mm. Found in houses, also in the open. Males fly incessantly around lights inside houses. Frequent.

Family Hippoboscidae
Flies which are generally dark brown. They are flattened, and suck the blood of birds and mammals. Some are wingless, and others have reduced wings. Every so often they give birth to fully developed larvae which soon pupate. 6 species, mostly found on birds.

Pigeon Louse-fly   p171
Ornithomyia avicularia   Dubbiena tal-Hamiem
5mm. Has normal wings. Found on pigeons, as well as on other birds, including migratory species. Sometimes enters houses. Occasionally frequent.

BUTTERFLIES and MOTHS
Order Lepidoptera

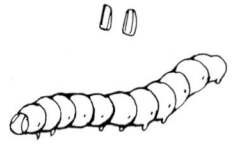

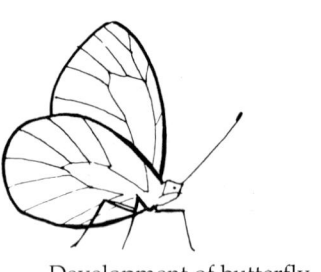

Development of butterfly
from egg to adult

An Order with about 150,000 species. The wings and a large part of the body are covered with minute scales similar to coloured dust particles. Most butterflies are colourful insects which fly by day and keep their wings folded vertically over the abdomen when not in flight. The antennae have clubbed tips. On the other hand, many moths fly by night and are of rather sombre coloration. Moths fold their wings horizontally over the abdomen, and their antennae are not clubbed.

Butterflies and moths have a **proboscis** or tubular mouth which they use to drink nectar from flowers, and occasionally other liquids. When not in use the proboscis is coiled beneath the head. Some moths have a markedly long proboscis, while in some species it is absent or non-functional. In many moths, the coloration of males and females is similar, while colour differences between the two sexes are common in butterflies.

Most larvae (caterpillars) feed on plant material, and they include several pests of crops. Some species feed on textiles and others on stored grains and seeds. Metamorphosis is complete: the egg hatches into a caterpillar, which later forms a pupa, from which the adult (or imago) emerges.

Family Cossidae
Good-sized moths, rather stout-bodied, usually with spotted wings. The caterpillars bore into tree trunks, some species causing damage. 1 species.

Leopard Moth   p173
Zeuzera pyrina   Bahrija tal-Langas
Male 25mm, female 25-30mm. A pest of fruit trees. Caterpillar takes 2-3 years to develop. Frequent.

Family Pyralidae
A large Family of small, delicate moths which vary in form and habits. The caterpillars feed on various materials such as stored foodstuffs and grain. Many cause considerable damage. The caterpillar of many species lives in a slender silk tube. About 100 species.

Meal Moth   p173
Pyralis farinalis   Bahrija tad-Dqiq
10-13mm. Caterpillar feeds on cereals and cereal products and is an important pest in places where cereals are stored, also in bakeries. Common.

Indian Meal Moth   p173
Plodia interpunctella   Bahrija tac-Cereali
8mm. Caterpillar has same feeding habits and behaviour as Meal Moth. Common.

Family Pterophoridae

Small, slender moths, usually grey or brown. The wings are generally split into two or three sections, giving them a feather-like appearance. At rest, the wings are spread out anteriorly. The caterpillars roll leaves or bore into twigs, often causing damage. About 20 species.

Plume Moth   p173

Emmelina monodactyla   Pjuma Komuni
12mm. Usually seen in summer. Caterpillar feeds on bindweeds. Common.

Family Geometridae

A large Family of moths which vary in size and form. They are slender, with an elongate body and very broad wings, often marked with a delicate pattern. In many species there are differences between the sexes, and in some females the wings are reduced or even absent. The caterpillars have a unique mode of locomotion, moving as though they are measuring the ground. When threatened, they often rear up on the posterior legs and mimic a twig. Many feed on the leaves of trees and shrubs. Over 80 species.

Vestal   p173

Rhodometra sacraria   Baħrija tal-Papa
15mm. Often migrates. Caterpillar feeds on flowers of the Family Asteraceae and Caryophyllaceae. Very common.

Family Lasiocampidae

Large moths, with a plump, hairy body. The wings are broad and generally dark brown. The caterpillars are also plump and hairy, and pupate in the grass. 4 species.

Lappet Moth   p173

Gastropacha quercifolia   Werqa Niexfa
40mm. Widespread. Caterpillar feeds on foliage of stone-fruits and pupates in the soil. Common.

Lappet Moth

Oak Eggar   p173

Lasiocampa quercus   Baħrija tal-Ballut
35-45mm. Found principally in the Buskett area. Hairy caterpillar feeds on Ivy. Frequent.

Family Sphingidae

Large, heavy moths with a powerful flight. The forewings are long and pointed. They often hover over flowers, whose nectar they drink by extending their proboscis and inserting it in the flower. Many of the caterpillars bear a horn-like process at the hind end. Pupation usually takes place in the soil or among leaf litter. The caterpillars of some species have two yellowish eyespots just behind the head region. When threatened, the head is retracted so that the eyespots are enlarged, making them appear more menacing. 6 species.

Death's Head Hawkmoth   p173

Acherontia atropos   Baħrija ta' Ras il-Mewt
50-60mm. The largest moth. Stout, with a short proboscis. Thorax bears skull-like pattern. Settles to suck nectar. Caterpillar feeds on leaves of potato plants, among others. Migratory. Scarce.

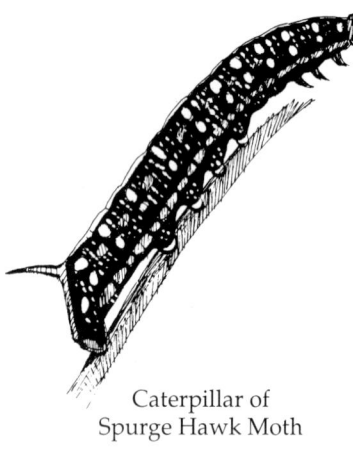

Caterpillar of
Spurge Hawk Moth

Convolvulus Hawkmoth p173
Agrius convolvuli Bahrija tal-Leblieb
50-60mm. Also migrates, often in large numbers. Proboscis extremely long. Principal foodplant of caterpillar is bindweed. Common.

Hummingbird Hawkmoth p173
Macroglossum stellatarum Habbara
25mm. Smallest species in this Family. Visits flowerbeds, occasionally straying inside houses. Unlike many other moths it is active by day. Caterpillar feeds on various species of Rubiaceae. Common.

Spurge Hawkmoth p173
Hyles euphorbiae Bahrija tat-Tenghud
40mm. Caterpillar feeds on spurge and has very vivid coloration. Common.

Striped Hawkmoth p173
Hyles lineata ssp. *livornica* Bahrija tad-Dwieli
40mm. Frequent migrant, occurring in large numbers. Caterpillar feeds on various plants, but is mostly found on grapevines and Rubiaceae. Common.

Family Lymantriidae
Both moths and caterpillars of this Family have irritant, stinging hairs. The chrysalis is loosely formed on the foodplant from the caterpillar's own hairs. 2 species.

Vapourer p173
Orgyia trigotephras Bahrija Tal-Frott Irqiq
Male 15mm. Found near Buckthorn, Bramble and stone-fruit trees, which are the caterpillar's foodplants. Male diurnal. Female wingless, staying near empty chrysalis. Harmful to fruit trees. Common.

Family Arctiidae
Moths which are either fat and hairy with broad wings and bright colours, or have slender wings and dull coloration. The caterpillars are hairy. 4 species.

Maltese Ruby Tiger Moth p173
Phragmatobia fuliginosa ssp. *melitensis* Rubin
20mm. Caterpillar feeds on Borage and bugloss. Endemic. Common.

Tiger Moth p173
Cymbalophora pudica Żarżur
22-25mm. Flies with buzzing sound. Caterpillar feeds on various plants, including nettles, dandelions, Borage and bugloss. Common.

Family Noctuidae
A large Family of mostly greyish or brownish moths. The hindwings are occasionally brightly-coloured. The caterpillars are generally hairless and pupate in the soil. About 135 species.

Bordered Straw Moth p173
Heliothis peltigera Bahrija tal-Lellux
18mm. Migratory, also breeding. Caterpillar feeds on both wild and cultivated plants, especially Crown Daisy. Very common.

DeLucca's Moth   p173
Blepharita deluccai   Bahrija ta' DeLucca
18mm. On the wing between late October and early February. Foodplants
include various wild and cultivated species. Endemic. Common.

Silver Y Moth   p173
Autographa gamma   Bahrija Gamma
20mm. Found in rural and urban areas and in gardens. Flies by night and by
day. Caterpillar feeds on various wild and cultivated plants, often causing
damage to the latter. Migrates in large numbers. Common.

Large Yellow Underwing   p173
Noctua pronuba   Bahrija Safra
28-32mm. Agile flier, which zigzags to evade predators. Hind wings bright
yellow. Caterpillar feeds on various herbaceous plants. Fairly widespread.
Very common.

Bloxworth Snout Moth   p173
Hypena obsitalis   Bahrija ta' l-Gherien
15mm. Found mainly in dense vegetation, such as Ivy, even in mouths of
caves and inside houses. Common.

Almond Tree Moth   p173
Diloba caeruleocephala   Bahrija tal-Lewż
18mm. Found near Almond Trees, on whose foliage the caterpillar feeds.
Very common.

Large Yellow Underwing
caterpillar (above) and
adult (below)

Family Hesperiidae
Generally small butterflies, with a stout body and short wings; they look more
like moths than butterflies. The flight is swift and haphazard. At rest, the
wings are held at an unusual angle. The caterpillars are hairless with a large,
retracted head. 1 species.

Pygmy Skipper   p175
Gegenes pumilio   Bahri
12-15mm. Widespread in virtually all valleys. Has two broods in April-June
and August-September. Caterpillar's foodplants include Bermuda Grass
and Meadow Grass. Pupates in folded leaves, held together with silk. Very
common.

Family Papilionidae
Large butterflies whose coloration usually includes black. The hindwings
have a pointed 'swallowtail' tip. The caterpillars are mostly hairless; when
threatened they emit a foul odour from special glands situated behind the
head. Others use a different defensive strategy: they have a pair of eyespots
which they suddenly enlarge and reveal by retracting their head. As a result
they appear larger, and are not attacked. The pupa is suspended by a slender
silk girdle. 1 species.

Swallowtail   p175
Papilio machaon ssp. *melitensis*   Farfett tal-Fejġel
35-46mm. Widespread. Produces two broods and sometimes a third. Male

Caterpillar of Swallowtail
two stages of development

and female coloration similar. Caterpillar feeds on Rue and Fennel. Subspecies *melitensis* is endemic. Common.

Small White

Family Pieridae
Medium-sized or small butterflies, generally white or yellow with black markings on the wings. The elongate pupa is attached by a silken girdle. Many species are common and migrate in large numbers. 5 species.

Large White   **p175**
Pieris brassicae   Farfett tal-Kaboċċi
26-34mm. Breeds repeatedly, almost all the year round. Caterpillar feeds on various plants of the cabbage Family, also on Caper in summer. Very common.

Small White   **p175**
Pieris rapae   Farfett tal-Kromb
22-28mm. Similar to Large White but smaller. Has similar habits. Very common.

Bath White   **p175**
Pontia daplidice   Farfett tal-Ġarġir
20-25mm. Migratory. Double-brooded. Caterpillar feeds on mignonette and rocket. Frequent.

Clouded Yellow   **p175**
Colias crocea   Farfett tas-Silla
22-28mm. Found from February to November. Frequent migrant. Female often of the form *helice*, which is much paler than the usual form. Caterpillar feeds on leguminous plants. Common.

Cleopatra   **p175**
Gonepteryx cleopatra   Farfett taż-Żiju
24-30mm. Usually found near Buckthorn shrubs, on which the caterpillar feeds, but male often flies considerable distances. Frequent.

Family Lycaenidae
Small, delicate butterflies, often brightly coloured. Some species are very common. The body is long and slender and the antennae often bear white striations. The caterpillars are flat and slug-like. Many emit a sweet substance which attracts ants. The pupa is generally smooth, and held in place by a silken girdle. About 6 species.

Small Copper   **p175**
Lycaena phlaeas   Farfett tas-Selq
12-15mm. Has one brood in early March and another in July-August. Sexes similar. Caterpillar feeds on Dock. Frequent.

Lang's Short-tailed Blue   **p175**
Syntarucus pirithous   Ikhal tad-Denb Qasir
13mm. Usually occurs near caterpillar's foodplant, Plumbago, frequently grown in gardens. Three broods between March and November. Frequent.

Long-tailed Blue   **p175**
Lampides boeticus   Ikhal tad-Denb Twil
14-19mm. Caterpillar feeds on leguminous plants, but rarely causes significant damage. Two broods produced from June onwards. Common.

Holly Blue   **p175**
Celastrina argiolus   Ikhal Fiddieni
14-18mm. Very localised, mostly in Buskett area. Two broods between March and late summer. Foodplants are Ivy and Bramble. Frequent.

African Grass Blue   **p175**
Zizeeria knysna   Ikhal ta' l-Afrika
10-12mm. Accidental visitor. Recorded three times. Very rare.

Brown Argus   **p175**
Aricia agestis   Kannelli ta' l-Anġlu
12-16mm. Caterpillar generally feeds on storksbill. Two broods in March-May and July-August. Frequent.

Common Blue   **p175**
Polyommatus icarus   Farfett ta' l-Anġlu
12-18mm. Found in certain valleys. On the wing from February to November. Caterpillar lives on various leguminous plants, both wild and cultivated. Common.

Family Danaidae
Large, brightly coloured butterflies, often brownish with black and white markings. The forelegs are small. They have a bitter taste, which serves as a defence mechanism. The caterpillars feed on Milkweed. The pupa is suspended with the head upwards. 1 species.

Plain Tiger   **p175**
Danaus chrysippus   Farfett ta' Danaus
40-45mm. Regular migrant in small numbers. Not recorded breeding as yet. Sexes similar. Flight unusual and eye-catching. Very scarce.

Family Nymphalidae
Common butterflies whose wings are brightly-coloured dorsally, but dark ventrally. The pupae are dotted with metallic markings, and are suspended with the head downwards. 2 species.

Red Admiral   **p175**
Vanessa atalanta   Farfett tal-Ħurrieq

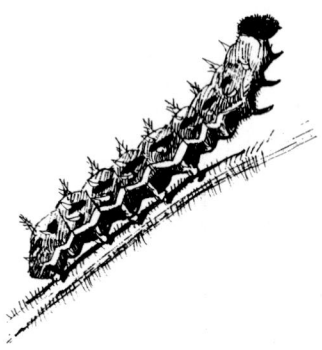

27-29mm. On the wing virtually all year round. Attracted to Lantana flowers and Orange Tree blossoms. Prefers wooded areas to open country. Sexes similar. Caterpillar feeds on nettles and Pellitory-of-the-wall. Common.

Painted Lady   **p175**
Cynthia cardui   Farfett tax-Xewk

Caterpillar of Red Admiral

27-29mm. More widely distributed than Red Admiral. Migrates in large numbers. Male and female similar. Foodplants include mallow, thistles and Borage. Very common.

Family Satyridae
Small or medium-sized butterflies, mostly brownish or greyish with eyespots on the wings. Pupation generally takes place in low vegetation. 4 species.

Speckled Wood

Meadow Brown   p175
Maniola jurtina ssp. *hyperhispulla*   Kannella Kbir
24-30mm. Appears between mid-April and early September. One brood from early May to September. The subspecies *hyperhispulla* is endemic. Very common.

Small Heath   p175
Coenonympha pamphilus   Kannella Żghir
14-16mm. Generally two broods, one in early spring, one in summer. Summer brood butterflies generally larger (up to 22 mm). Frequent.

Speckled Wood   p175
Pararge aegeria   Kannella tad-Dell
18-23mm. On the wing from March onwards, with several broods. Prefers open areas. Various foodplants. Frequent.

Wall Brown   p175
Lasiommata megera   Kannella tax-Xemx
18-25mm. Found mainly in dry, sunny situations. Several broods and may be seen all year round. Common.

ANTS, BEES and WASPS
Order Hymenoptera

A large and important insect Order, including many species which are beneficial to humans because they pollinate flowers, or else prey on or parasitise harmful insects. They are very variable in their habits. Certain species have reached a peak in development, having adopted a social way of life.

Winged forms have two pairs of membranous wings, the hind pair being smaller and joined to the forewings by a row of minute hooks. Venation is reduced, in some forms almost completely lacking. The females of many species have an ovipositor which is modified as a sting, used for attack or defence. Metamorphosis is complete, including egg, larval and pupal stages. Sex is dependent on whether the ovum is fertilised or not: fertilised ova develop into females and unfertilised ones into males.

Family Tenthredinidae
Structurally primitive wasps, poorly represented in the Maltese fauna. Most larvae chew leaves, but a few are leaf-miners. Others live in wounds they themselves cause in leaves and other plant tissues. Some species can be harmful to crops. 2 species.

Common Sawfly   p177
Athalia glabricollis   Żunżan ta' Bla Qadd
7-8mm. Sluggish. Mostly found on flowers of Ivy. Frequent.

Family Ichneumonidae

A large Family of parasites of invertebrates and other insects. They vary in shape, size and colour, but they mostly resemble bees and wasps. The antennae are very long and are constantly in motion. In many species, there is a long, terminal ovipositor. Some species show sexual differences in colour, size and structure, including the presence or absence of wings. They can be found everywhere, especially among vegetation. Several species occur, and are still being studied.

Large Red-legged Ichneumon Fly   p177

Pimpla instigator   Teftufi

Male 16mm, female 21mm. Parasitises caterpillars of butterflies, including those of Whites and Swallowtail. Often searches among vegetation. Common.

Family Evaniidae

A very small Family of parasitic wasps whose abdomen is held in an unusual uplifted position. 1 species.

Black Ensign Wasp   p177

Evania appendigaster   Żunżana taċ-Ċurniena

8-9mm. Often enters houses in search of cockroach egg capsules which it parasitises. Frequent.

Ensign Wasp
and wing

Family Chrysididae

Small to medium-sized parasites, usually metallic blue, red or green. The hard integument is engraved, and the abdomen is concave ventrally, so that they can roll up into a ball when threatened. Many species lay their eggs in the nests of ants and of other wasps which they parasitise. About 15 species.

Ruby-tailed Wasp   p177

Chrysis ignita   Żunżana Dehbija

8-9mm. Often seen basking in early morning sun on rubble walls, Prickly Pear cladodes or Fig leaves. Fairly widespread. Common.

Family Formicidae

The Ant Family. Social insects which live in colonies and display division of labour. Typically, the colony is founded by the queen, which lays large numbers of eggs throughout its life. Most of these develop into worker ants, whose duties include caring for eggs and newly-hatched larvae, enlargement of the nest when required, food gathering and defence. Once a year the queen lays special eggs from which other queens and males will hatch, all winged. These remain in the nest, tended and fed by the workers, until it is time for their nuptial flight, when they leave the nests together to mate in mid-air. Many are destroyed by insectivorous birds. The few survivors settle, the queens seek out likely spots and establish a new colony; the males perish. On finding a suitable spot, in a log or hole in the ground, or underneath some flower pot, the queen sheds its wings lays some eggs and lives on its food reserves without leaving the nest. The eggs develop into workers and these take over all the work. This behaviour varies according to the species. About 50 species, some of which are very rare.

Red Harvester Ant   p177
Pheidole pallidula   Ħażżien Aħmar
Male 5mm, female 7mm, worker 2-4mm. Nests in cracks or crevices, often under kerbstones, in courtyards and gardens. Mostly nocturnal. Lives on food fragments, seeds and similar items. Foraging workers form long columns leading back to nest. Queens and males fly in late summer, and are frequently attracted to artificial lights. Very common.

Carpenter Ant   p177
Camponotus barbaricus   Zokkrin
Male 9mm, female 14mm, worker 8-12mm. Forms large, extensive colonies in soil. Found in both rural and urban areas, especially in gardens. Active by night. Strongly attracted to sweet substances. Common.

Acantholepis Ant   p177
Acantholepis velox   Żvelt Iswed
Male 2mm, female 5mm, worker 3mm. Found in countryside, also in urban localities. Prefers roofs and external walls for foraging, but often seen on flowers. Very swift-moving, and active throughout the day, even during the hottest part of the day. Often catches other insects. Very common.

Black Harvester Ant   p177
Messor capitatus   Ħażżien Iswed
Male 10mm, female 13mm, worker 5-10mm. Found in large numbers, mostly in the countryside, where it gathers various seeds, forming long columns. Underground nests often very extensive. Common.

Maltese Slave-keeping Ant   p177
Strongylognatus insularis   Nemlu ta' Kemmuna
Worker 3mm. Lives in nests of the ant *Tetramorium semilaeve*, feeding on food provided by the latter. Does not carry out nest maintenance or food gathering - a type of social parasitism found in ants. Discovered by an Italian entomologist on Comino. Since then only recorded twice. Males not known. Endemic. Very rare.

Cocktail Ant   p177
Crematogaster scutellaris   Nemlu Rasu Ħamra
Male 4mm, female 8mm, worker 5-6mm. Found on trees and bushes, forming columns of foraging workers. When threatened, cocks rear end. Nests in logs and dead tree stumps. Frequent.

Cocktail Ant
with raised abdomen

Family Mutillidae
Wasps which resemble ants, but have a velvety fur and are rust-coloured with white abdominal stripes. They are parasites of other wasps and bees, in whose nests the females lay their eggs. Some species squeak faintly. Only the males are winged, and they are good fliers, often seen on flowers. The females wander about on the ground, especially in areas where bees and wasps nest. About 20 species, including races which are probably endemic.

Velvet Ant   p177
Stenomutilla hottentota   Naħla tal-Pil
6-11mm. Found in various habitats and probably parasitises Mason Bee. Generally active in the evening. Frequent.

Family Scoliidae

A small Family of large, strong wasps. Most are very hairy and are black with yellow markings. They have a heavy but strong flight. The larvae are parasitic on the larvae of Scarabeid beetles. The female digs in the soil, using its tough forelegs until it finds a suitable grub, which it paralyses with its sting and pushes deeper into the soil. When the wasp larva hatches, it feeds on the paralysed grub. 8 species.

Large Yellow-banded Scolid Wasp   p177

Megascolia flavifrons   Qerd iż-Żaqquq

Male 30mm, female 40mm. Large and conspicuous. Visits the purple flowers of Wild Artichoke. Parasitises larvae of Rhinoceros Beetle. Fairly common.

Family Pompilidae

Medium to large hairless, shiny insects. Very good fliers, often seen wandering among vegetation in search of spiders, which they sting and paralyse. Some species carry the paralysed spider to a hole in the ground or a crack in a tree trunk. Others do not move the victim and lay their eggs in the spider's nest. At least 10 species, including one which is endemic.

Black Spider-hunting Wasp   p177

Anospilus orbitalis ssp. *luctiger*   Qerd il-Brimb

Male 10mm, female 12mm. Very active. Found rummaging among vegetation in various habitats. Common.

Family Eumenidae

Solitary wasps of medium size, and almost always black and yellow. When at rest, the wings are folded above the abdomen. They have different methods of nest building; some use cracks in tree trunks or in timber, others burrow underground. Some construct a nest from mud or clay. About 20 species.

Common Potter wasp   p177

Eumenes lunulatus   Żunżan tal-Ġarra

10-20mm. One of six very similar species with similar habits. Female forms nest from mud in the shape of an inverted vase, attached to some stalk. It then stocks the nest with caterpillars and lays a single egg in the nest, which it seals. Common.

Family Vespidae

A small Family which includes some very common species which are found everywhere in large numbers. Most species are black and yellow. At rest the wings are folded lengthwise above the abdomen. These wasps are social insects and the individuals in the colonies are of three castes - queens, female workers and males. Only the males lack a sting. There are no great differences between the queen and the female workers apart from size. These wasps build a nest (comb) from a paper-like material which consists of wood particles which the wasps chew and work to the right consistency. The queen lays an egg in each cell and the larvae which hatch are cared for by the workers. They are fed on insects and other organisms supplied by the workers. 4 species, one of which has been virtually exterminated, while another was recently introduced and is spreading and increasing.

Common Paper Wasp

Common Paper Wasp   p177
Polistes omissus   Żunżan tax-Xehda
13mm. Builds circular nest, usually in shelter of rubble walls. Colony often quite sizeable. Very common.

Large Paper Wasp   p177
Polistes gallicus   Żunżan tax-Xehda Kbira
14-17mm. Resembles Common Paper Wasp and has similar habits. Nest is larger and lacks regular round shape. Very common.

German Wasp   p177
Paravespula germanica   Żanżun
13-18mm. Found in various localities. Workers often seen on sandy beaches, and are easily attracted by sweet substances. Nests in holes in the ground or in corners of ceilings. Common.

Family Sphecidae
A large Family of solitary wasps. Some nest near each other, showing the first indications of social life. They build various types of nest: some dig in the ground, others use holes and natural cracks in hollow twigs or logs, others build a nest of mud. The larvae eat various types of food, but some are very particular. A number do not build a nest but lay their eggs in the nests of other wasps, the resulting larvae feeding on the food stores. Very variable in size. About 60 species.

Mud-dauber   p177
Sceliphron spirifex   Żunżan taz-Zokk
20-25mm. Found in the country and in gardens. Builds sizeable nest attached to walls, stones, trees or twigs, generally at considerable heights. Spiders, caught by the female, are stored in the nest. Frequent.

Digger Wasp   p177
Ammophila heydeni   Żunżan Ballât
Male 15mm, female 19mm. Nests in the ground, usually in sandy soil. Stocks nest with caterpillars and seals it by pounding the soil with its head or using small pebbles carried in the mandible. Common.

Bee-killer
attacking Honey Bee

Bee-killer   p177
Philanthus triangulum   Qerd in-Nahal
Male 11-13mm, female 15mm. Found mainly in sandy localities. Female digs nest in sand and stocks it with Honey Bees which it catches. Frequent.

Weevil Wasp   p177
Cerceris quadricincta   Qerd il-Bumunqar
9mm. Found on various plants, especially Pennyroyal. Stocks underground nest with a variety of beetles, especially weevils. Several similar species occur. Common

Family Halictidae
Small to medium-sized bees. Most nest in holes in the ground, forming a number of separate cells with a common entrance. Large numbers often nest close to each other and often use the same exit passage. About 16 species.

Common Halictid Bee   p177
Lasioglossum malachrum   Nahla ta' l-Art
8mm. Visits various flowers, including Pennyroyal, Fennel, Caper and
Squirting Cucumber. Male found in two colour morphs. Very common.

Yellow Halictid Bee   p177
Halictus fulvipes   Nahla Rqiqa Safra
10-13mm. Visits thistles, Pennyroyal, Golden Samphire and fleabanes. Very
common.

Family Andrenidae
Small or medium-sized bees which nest in holes in the ground in the same
way as the Halicitid Bees. Some species nest very near to each other, usually
on hard, bare ground. About 10 species.

Black Mining Bee   p177
Andrena carbonaria   Nahla Sewda
10-14mm. Found mainly on flowers of Pennyroyal. Frequent.

Family Megachilidae
Medium to large bees, generally rather stout. Females carry pollen beneath
the abdomen, not on the hind legs as in many other bee species. Some species
cut circular fragments from leaves with their mandibles and use them to line
the inside of their nest. Some are parasitic. Nests constructed in various
places: holes in the ground and other dark hollows, especially in timber and
logs. Some species are important pollinators. About 15 species.

Megachilid bee
head of female

Yellow-striped Megachilid Bee   p177
Anthidium florentinum   Nahla tal-Granfi
Male 15-20mm, female 10mm. Found on flowers, especially Bramble. Larger
size of male unusual in the insect world. Nests in holes in ground, trees or
walls. Lines nest with plant hairs. Frequent.

Common Leaf-cutting Bee   p177
Megachile schmicdeknechti   Mqass tal-Weraq
10mm. Found on various plants. Cuts circular pieces from leaf edges to line
nest. Common.

Kohli's Megachilid Bee   p177
Osmia kohli   Nahla tat-Toqob
10-12mm. Nests in houses and gardens, in hollows such as keyholes, snail
shells and holes in walls. Various colour forms. Fairly widespread. Common.

Mason Bee   p177
Chalicodoma sicula ssp. *balearica*   Nahla tal-Koppla
14mm. Found in many valleys. Female collects dust and gravel to form mud
and constructs dome-like nest attached to walls or stones. Common.

Family Anthophoridae
Strong, hairy bees of medium size. They nest underground and line the cells
with a shiny, waxy substance. Not very well studied. About 10 species.

White-banded Digger Bee   p177

Amegilla quadrifasciata   Naħla tal-Ġonna

11-13mm. Widely distributed in countryside and gardens, appearing late in the year. Common.

Long-horned Digger Bee   p177

Tetralonia berlandi   Bomblu tal-Qrun Twil

18-20mm. Heavy-set. Appears early in the year on various flowers such as Cape Sorrel and Crown Daisy. Sexes different. Frequent.

Family Apidae

Medium to large bees with social habits. Very important plant pollinators. Bees of the genus *Bombus* are strong with a globular shape, covered with long yellow, black or white hairs. They form a new colony every year. Only fertilised females survive winter and form a new colony in the following spring. They usually nest underground, often in old rat holes, sometimes at the base of tall vegetation in sunny positions. Nest consists of a clump of grass enclosing waxy cells. Larvae fed on pollen and nectar. 2 species.

Bumble Bee   p177

Bombus terrestris   Bomblu

16-22mm. Occurs in countryside and gardens. Nests underground forming a new colony every year. Only fertilised females survive winter. Beneficial to humans, as it pollinates many types of flowers. Frequent.

Honey Bee   p177

Apis mellifera   Naħla ta' l-Ghasel

14mm. Social, living in large permanent colonies. In the wild, colonies are generally established in hollow tree trunks or in holes in walls. Colony consists of queen (fertilised female), workers (sterile females) and drones (males). Queen lays numerous eggs while workers forage for food away from hive. Many races known. Common.

Family Xylocopidae

Mostly small bees, although some are large, strong species. The smaller species nest by hollowing out stems and twigs. Large and massive species (genus *Xylocopa*) bore into timber. 3 species.

Large Carpenter Bee   p177

Xylocopa violacea   Bomblu Iswed

26mm. Large and stout. Found in countryside and in gardens. Bores into wood, often nesting in Giant Reed stalks used for windbreaks. Strong flier with loud buzzing sound. Common.

Large Carpenter Bee

CRUSTACEANS

The Crustacea forms one of the Classes of the Phylum ARTHROPODA, and is itself classified into five groups. Crustaceans number upward of 44,000 species, with great variation in morphology and habitat. Some species are less than 1mm in length, some others have leg spans of up to 4m and weigh up to 8kg.

Most crustaceans live in the sea. Others live in fresh or brackish water and a smaller number are terrestrial, although they are mostly restricted to damp or humid habitats.

Crustaceans are of great economic importance. Some of the larger species, such as crabs and prawns, have been eaten by humans since prehistoric times, while others are important as food for fish.

The simpler crustaceans consist of a **head** and an elongate **body**, to which are attached several paired **appendages** made up of many similar segments. In other species, the body is divided into two parts each of which is further subdivided. Many have a hard covering over the entire body or a kind of **helmet** covering the head. The word crustacean, in fact, is derived from the Greek word for skin.

Crustaceans have two pairs of **antennae** on the head; one pair of these is used for swimming in many species, especially the smaller ones. The appendages are always numerous, and are used not only for the locomotory functions of swimming or walking, but also for food gathering, for the extraction of oxygen from the water, and for reproduction.

The mode of locomotion also varies. Most swim or walk, others jump; some burrow in the bottom mud or sand, while others attach themselves to other organisms. The swimming forms, such as shrimps and swimming crabs, use their appendages as oars. Many are capable of dashing through the water at great speed in order to escape predators. Many species walk forwards and backwards, and, in the case of crabs, sideways. Water fleas, clam shrimps and ostracods use their antennae to propel themselves through water, while some species of semi-terrestrial amphipods are capable of long leaps.

Crustaceans may be carnivorous, herbivorous or detritus-feeders, the latter feeding on decaying organic matter. Most, however, are omnivorous, feeding on whatever food comes their way. Several are parasitic and attach themselves to other animals from which they obtain the nutrients they require.

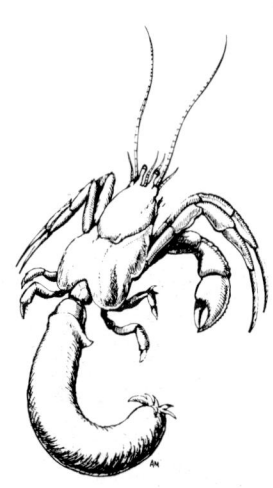

Hermit crab
outside the shell

Many of the aquatic species have specialised mechanisms for feeding on suspended detritus or catching minute organisms. Some species use their appendages to create a current of water in the direction of their mouth. This current conveys microscopic plants and animals towards the appendages, where they are entangled in net-like hairs, passed to the mouth and ingested.

Another feeding mechanism involves the use of appendages or hard mouthparts to scrape off algae, small encrusting animals or other organic matter from rocks or other substrata. The material removed in this way is ingested through the mouth.

Carnivorous crustaceans employ various methods to capture their prey. Some lie in wait while others, though not many, search out their prey actively. When the prey is captured, it is held fast by the appendages, bitten to death and ripped apart.

Aquatic crustaceans obtain their oxygen requirements in various ways. Some of the smaller species with a thin body wall, such as copepods, absorb oxygen directly through the surface into the blood. Others have a thin membrane lining the body wall internally which is permeable to oxygen.

Most crustaceans respire through specialised appendages which have a hollow, thin-walled part, rich in blood vessels. The blood passing through absorbs oxygen from the water. In many cases, the water is circulated around the crustacean in order to increase the efficiency of oxygen absorption. Terrestrial crustaceans, such as isopods, have very small apertures in some of their appendages through which air can enter.

The appendages and other parts of the body are covered with fine hairs which are very sensitive to water movements and to the animal's own activities. They also possess bristle-like sense organs on the antennae or in the vicinity of their mouth which can detect chemical changes in the water.

Crustaceans can have two types of **eyes**: the simple eye and the compound eye. Many have both types. The simple eye is only used to detect the direction and intensity of light. The compound eyes can distinguish form, movement and colour. Some species have the compound eyes raised on stalks in order to increase the field of view.

Most species have separate sexes. In the smaller and more primitive forms, the female is invariably larger than the male, and in some species, males are lacking altogether. In many of these forms, even where males are known, females can produce offspring without being fertilised by a male. This method of reproduction is termed parthenogenesis.

The females of certain species retain the eggs until they hatch. The larval crustacean is known as a **nauplius** and is completely different from the adult. After some time the nauplius moults and changes form. This process is repeated several times, until the larva assumes the shape and structure of the adult. In some species a number of different larvae forms between the nauplius and the adult exist, while in others the nauplius stage is suppressed and is spent in the egg.

The Branchiopoda, Maxillopoda and Malacostraca are three of the five Divisions of the Class Crustacea which are represented in Malta.

The Branchiopoda are vary variable. Almost all of them live in fresh or

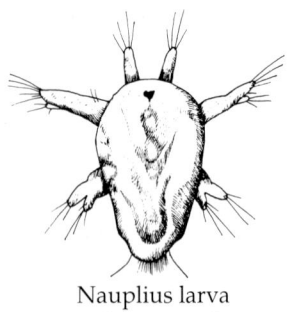

Nauplius larva
of a copepod

brackish water, and have numerous thin, broad, leaf-like appendages. They include fairy shrimps, water fleas, tadpole shrimps and clam shrimps.

The Maxillopods include the ostracods, the copepods and the cirripedes.

Ostracods are small with a bean-shaped shell-like cover. The shell can be opened to allow the animal to extend its appendages for swimming, walking or feeding. Ostracods include both marine and freshwater forms. They are capable of swimming, but spend most of their time on the bottom, where they feed on organic matter.

Copepods are common in both marine and freshwater environments. Few exceed 1cm in length, although some parasitic forms can reach a length of 25cm. They have an elongate body made up of three regions: the head, a middle region and a posterior region. The head bears two pairs of antennae, one of which is generally long and used for swimming. Over 1000 species of copepods are parasites. Many live on the gills, fins and other body parts of fish. Others parasitise marine annelids, echinoderms and sea-anemones. The morphology of the parasitic forms differs considerably from that of the free-living copepods and some parasites are hardly recognisable as copepods.

Barnacle with extruded appendages

Cirripedes include the barnacles. They are completely unlike other crustaceans, and for a long time were considered to be molluscs. All barnacles live in the sea. The adults are usually attached to rocks, mollusc shells, corals or to the hulls of seacraft and floating objects. Certain species adhere to the bodies of other marine animals such as fish, turtles and whales. Barnacles generally have a hard 'shell' which encloses the whole animal. They feed on microscopic plants and animals and on particles which they capture by means of a current they create using their appendages. The latter are also used to sieve out the food.

The Malacostraca comprise three quarters of all known crustaceans, including the larger forms such as crabs, lobsters and prawns. Most are marine, but some live in freshwater and a few are terrestrial. This Division also includes the woodlice and sandhoppers.

Order Anostraca
Family Branchiopodidae

Fairy Shrimp   p179
Branchipus schaefferi   Gamblu ta' l-Ghadajjar
2-3cm. Found in rainwater pools from September to April. Light brown, although other colours may be present, especially green, due to ingestion of microscopic algae. Has 11 pairs of appendages which are used as oars, the shrimp swimming on its back. Feeds on organic matter and minute algae which are filtered from the water. Has two prominent eyes raised on stalks. Male has antennae resembling downward-pointing horns. Female has a coloured egg sac. Frequent.

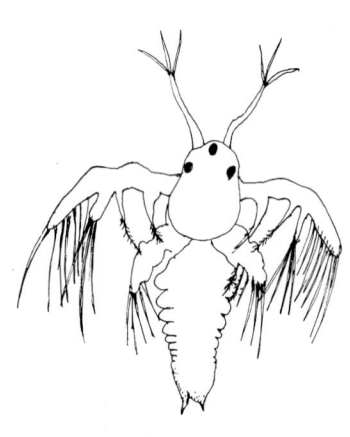

Nauplius larva
of a fairy shrimp

Order Notostraca
Family Triopsidae

Tadpole Shrimp   p179
Triops cancriformis   Gamblu ta' l-Elmu
5-6cm, including tail. Lives at the bottom of rainwater pools. Head region is

protected by a helmet-like carapace. Posterior part elongate, consisting of several segments ending in a long, forked tail. A pair of small eyes are present on carapace. Colour generally brownish, sometimes dark green. Feeds on small plants and animals as well as bottom detritus. Can swim, but only for short distances. Very rare.

Order Conchostraca
Family Cyzicidae

Clam Shrimp   p179
Cyzicus tetracerus   Gamblu tal-Qoxra
1cm. Found at the bottom of rainwater pools on karstland between September and April. Has a clam-like shell which encloses whole body. The animal is reddish or brown and feeds on small plants and animals and other organic matter which is located by burrowing in the bottom mud. Uses the antennae for swimming but, owing to the heavy body, soon returns to the bottom. Scarce.

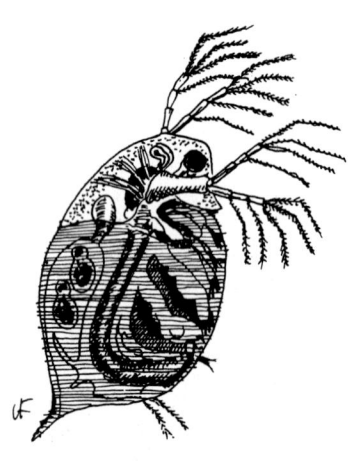

Water flea

Order Cladocera
Family Daphniidae

Water Flea   p179
Daphnia pulicaria   Żagħrun tal-Ġwiebi
3-4mm. Lives in freshwater, and is usually found in reservoirs and other places where water is present all year round. Rarely seen in pools which dry up during summer. Transparent, but takes on a reddish hue when living in poorly-oxygenated water. Uses antennae for swimming, which is usually rather jerky. Feeds by filtering microscopic organisms and other food particles from the water. Common.

Pool Flea   p179
Ceriodaphnia quadrangula   Żagħrun ta' l-Għadajjar
1-2mm. Found in rainwater pools which dry up in summer. Similar in structure and habits to Water Flea. Females lay hard-shelled fertilised eggs which sink to the bottom sediment and can withstand the intense summer heat when pool dries up. Eggs hatch when pool fills up again with the autumn rains. Common.

Family Chydoridae

Chydorid Water Flea   p179
Pleuroxus latourneuxi   Żagħrun Skur
1mm. One of the smallest arthropods. Lives on mud at the bottom of rainwater pools. Dark brown. Form is flattened with an elongate beak. Eyes close to each other. Swims by means of antennae, and capable of rapid movements. Feeds in the same way as Water Flea and Pool Flea. Common.

Order Podocopa
Family Cyprididae

Seed-shrimp   p179
Cypris pubera   Ostrakodu Kbir
2-3mm. Lives at the bottom of rainwater pools, where it is often abundant.

Feeds on organic matter and crawls and swims quite rapidly using its antennae. When threatened, the bean-shaped shell can be closed. Eggs laid in late spring and withstand the summer heat when pool dries up. No males have ever been recorded. Frequent.

Golden Seed-shrimp   p179
Herpetocypris reptans   Ostrakodu Isfar
2-3mm. Similar to Seed-shrimp in habitat and behaviour. Shell golden brown. Males unknown. Eggs can resist summer temperatures and dehydration. Very common.

Order Cyclopoida
Family Cyclopidae

Common Copepod   p179
Cyclops vulgaris   Kopepodu ta' l-Ghadajjar
1mm. Found in rainwater pools. Swims jerkily using antennae as well as other appendages. Feeds on algae and microscopic animals which it filters from the water. White, but reddish in poorly aerated water. Female can be distinguished by the paired lateral egg-sacs. Some of the eggs are deposited in the bottom mud, where they can survive the summer drought. Very common.

Order Thoracica
Family Lepadidae

Goose Barnacle   p179
Lepas anatifera   Koċċla ta' l-Ghonq
Shell 5cm + neck 15cm. Attached to hulls of boats and floating timber. Has long stalk-like neck below shell. Feeds by filtering organic matter from surrounding water. Common.

Family Chthamalidae

Goose Barnacles

Flattened Barnacle   p179
Chthamalus depressus   Koċċla Ċatta
1-1.5cm. Found in the splash zone of rocky shores, where it is subject to frequent exposure due to wave action. Can live out of water, but not for extended periods. Body enclosed in pyramidal shell consisting of six plates. Appendages are able to extend out through oval aperture at the top to form net-like filter for planktonic organisms. These are ingested when appendages are retracted. Common.

Star Barnacle   p179
Chthamalus stellatus   Koċċla Komuni
5-10mm. Attached to rocks on the lower regions of rocky shores. Whitish shell composed of six plates, with a round aperture through which appendages are extended. Feeds in the same way as Flattened Barnacle. Often abundant. Common.

Order Isopoda

Small crustaceans which live in the sea, on the shore in brackish or fresh water or on land. Their body is segmented and semicircular in section.

Family Sphaeromatidae

Shore Louse   p179
Sphaeroma serratum   Ħanżir l-Art tax-Xatt
1cm. Found in shallow marine waters among rocks and pebbles and when threatened hides beneath them or in rock crevices. Resembles woodlice in appearance. Feeds on decaying remains of dead plants and animals. Common.

Family Ligiidae

Sea-slater   p179
Ligia italica   Dudu tas-Sajd
1-2cm. Roams about on rocks very close to the sea's edge. Very agile and hides in rock crevices at the slightest sign of danger. Mostly nocturnal, but often seen during the day. Lives on land but also spends some time in the sea; often found in rock pools. Used as bait by anglers. Very common.

Family Porcellionidae

Maquis Woodlouse   p179
Porcellio laevis   Ħanżir l-Art tal-Makkja
2cm. Lives in various terrestrial habitats including maquis, coastal areas and gardens. Usually found under stones and among leaf litter, especially in sheltered, damp situations. Does not roll up into a ball when threatened. Common.

Family Oniscidae

Garigue Woodlouse   p179
Chaetophiloscia elongata   Ħanżir l-Art tax-Xagħri
1cm. Lives in very humid conditions. Mostly found under stones in maquis, garigue or along watercourses. Does not roll up when threatened. Very common.

Family Armadillidiidae

Common Maltese Woodlouse   p179
Armadillidium schmalfussi   Ħanżir l-Art ta' Malta
2cm. Lives in similar conditions as Garigue Woodlouse. Dehydrates and dies rapidly unless sheltered from the heat. Feeds on plant remains. Rolls up into tight ball when threatened. Commonest woodlouse. Endemic. Very common.

Common Woodlouse   p179
Armadillidium vulgare   Ħanżir l-Art Komuni
2cm. Lives in very damp habitats, under stones and leaf litter in maquis. Rolls up when threatened. Feeds on vegetable matter in the soil. Absent from Gozo and Comino. Common.

Common Woodlouse
rolled up

Order Amphipoda

Small crustaceans which live in the sea or fresh water. Certain species can live away from water, but always in very humid conditions.

Family Talitridae

Sandhopper   p179
Talitrus saltator   Berghud tar-Ramel
1cm. Found on sandy beaches. Burrows into sand, where it finds sufficient moisture and shelter. Also found in banks of Posidonia washed up by the waves, feeding on the decaying leaves. Retreats into the damp sand when Posidonia dries up. Leaps rapidly about when exposed, and soon digs back into sand. Often used as bait by anglers. Common.

Common Amphipod   p179
Orchestia gammarellus   Amfipodu Komuni
2cm. Found in various habitats, including brackish water pools, valleys with natural springs and dry but humid valleys. The only amphipod which can survive away from water. Resembles Sandhopper. Feeds on plant and animal remains. Common.

Order Stomatopoda

Marine crustaceans. Carnivorous, feeding on fish, crabs, shrimps and molluscs by piercing or cracking their shells. Flattened, with a small carapace.

Family Squillidae

Spot-tailed Mantis Shrimp   p181
Squilla mantis   Ċkala Bajda
15-20cm. Lives at depths of about 55-200m, preferring rocky and sandy bottoms. Lives in a burrow and defends a territory. Spends most of the time hidden on the bottom, but occasionally swims up to catch small animals, using two long, pointed appendages which resemble the raptorial forelegs of the Praying Mantis. Two distinctive black spots on tail. Used as bait. Scarce.

Mantis shrimp attacking prey

Order Decapoda

Lobsters, shrimps, crabs and hermit crabs. Have five pairs of walking appendages. The first pair are pincer-like claws. Most live in the sea, but some live in fresh water and some are terrestrial. Some swim for long periods while others do not swim but crawl on the bottom. All Maltese species are marine except for the Maltese Freshwater Crab.

Caramote Prawn   p181
Penaeus kerathurus   Gamblu Imperjali
Male 14cm, female 18cm. Lives on sandy or muddy bottoms at depths of about 40-90m. Flattened, with short appendages used for swimming. Does not swim much, mostly remaining on the bottom. One of the pairs of antennae is longer than body. Tail bears three spine-like plates, used for steering. Feeds on small bottom-living organisms. Rare.

Family Crangonidae

Common Shrimp   p181
Crangon crangon   Gamblu tar-Ramel
9cm. Lives near the shore, on sand or among seaweeds at depths down to

20m. Transparent or sand-coloured and difficult to spot when at rest on the sand. Swims for short periods, but normally remains on the bottom, where it feeds on small animals. Edible. Scarce.

Family Hippolytidae

Monaco Shrimp   p181

Lysmata seticaudata   Suldat

3-6cm. Lives in sea-grass meadows at depths down to 60m. Also found close to the shore. One of the pairs of antennae is longer than body. Feeds on small, bottom-living animals. Frequent.

Family Processidae

Processa Shrimp   p181

Processa canaliculata   Gamblu tal-Fond

5-7cm. Lives at depths of 70-600m. Red with orange stripes. Swims for short periods. Feeds on animals living in the bottom mud. Rare.

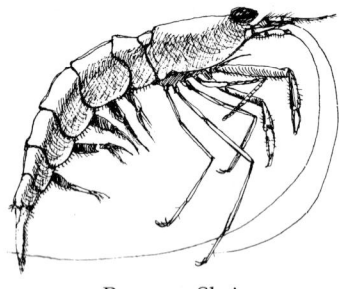

Processa Shrimp

Family Palaemonidae

Glass Prawn   p181

Palaemon elegans   Gamblu tax-Xatt

3-4cm. Lives on rocky bottoms. Found in shallow water on the shore down to depths of about 10m. Frequently found in rock pools. Lives on organic remains found on the bottom. Anterior part of carapace is saw-like, bearing a number of teeth. Frequent.

Family Palinuridae

Common Spiny Lobster   p181

Palinurus elephas   Awwista

50cm. Lives at depths down to 160m on rocky or sandy bottoms, hiding in crevices or among rocks on the bottom. Does not swim. Has no oar-like appendages or pincers. Carapace and tail very spiny. Antennae are banded, one pair considerably longer than the body. Feeds on smaller animals, including snails whose shell it breaks to reach the softer parts. Edible. Frequent.

Family Scyllaridae

European Paddle-nosed Lobster   p181

Scyllarus latus   Ċkala Ħamra

40cm. Found on muddy or rocky bottoms and near sea-grass meadows at depths exceeding 3m. Antennae very short and pincers are absent. Does not swim, but walks on the bottom. One of the pairs of antennae is paddle-shaped, used for burrowing in the mud, as well as for defence. Edible. Frequent.

Family Nephropidae

European Lobster   p181

Homarus gammarus   Ljunfant tal-Bahar

50cm. Largest crustacean in Malta. Found at depths down to 150m in caves and crevices. Does not swim. Territorial. One pair of antennae is as long as its body, while the other pair is short. Anterior appendages armed with very large pincers which are used to break the shells of its prey. Scarce.

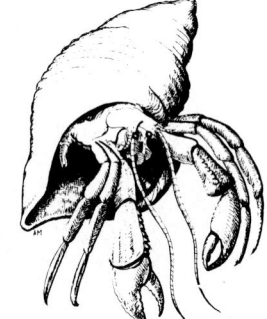

Hermit crab

Family Paguridae

Deep-water Hermit Crab   p183
Dardanus arrosor · Granċ tal-Bebbuxu tal-Fond
8cm. Found on muddy and rocky bottoms at around 30m. Lives in the empty shell of a snail, which is dragged around when the crab walks and into which it retreats when threatened. Shell often bears sea-anemones or sponges which serve as camouflage. As the crab grows, it occupies larger shells. Used as bait by anglers. Common.

Shore Hermit Crab   p183
Clibanarius erythropus   Granċ tal-Bebbuxu tax-Xatt
2cm. Found in shallow water near the shore and in rock pools. Hides among pebbles. Same habits as Deep-water Hermit Crab, but does not bear sea-anemones or sponges. Feeds on organic remains found on the bottom. Common.

Family Dromiidae

Sponge Crab   p183
Dromia personata   Kapott
8cm. Found mostly in deep water. Often carries pieces of living sponge on its back for camouflage, keeping it in place with its hind legs. Sponge continues to grow and assumes the shape of the crab's carapace, but does not adhere to it. When threatened, the crab often abandons the sponge and flees without it. When no sponge can be found, it uses bits of shell and other bottom debris. Carapace is dome-shaped with hairy covering. Armed with two strong pincers which have dark-coloured fur except for the bare tips, which are pinkish. Common.

Family Calappidae

Shame-faced Crab   p183
Calappa granulata   Serduq
11cm. Buries itself in sandy bottoms. Feeds on small animals, such as clams and cockles which it finds by burrowing. Very light brown with reddish spots on back and on pincers. The dorsal part of the claws resembles a cock's comb. When threatened, it retracts all appendages to form a ball. Common.

Family Leucosiidae

Nut Crab   p179, p181
Ilia nucleus   Mewt
3cm. Bottom-dwelling, in both coastal and deep waters. Found in mud or among pebbles and seaweed. Body spherical, with numerous humps on posterior part of carapace. Long, slender appendages. Can be light brown or reddish. Rare.

Family Pirimelidae

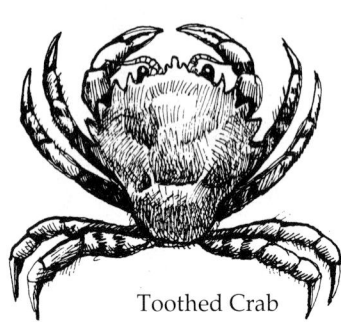
Toothed Crab

Toothed Crab   p183
Pirimela denticulata   Granċ tas-Snien
2.5cm. Lives on shallow, sandy bottoms, sometimes also found in rock pools on the shore. Carapace is toothed anteriorly, with three teeth between the eyes. Anterior appendages with small pincers, and the others with a single claw. Common.

Family Portunidae

Green Crab   p183
Carcinus aestuarii   Granċ tal-Marsa
4cm. Found mostly on muddy bottoms in shallow water, feeding on small organisms which live in the mud. Very agile, and hides at the slightest sign of danger. Dark green. Common.

Arched Swimming Crab   p183
Liocarcinus arcuatus   Farfett tar-Ramel
2cm. Buries itself in sand and occurs at depths down to about 40m. Also found among seaweed. Posterior part of carapace is arched laterally. Has numerous bristles between eyes. Hind legs oar-like. Common.

Velvet Swimming Crab   p183
Liocarcinus puber   Farfett il-Bahar
5cm. Found mostly in deep water. Can swim, the hind legs being oar-like. Feeds on other swimming animals, including small fish and shrimps. Carapace covered with short brown hairs. Bare parts are bluish or reddish. Rare.

Family Xanthidae

Spiny Crab   p183
Eriphia verrucosa   Grottlu
8-10cm. Lives on the shore in cracks on seaweed-covered rock, retreating to greater depths in rough weather. Carapace and legs very hairy. Has a pair of very strong pincers. Feeds on small bottom-living animals, including snails. Breaks shells with pincers and consumes soft inner parts. Widely used as live bait for octopus fishing. Edible. Common.

Stone Crab   p183
Xantho poressa   Grottlu Żghir
3cm. Lives on shallow, rocky bottoms, on or among stones. Legs short compared to body. Front legs armed with unequal pincers of a brownish colour. Very common.

Family Goneplacidae

Angular Crab   p183
Goneplax rhomboides   Zakak
3cm. Burrows in muddy bottoms at depths of up to 100m, but has also been found at depths of 300m. Body rectangular. Male has very long pincers. Frequent.

Family Grapsidae

Mediterranean Shore Crab   p183
Pachygrapsus marmoratus   Granċ tax-Xatt
3cm. Found on all rocky shores. Flattened for easy retreat into rock crevices.
Can walk forwards, backwards and sideways so that it can manoeuvre in
confined spaces. Very common.

Family Parthenopidae

Long-armed Crab   p183
Parthenope angulifrons   Granċ Idejh Twal
2-2.5cm. Lives among bottom gravel and on sand at depths of 5-40m. Pincers
very long, and when retracted give the crab a triangular appearance.
Carapace dorsally very rough, not easily seen when animal is at rest on the
bottom. Scarce.

Family Majidae

Spiny Spider Crab   p183
Maia squinado   Għaġuża
25cm (breadth 50cm including legs). Lives on the bottom at considerable
depths. Largest Mediterranean crab. Carapace bears short thick spines
dorsally. Legs long and slender. Camouflages itself with pieces of seaweed,
which it places on its back using pincers. After moulting , it 'plants' fresh
seaweed on the bare carapace. Its chief predators are octopuses. Often used
as octopus bait. Frequent.

Spiny Spider Crab

Four-horned Spider Crab   p183
Pisa tetraodon   Għaġuża ta' Erba' Qrun
4cm. Lives in both deep and shallow waters in sea-grass meadows. Has four
anterior, horn-like projections. Common.

Round-jointed Spider Crab   p183
Lissa chiragra   Għaġuża tal-Hotob
4cm. Found on muddy bottoms at 30-80m. Carapace pear-shaped with large
lateral spines. Often encrusted with algae or small organisms. Carapace
extends forwards forming T-shaped projection. Dorsal part of carapace
bears two large overlapping humps. Appendages with bead-like joints.
Rare.

Clinging Crab   p183
Acanthonyx lunulatus   Għaġuża tal-Plajja
3cm. Clings to seaweed on the shore, using small pincer-like claws. Hangs
on even in rough weather. Carapace elongate, the rear part being rounded
and the front armed with several straight spines. Frequent.

Long-legged Spider Crab   p183
Macropodia rostrata   Brimba
2cm. Lives on muddy and sandy bottoms down to 85m. Legs long and
delicate compared to body, which is triangular and extends forward to form
pointed projection. Feeds on small animals and organic remains which it
finds on the bottom. Scarce.

Family Potamonidae

Maltese Freshwater Crab

Potamon fluviatile ssp. *lanfrancoi*

p183

Qabru

7-8cm. Found at Bahrija, Imtahleb, San Martin and Lunzjata Valley (Gozo), where running water is present all year round. Lives near pools and springs. Hides under stones in the water, among vegetation, or by retreating into burrows which it excavates in the mud or clay. These burrows have two openings and often exceed 50cm in depth. Internal part of burrow often flooded. Forages for food after sunset. Carnivorous and feeds on smaller animals, including snails and tadpoles. Has disappeared from a number of valleys because of drying up or pollution of the springs, and because it is often caught by humans. Up to a century or so ago, it was used by poor people to make soup on fasting days. It apparently caused bowel movements. The subspecies *lanfrancoi* is endemic. Very rare.

Maltese Freshwater Crab

ARACHNIDS

Arachnids (Class ARACHNIDA) can be distinguished from other arthropods because the first pair of appendages are pincer-like claws termed **chelicerae**. They are used to catch and grasp prey or other objects. All living arachnids are in fact carnivorous, except for some which live by sucking plant sap.

Besides the chelicerae, arachnids have another pair of specialised appendages called **pedipalps**, as well as four pairs of walking **legs**. They lack wings and antennae. The **eyes** are simple, not compound as in the insects, and their number may vary from two to twelve; some are eyeless. The body is generally divided into two, although in some cases it appears to be undivided.

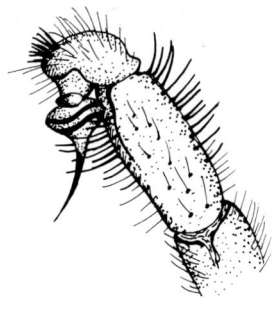

Pedipalp of
male Trapdoor Spider

The arachnid Class is divided into eleven Orders, only six of which include species which live outside the tropics. These are the scorpions, the pseudoscorpions, the acarines, the spiders, the palpigrades and the harvestmen. These six Orders are all represented in the Maltese fauna.

SCORPIONS
Order Scorpiones

Scorpions are medium-sized to large arthropods, some of which can reach lengths of 20cm. They are generally found in dry habitats. By day they hide in crevices or beneath stones, emerging to search for prey at dusk. In order to capture their prey they have two important organs. Anterior to the four pairs of walking legs are a pair of very large pincer-like pedipalps, which are used to catch and hold the prey but which also have a defensive function. In scorpions the chelicerae are very small and their only function is to manipulate food particles towards the mouth. The other predatory organ is the long 'tail' whose tip bears a swollen venom gland armed with a sharp sting. When the scorpion encounters its victim, it grasps it in the pedipalps and curves its tail forwards over the back to sting the prey and inject its venom, which rapidly induces paralysis. The venom of some scorpion species is very powerful and can be dangerous to humans. 1 species.

Family Chactidae

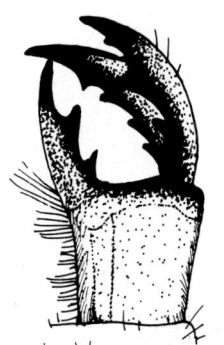

Scorpion   p185
Euscorpius carpathicus   Skorpjun
50mm (including tail). Head and tail dark brown, abdomen paler brown.

Chelicera of a scorpion

Mostly found among leaf litter, under stones and even in houses, usually in cellars. The venom is not very strong, and its effect on humans is equivalent to that of a bee sting. Preys on insects and other small organisms, including some pest species. Common.

PSEUDOSCORPIONS
Order Pseudoscorpiones

Pseudoscorpions are very small arachnids whose body consists of a **cephalothorax** (fused head and thorax) and an abdomen. Some species have one or two pairs of eyes, while others lack these organs. They generally live in dark habitats such as caves or beneath stones, so vision is not very important for these animals. In order to sense what happens around them, they have very long, delicate hairs which are very sensitive to contact and to the slightest of air movements.

As in the scorpions, the chelicerae are reduced and are found at the anterior tip of the cephalothorax. They have a number of functions that include food gathering, production of silk and detection of changes in their environment. The pedipalps are as prominent as those of the scorpions and are situated between the chelicerae and the walking legs. They are also pincer-like and are used to catch and retain prey. Like the chelicerae, they bear sensory hairs; they also play a part in mating. The pedipalps can also inject a poison which paralyses the prey. There is no venomous 'tail' as in the scorpions, and this is the easiest way to distinguish between the two Orders.

About 23 species of pseudoscorpions occur in Malta, although they are little known owing to their small size: the largest species is less than 1cm, and most are less than 3mm in length. Besides, they hide during the day. Three species are endemic and very rare.

Pseudoscorpion

Family Chthoniidae

Green Pseudoscorpion   p185
Chthonius tenuis   Psewdoskorpjun Ħadrani
1.5-2.3mm. Lives beneath stones in dry habitats. Common.

Family Neobasiidae

Red Pseudoscorpion   p185
Roncus lubricus   Psewdoskorpjun Ħamrani
2.5-3mm. Found in the same situations as Green Pseudoscorpion. Common.

ACARINES
Order Acari

Acarines have an apparently undivided body, but this is not in fact true. They generally have four pairs of walking legs, although in some Families one, two or even three pairs may be lacking. The anteriorly placed chelicerae are either pincer-like for grasping, or pointed for piercing. The pedipalps resemble the walking legs.

Many acarines are very small, with a length of less than 1mm; others are larger, but rarely exceed 6mm.

Acarine habits are very variable. Some are predators while others are ectoparasites of reptiles, birds and mammals (including humans). These parasitic forms include a number of species which are harmful to livestock, either directly or else by acting as vectors of disease pathogens. A considerable number of acarine species feed on plants by piercing the leaf epidermis and sucking the sap. These forms include a number of species which are important pests, causing severe damage to agricultural crops.

Other species, of minute size, live in stored grain, cereals, flour and similar goods. They feed on tiny fragments of the stored product and cause little damage.

Although Maltese acarines have received little scientific attention, it can be safely said that numerous species occur, including both free-living and ectoparasitic forms.

Family Ixodidae

Common Tick   p185
Ixodes ricinoides   Qurdiena
6-20mm. The most familiar species. Ectoparasitic on various animals, especially dogs, piercing the skin and sucking blood. The normal size is about 6 mm, but it becomes much larger when gorged with blood. Common.

Family Tetranychidae

Red Spider Mite   p185
Tetranychus telarius   Brimba Hamra
1.5mm. Small, hardly visible. Very harmful, especially to greenhouse crops, fruit trees and ornamental plants. Often preyed upon by other mite species, which thus remedy some of the damage caused. Very common.

SPIDERS
Order Araneae

The spiders are one of the most successful group of arachnids. The Order comprises thousands of species classified in a number of Families. Spiders are found in all parts of the world. Their body consists of two regions: the anterior fused head and thorax (cephalothorax) and the posterior abdomen. The cephalothorax bears four pairs of walking legs.

Borne dorsally on the head are the eyes, usually four pairs, although some species have less. The chelicerae are adapted for the capture of insects and other small creatures and for injecting venom.

The pedipalps of the female spider resemble the walking legs. However, in the male, they are specialised in both structure and function. They often have a strange, complicated structure, including sac-like swellings, rings and spiny outgrowths. The male pedipalps are used during copulation, and function in sperm transfer.

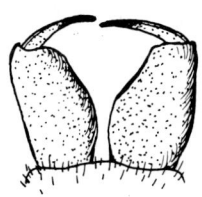

Chelicerae of a spider
underside view

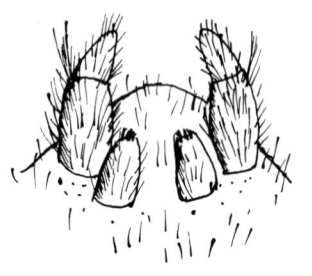

Spinnerets of a spider
underside view

Spiders are renowned for their ability to produce silk. Although found in other arachnid Orders, in none of them does this ability reach the level of development found in spiders. The silk is produced by the **spinnerets**, specialised organs located at the rear of the abdomen. The spinnerets produce a stream of liquid which solidifies instantaneously to form long, delicate silk threads. The silk is used for various purposes, especially for the construction of webs which serve to trap insect prey. These webs can take various forms, ranging from simple ones involving a few silk strands, to larger, complex structures made of large quantities of silk. The orb-web, shaped like a cartwheel, is probably the most familiar, although this type is in fact found in a relatively small number of Families.

Maltese spiders have not yet been fully studied, and numerous species still await identification, among them those of the Family Linyphiidae. This Family includes many species of very small size, which are almost certainly very numerous in Malta. The number of Maltese spider species probably lies between 200 and 500.

Family Nemesiidae

Trapdoor Spider   p185
Nemesia macrocephala   Brimba tal-Bejta
18mm. Lives in a tubular retreat in the soil on the sides of valleys, emerging only to capture passing insects. Nest can be closed by means of a hinged lid or 'trapdoor'. Scarce.

Family Dysderidae

Red-headed Spider   p185
Dysdera crocata   Brimba Rasha Hamra
14mm. Lives under stones and among leaf litter on the soil surface. Has a pair of strong chelicerae. Cephalothorax reddish, contrasting sharply with whitish abdomen. Frequent.

Family Pholcidae

Daddy-long-legs Spider   p185
Pholcus phalangioides   Brimba tad-Djar
5-8mm. Body small with very long legs. Builds tangled webs on ceilings of houses, which trap large numbers of flies and mosquitoes. When disturbed, vibrates vigorously on the web and becomes difficult to see. Very common.

Family Salticidae
Spiders which use their jumping ability to catch insects such as flies and mosquitoes. For this they require very good multi-directional vision, which is provided by four pairs of eyes.

Schembri's Jumping Spider   p185
Aelurillus schembrii   Brimba Qabbeżija ta' Schembri
4mm. Found on dry ground among stones. Described from specimens found in Malta. Endemic to Malta and Sicily. Scarce.

Jumping Spider   **p185**
Hasarius adansoni   Brimba Qabbeżija tad-Djar
7mm. Often seen hunting flies on both internal and external walls of houses.
Common.

Family Thomisidae
Spiders in this Family superficially resemble crabs in structure and movement.
They hide among foliage and lie in wait for their prey, usually bees or flies.
In order to escape detection, their body colour often matches that of the
flowers or leaves on which they live.

Crab Spider   **p185**
Synaema globosum   Brimba tal-Fjuri
Female 8mm, male 3.5mm. Can be white, yellow or red, depending on the
flowers of the plants it is living on. Distinctive black pattern on the dorsal
surface of abdomen. Common.

Humped Crab Spider   **p185**
Thomisus onustus   Brimba tal-Fjuri Mhattba
Female 8mm, male 4mm. Posterior part of abdomen bears two dorsal,
hump-like protuberances. Found on flowers, especially those of Crown
Daisy. Frequent.

Family Agelenidae

Funnel-web Spider   **p185**
Tegenaria parietina   Brimba tal-Kantini
18mm. Constructs a triangular web in the corners of rooms which are little
frequented, such as cellars and outhouses. Hides in a funnel-like tube made
of silk. Darts out to seize insects such as flies and mosquitoes which become
entangled in the web. Common.

Family Argiopidae

Lobed Argiope   **p185**
Argiope lobata   Brimba Kbira tal-Widien
Female 25mm, male 7mm (excluding legs). Largest Maltese spider: legs
often reach length of 40mm. Blackish with pale grey stripes on back. Builds
large orb web. Found mostly in valleys and wooded areas. Frequent.

Cathedral Spider   **p185**
Cyrtophora citricola   Brimba tal-Pal tal-Bajtar
10mm. Constructs web in bushes, especially those of Prickly Pear. Web very
complicated, hence comparison to Gothic cathedral! Very common.

Family Theridiidae

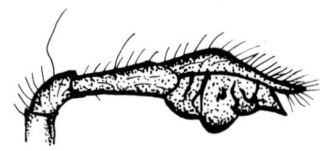

Beady Spider   **p185**
Steatoda paykulliana   Brimba Mżebbġa
10mm. Globular in shape, shiny black with a pink stripe between
cephalothorax and abdomen. Its venom is said to be dangerous to humans,
but no cases of poisoning are known to have occurred in Malta. Frequent.

Pedipalp of a male
Beady Spider

Family Lycosidae

Wolf Spider   p185
Lycosa narbonensis   Brimba Ħaddiela
27mm. Wanders about on the ground, hiding in holes and crevices. Female carries young, often very numerous, on her back until they can fend for themselves. Scarce.

PALPIGRADES
Order Palpigrada

Palpigrades are small, eyeless arachnids with a long 'tail'. The chelicerae are pincer-like and the pedipalps resemble the walking legs. They are a primitive Order, first discovered in Sicily towards the end of the 19th century. They About 50 species worldwide. 1 species in Malta.

Family Koeneniidae

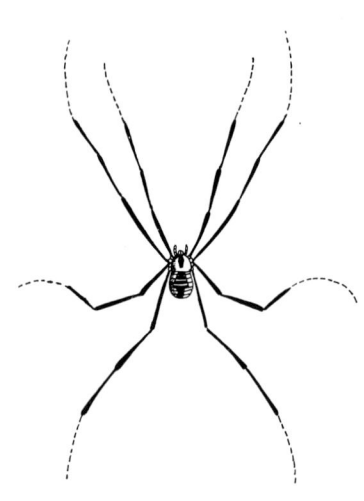

Harvestman

Maltese Palpigrade   p185
Eukoenenia christiani   Palpigrad ta' Malta
1.2mm. Only one specimen has so far been found, in a cave at Girgenti in 1988. Endemic. Very rare.

HARVESTMEN
Order Opiliones

Harvestmen are probably the strangest of living arachnids. At first sight they look like spiders, but closer examination reveals a unique structure, with a number of characteristics not found in any other arachnid group. Their body appears to consist of a single part, with a pair of eyes at the top of a raised hump. The legs are generally long and slender, appearing extremely fragile. 6 species.

Family Phalangidae

Harvestman   p185
Phalangium sp.   Brimba Saqajha Twal
4mm (excluding legs). Often seen on vegetation, especially during autumn. Body small with long, slender legs. Common.

Family Dicranolasmatidae

False Spider   p185
Dicranolasma sp.   Brimba Saqajha Twal tal-Ħamrija
5mm (excluding legs). Lives under stones. Covers itself with a layer of mud which dries so that it is perfectly camouflaged against the soil. Scarce.

ECHINODERMS

Echinoderms (Phylum ECHINODERMATA) are a group of invertebrates with a generally spiny body. The name is in fact derived from the two Greek words *echinos* (spine) and *derma* (skin). These spines can be very small and inconspicuous or they can be long and pointed.

The ECHINODERMATA consists of six Classes, including the ASTEROIDEA (starfish), the ECHINOIDEA (sea-urchins), the HOLOTHUROIDEA (sea-cucumbers) and the OPHIUROIDEA (brittle-stars).

All species live in the sea, and although the Classes appear to be very diverse, they have a number of common characteristics: the **skeleton**, for example, is made up of calcareous plates. In the starfish and the brittle-stars, these plates articulate freely, but they are fused together to form a rigid **test** in sea-urchins. The delicate **spines** of starfish and brittle-stars, as well as the long spines of the sea-urchins, form part of the skeleton. In the case of the sea-cucumbers, the calcareous skeletal plates are minute and are not joined together. These animals therefore have a relatively soft body, unlike the other echinoderms.

Most echinoderms have a body divided into five sections (pentamerous symmetry). This is clearly evident in the starfish and the brittle-stars, which normally have five **arms**. It can also be seen in the spherical test of the sea-urchins, which consists of five segments. These segments have rows of minute holes through which emerge slender tube-feet with a terminal sucker termed **podia**. The sea-urchin uses these podia for locomotion and adherence to rocks, although the spines are also involved in locomotion. Starfish also have podia which have a locomotory function. They are located in a ventral groove running along each of the arms. Brittle-stars are similar but in this group the podia are used mainly for feeding.

In the case of starfish, brittle-stars and sea-urchins, the mouth is located ventrally, that is, on the surface touching the bottom. In sea-cucumbers the mouth is at one end of the long cylindrical body.

Most echinoderms are bisexual. Most commonly, the sperm and ova are released into the water, fertilisation taking place externally. The fertilised eggs hatch into larvae which lead a planktonic existence until they settle on the bottom and assume adult characteristics. Although there is much variation among larvae of different Classes, they all have rows of **cilia** which are used for swimming.

Common Starfish

STARFISH
Class ASTEROIDEA

These familiar animals have a star-shaped body with five arms, although some species can have seven, ten or more. In others the arms are so short that the body resembles a flat, pentagonal saucer.

Most starfish are carnivorous. Some species capture and ingest smaller animals such as annelids, snails and bivalves. Others attack the larger bivalves by enveloping them in their arms, which attach to the shell by the terminal suckers on the podia. The two shells of the bivalve are slowly prised apart, and as soon as a crack between them appears, the starfish everts its stomach and introduces it into the bivalve. The stomach juices digest the soft parts of the mollusc to a liquid, which is then ingested by the starfish. Over 20 species.

Starfish feeding
on a bivalve

Order Spinulosa
Family Echinasteridae

Common Starfish   p185
Echinaster sepositus   Stilla Hamra
20cm. Lives in shallow water among seaweed, almost up to the seashore. Has five arms and a bright red colour. Common.

Family Asterinidae

Cushion-star   p185
Asterina gibbosa   Stilla Hadra
4cm. Lives among seaweed and beneath stones. Small, with yellowish-green body. Arms very short, so that the body has a pentagonal shape. Common.

Order Phanaerozonia
Family Ophidiasteridae

Red Starfish   p185
Hacelia attenuata   Stilla Hamra Lixxa
15cm. Lives on rocks among seaweed. Resembles Common Starfish, but has a smoother skin. Frequent.

Violet Starfish   p185
Ophidiaster ophidianus   Stilla Hamra Kbira
30cm. Lives on shallow, rocky bottoms among seaweed. Has swollen, round arms with blunt ends. Frequent.

Family Astropectinidae
The starfish in this Family live on sandy bottoms. The podia lack terminal suckers, since they would be useless on such a substratum, and in their place are paddle-like structures which enable them to move through the sand. The dorsal surface is smooth, except for marginal rows of long, sharp spines. They dig themselves into the sand and feed on all types of small animals they encounter during their burrowing activities. 3 species.

Red Comb-star   p185
Astropecten aranciacus   Stilla tar-Ramel Kbira
30cm. Lives at depths of 5-50m. Largest species in this Family. Bright orange.
Frequent.

Order Focipulata
Family Asteriidae

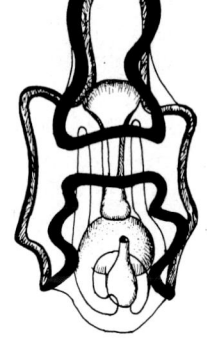

Blue Starfish   p185
Coscinasterias tenuispina   Stilla ta' Ħafna Swaba'
9cm. Lives in shallow water down to 30m. Has more than five arms, usually
seven, sometimes more. Arms not all the same length. Dark brown with
bluish tones. Common.

Spiny Starfish   p185
Marthasterias glacialis   Stilla tal-Felul
35cm. Lives in shallow and deep water, down to 180m. The dorsal surfaces
of its very flexible arms have rows of warty protuberances, each bearing a
hard spine. Brown or greenish. One of the largest starfishes. Frequent.

Larva of a starfish

BRITTLE-STARS
Class OPHIUROIDEA

Brittle-stars are easily distinguished from true starfish by the long snake-like
arms emerging from a small, flat, disc-like body. Instead of using the podia
on the arms for locomotion, brittle-stars use the actual arms in order to pull
themselves swiftly over the bottom.

Order Ophiurae
Family Ophiodermatidae

Brown Brittle-star   p185
Ophioderma longicauda   Stilla Qarnita Kbira
25cm. Lives among rocks and seaweed, in both shallow and deep waters.
Arms can be up to 15cm long, but body only grows to a diameter of 2.5cm.
Dark, ranging from brown to olive green with darker blotches. Very common.

SEA-URCHINS
Class ECHINOIDEA

Sea-urchins have no arms, their bodies taking the shape of a more or less
flattened ball. Two types exist: those with a radially symmetrical, sub-
spherical body, and those with an elongate, bilaterally symmetrical shape.
The former live on rocky substrata or on the surface of sand or mud; the
others, known as heart-urchins or pea-urchins, burrow into sandy or muddy
bottoms.

The skeleton of a sea-urchin (test) is covered with spines which are sharply
pointed in many species. In the round urchins, the spines are long and stout,
while in the heart-urchins they are short and weak, resembling thick fur.
This has an important function in preventing abrasion of the test by the

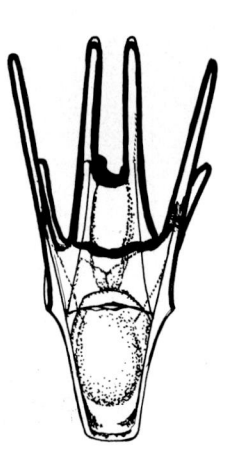

Larva of a sea-urchin

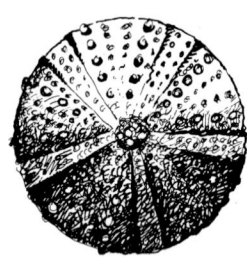

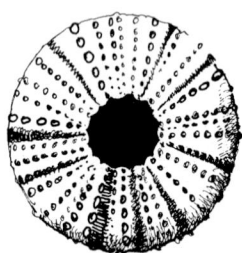

Test of
Rock-urchin

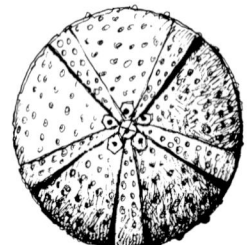

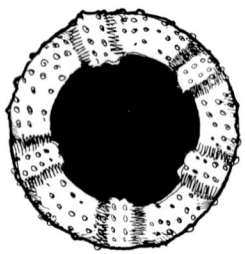

Test of
Black Sea-urchin

sediment particles during burrowing. In the round urchins, the spines are attached to the test by means of a joint which allows movement in any direction. These urchins use their spines in order to move about.

The mouth of round urchins comprises five long, chisel-like teeth. These move by a complicated arrangement of muscles and calcareous plates termed 'Aristotle's Lantern'. Moving slowly over the rock, the urchins use their teeth to scrape off any encrusting plants and animals they encounter. The teeth are so strong that even the rock surface itself is scratched.

The heart-urchins feed on organic matter which they obtain from the sand and mud around them, and so they do not require strong teeth. In fact both teeth and Aristotle's Lantern are much reduced or lacking altogether. Six or seven species of heart-urchins are found in Maltese waters, and these are usually trawled up from sandy or rocky bottoms. Except for a single small species, they grow to lengths of up to 13cm.

Order Diadematoida
Family Echinidae

Rock-urchin   p185
Paracentrotus lividus   Rizza
8cm. Lives on rocks among seaweed and among Posidonia leaves, even in very shallow waters. Excavates a small depression by abrasion of the rock using teeth and spines. Covers itself with bits of shell and seaweed, probably to reduce its exposure to light. Colour very variable, usually greenish, but often brown, red or purple. Edible. Has almost disappeared from certain localities in recent years, probably because of a disease epidemic. Very common.

Family Arbaciidae

Black Sea-urchin   p185
Arbacia lixula   Patri
7cm. Prefers shallow, rocky bottoms in rather dark places, such as vertical rock faces, rock crevices or among stones. Always black. Often wrongly believed to be the male Rock-urchin. Very common.

Family Toxopneustidae

Violet Sea-urchin   p185
Sphaerechinus granularis   Rizzun
16cm. Found singly in fairly deep waters, on rocks or among Posidonia. Can be distinguished from Rock-urchin and Black Sea-urchin by its larger size and white-tipped pale violet spines. Frequent

Order Cidaroida
Family Cidaridae

Red Lance-urchin   p185
Stylocidaris affinis   Raddiena
20cm. Lives on fine sand or mud in deep waters. Spines are few, but long and very stout, preventing it from being engulfed by the sand or soft mud. Frequent.

Order Clypeasteroidea
Family Fibulariidae

Pea-urchin   p185

Echinocyamus pusillus   Ġurdien Żgħir
1cm. Lives among gravel and small pebbles which collect around the bases
of Posidonia plants. Has a felt-like covering of very short, dense spines.
Greenish. After death, the spines drop off leaving only the whitish test. A
handful of gravel may contain several empty tests. Very common.

Sea-cucumber

SEA-CUCUMBERS

Class HOLOTHUROIDEA

Probably the most aberrant of the echinoderms. At first sight they seem to
lack pentamerous symmetry, as well as the spines and skeletal plates
characteristic of other echinoderms. On closer examination, however, the
pentamerous symmetry becomes apparent. As the name implies, sea-
cucumbers are elongate creatures, and they lie horizontally on the bottom.
The mouth is at one end of the body.

Three of the five rows of podia are in contact with the bottom. While the other
two are situated on the dorsal surface. The ventral podia resemble those of
other echinoderms, and have a locomotory function. The dorsal podia are
much reduced in some species and in others they take the form of warty
outgrowths, completely different from the ventral podia.

The podia round the mouth have a specialised structure and function. They
take the form of small, thick tentacles covered with sticky mucus, and are
used for food gathering. In some species, these tentacles are dragged along
the bottom, collecting organic debris. In others they are spread fan-wise to
capture food particles from the water. The tentacles are then inserted in turn
into the oral cavity and licked clean.

When threatened, some species of sea-cucumber can shoot out a liquid
secreted by specialised glands, which solidifies on contact with the water
and turns into a mass of sticky threads. If this is not enough to deter
aggressors, the animal ejects its stomach and intestines through its mouth.
After a few weeks, new stomach and intestines are regenerated.

Several species of sea-cucumber are found in Maltese waters. They have
never been studied scientifically, so that the precise identity and number of
species present is unknown.

Order Aspidochirota
Family Holothuriidae

Black Sea-cucumber   p185

Holothuria tubulosa   Bużżu tar-Ramel
25cm. Lives on sand in Posidonia meadows, crawling along and ingesting
the sediment, from which it retains any nutrient matter. The rest is eliminated
at the posterior opening. Several specimens often encountered on sandy
bottoms, each with its own trail of sand. Very common.

FISH

Typical cartilaginous fish

Typical bony fish

Around 45,000 species of fish are known worldwide, making up 40% of all vertebrates. They show great variation in structure, size and colour. Fish are the ancestors of amphibians, reptiles, birds and mammals.

Fish can be divided into two Classes: the CHONDRICHTYES (cartilaginous fish) and the OSTEICHTYES (bony fish). Another fish-like vertebrate Class is the AGNATHA, but these are more primitive and are not considered to be true fish.

Cartilaginous fish have a **skeleton** made of cartilage, not bone, although in some cases calcareous substances are present. The **skin** is covered with small, backward-pointing **scales**, which give it a very harsh texture. The dorsal, ventral and pectoral **fins** are not stretched membranes. The **tail**, or caudal fin, is forked, but the upper lobe is longer than the lower. About 50 species in 20 Families have been recorded from Maltese waters.

Bony fish have a skeleton made of bone. The gill-slits are covered with a hard lid or **operculum**. The two parts of the forked tail are normally identical in size and shape. About 85 Families with around 240 species are found in the seas around Malta.

Fish are admirably adapted for life in an aquatic environment. Some species live in shallow water while others are found at greater depths. Some live among rocks and shoals while others are open water species.

Fishes respire by means of **gills**, normally situated just beneath the gill slits near the head. The water enters the mouth and passes over the gills, where oxygen enters the blood and carbon dioxide is released; it then leaves through the gill-slits. Fish can detect vibrations caused by sound or changes in water pressure by means of specialised **lateral line organs** stretching from head to tail on either side.

The morphology of fishes is related to their habitat and mode of life. Species which swim constantly, especially migratory species which swim close to the surface, such as Tuna and Common Dolphin-fish, have a smooth, streamlined body. The tail is generally forked for faster swimming and they rarely venture down to the bottom. These surface-dwelling species are not normally very colourful, being grey or bluish above and white or silvery underneath; this makes them less visible both from above and from below.

Species which have a straight or rounded tail, such as gurnards, scorpion-fish and wrasse, which are not migratory and are normally not fast swimmers, prefer to remain near rocky, weedy bottoms close to the shore. Such species are generally quite colourful. Flattened forms, such as rays, soles and anglerfish, have eyes which look upwards, and can bury themselves in sand or mud, so that only their eyes are exposed as they lie in wait for their prey.

Bony fish have fins which usually consist of a number of spines joined by a thin membrane. They are either single or paired and include the dorsal, pectoral, ventral and anal fins, depending on the species. The fins are used for swimming and to maintain stability in the water. The spines of the fins can be soft or hard, and in some cases the same fin can have both soft and hard spines. The membrane stretched between the spines can be transparent or coloured.

Most fish are covered with scales, which vary in size and distribution depending on the species. Glands in the skin secrete a slippery mucus, which is very useful, especially in fast-swimming forms. Some species, such as the Greater Weever, the Scorpionfish and the Stingray, have venom glands, while others, such as the Torpedo Ray can generate electricity in order to stun their prey or to deter aggressors.

Fast-swimming fish are usually predators of smaller fish, which are swallowed whole or, as in the case of the sharks, torn to pieces and then swallowed. Sluggish, often colourful, species generally feed on seaweed or on small animals living on the rocky substratum.

Generally, marine species are incapable of living in fresh water; the contrary applies to freshwater species. Certain species, however, such as Mullet and Eels can tolerate changes in the salt content of the ambient water. These are often found in brackish water or sea water into which sewage or rainwater is flowing.

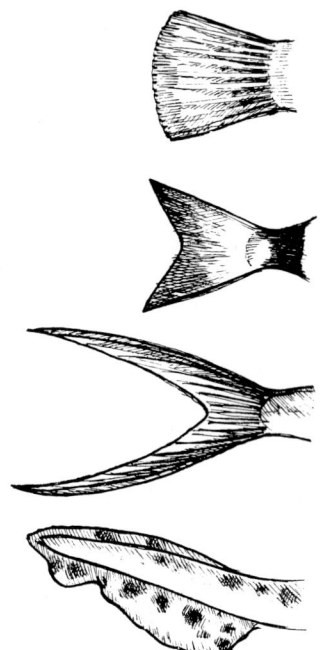

Different shapes of tails

Like many other animals, fish develop from eggs. The first important change involves metamorphosis from the larval to the adult form. During their lifetime, some species change their appearance in both form and colour, especially in the profile of the head. In the Common Dolphin-fish, the shape of the head changes from a pointed snout in the younger fish to a vertical profile in the older individuals. Major changes take place in the Flatfish, the laterally-placed eyes ending up on one side of the head.

In most bony fish the male releases the sperm into the water and this fertilises the ova which are laid by the female. As the eggs are not normally protected by the parents, a large proportion of these eggs are destroyed. In order to make up for these losses, thousands of eggs are laid. Some species are exceptional in remaining near their eggs; male seahorses keep the fertilised eggs and newly-hatched young in a pouch.

In cartilaginous forms like the dogfish, sharks and rays, fertilisation is internal, and the female retains the eggs inside her body until the embryo is fully developed. Such eggs receive parental protection and there is therefore no need for large numbers, as in the bony fish. Certain cartilaginous species lay eggs in a large egg case with tendril-like projections which become entangled in seaweed. In others, the mother retains the few eggs inside her until they hatch, and then gives birth to the young.

Some species in the wrasse Family change sex: they are initially female, gradually changing to males as they grow, their colour also changing. Other species change colour during the breeding season. Colour can also change depending on the habitat, while the colour of some species changes on being taken out of the water.

CARTILAGINOUS FISH
Class CHONDRICHTYES
Order Pleurotremata

Sharks in which the lateral gill-slits are anterior to the pectoral fins, which are separate from the head.

Family Lamnidae
With 5 gill-slits and a tail bearing lateral flanges. 3 species.

Short-fin Mako Shark   p187
Isurus oxyrinchus   Pixxitondu
300-400cm. Swims close to surface in open water of any depth. A powerful swimmer which hunts among schools of smaller fish. Often leaps out of water. Dangerous to humans. Frequent.

Family Alopiidae
5 gill-slits. The dorsal lobe of the tail is as long as the rest of the body. 1 species.

Thresher Shark   p187
Alopias vulpinus   Pixxivolpi
400-500cm. Prefers deep waters, where it feeds among schools of small fish. Tail long. Young appear mostly during summer. Rare, frequent in certain years.

Family Scyliorhinidae
Small sharks with 5 gill-slits; no lateral flanges on caudal fin. Olfactory openings touching mouth. 3 species.

Nursehound

Blackmouth Cat-shark   p187
Galeus melanostomus   Gattarell Ħalqu Iswed
50-90cm. Nocturnal. Feeds on fish and other animals. Egg case yellowish. Prefers depths below 200m, sometimes encountered in shallow water. Frequent.

Nursehound   p187
Scyliorhinus stellaris   Gattarell tar-Rukkal
100-170cm. Found in clear waters among rocks and sand. Flesh (especially liver) inedible because of its taste and the toxic substances it contains. Common.

Family Carcharhinidae
Sharks of considerable size, with 5 gill-slits. No eyelids. 2 species.

Blue Shark   p187
Prionace glauca   Ħuta Kaħla
250-300cm. Mostly nocturnal, keeping to the surface in deep waters. Sometimes seen close to shore. Teeth of upper jaw in four rows, pointed in adults, smooth in young. Omnivorous. Frequent.

Family Triakidae
Small sharks which live in shallow waters. The eyes have a ventral fold. The 5 gill-slits are short and of equal length. 3 species.

Starry Smooth Hound   **p187**
Mustelus asterias   Mazzola tat-Tbajja'
80-130cm. Bottom-living, found in both deep and shallow waters. Mostly nocturnal. Feeds on crustaceans, such as shrimps and crabs, and on molluscs, such as cuttlefish. Common.

Family Sphyrnidae
Hammerhead sharks. 2 species.

Smooth Hammerhead Shark   **p187**
Sphyrna zygaena   Kurazza Komuni
300-400cm. Keeps to deep water, but often enters shallow water. Head shaped like a hammer with eyes at lateral extremities. Can be dangerous. Preys on animals of all kinds. Frequent.

Family Oxynotidae
Small, stocky sharks with a humped back. 1 species.

Angular Rough Shark   **p187**
Oxynotus centrina   Pixxiporku
50-150cm. Prefers deep waters. Skin very rough, formerly used as sandpaper, as was the skin of other cartilaginous fish. Frequent.

Family Squalidae
Small sharks of deep, open water, without ventral fins. Olfactory openings do not touch the mouth. 7 species.

Gulper Shark   **p187**
Centrophorus granulosus   Żaghrun
100-150cm. Lives in deep water. Upper teeth have smooth edges, while the lower ones are serrated. Frequent.

Longnose Spurdog   **p187**
Squalus blainvillei   Mazzola tax-Xewka
60-100cm. Generally found in deep water, even down to hundreds of metres, but sometimes seen in small groups near shore. Frequent.

Family Squatinidae
Flattened; pectoral fins continuous with head. 2 species.

Angel Shark   **p187**
Squatina squatina   Xkatlu Komuni
50-200cm. Lies on the bottom at depths down to 100m, often half-buried in sand. Young born in winter, in shallow water. Skin formerly used as sandpaper. Frequent.

Order Hypotremata

Gill-slits ventrally placed under head. Pectoral fins continuous with head.

Family Rhinobatidae
Flattened; anterior body laterally extended and pointed. 2 species.

Angel Shark

Common Guitar Fish   p187

Rhinobatos rhinobatos   Vjolin
50-100cm. Lies half buried in sand, feeding on passing fish and other animals. Found near the shore in spring during the breeding season. Rare.

Family Torpedinidae
Flat and round; skin smooth, without scales. Have an internal electric organ. 3 species.

Common Torpedo   p187

Torpedo torpedo   Haddiela ta' l-Ghajnejn
25-35cm. Lies buried in sand or hidden among seaweed with only eyes showing. Electrocutes animals which get too near and feeds on them. Found in waters down to 100m deep. Delivers electric shock when touched. Skin appears smooth. Common.

Family Rajidae
Flattened, sides and head pointed. Tail slender; skin rough and spiny. 8 species.

Longnose Skate   p187

Raja oxyrinchus   Rebekkin Geddumu Twil
50-100cm. Lies buried in sandy or muddy bottoms. Adults found even at depths in excess of 100m. Frequent.

Maltese Brown Ray   p187

Raja melitensis   Raja ta' Malta
40-50cm. Very similar to other rays, especially Brown Ray. Frequent.

Brown Ray   p187

Raja miraletus   Raja Lixxa
45-60cm. Buries itself in the bottom, at depths down to 300m. Often approaches shore in summer. Common.

Family Dasyatidae
Flattened and rounded, with one or two venomous spines on the tail. The skin is smooth. 3 species.

Common Stingray

Common Stingray   p187

Dasyatis pastinaca   Boll Komuni
40-50cm. Lies in wait for prey half buried in the bottom, at depths down to 60m. Flesh not very good to eat. Liver, as in other cartilaginous fish, was formerly used to treat wounds. Has venomous spine on tail which can cause intense pain. Adults often grow an additional spine beside the old one. Common.

Family Myliobatidae
Flattened, the sides pointed and wing-like; the slender tail bears a venomous sting. 2 species.

Common Eagle Ray   **p187**
Myliobatis aquila   Ħamiema Komuni
50-70cm. Flattened. Normally found at depths down to 300m, but often comes to the surface, often emerging partly out of water as it hunts for fish. Frequent.

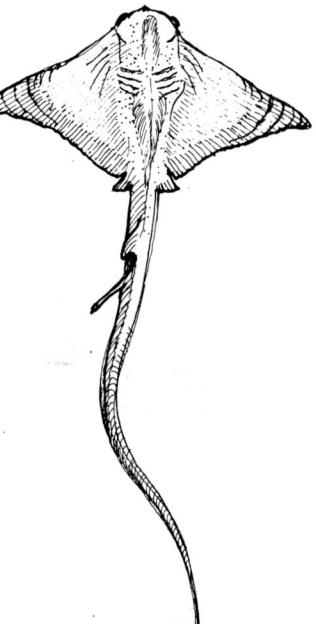

Common Eagle Ray

BONY FISH
Class OSTEICHTYES
Order Isospondyli

Gregarious, surface-living fish with an elongate, slender body. No lateral line organ. Dorsal fin single.

Family Clupeidae
Elongate and streamlined for fast swimming in open water. Sizeable scales. 5 species.

Twaite Shad   **p189**
Alosa fallax   Laċċi tat-Tbajja'
25-50cm. In countries with rivers, often swims upriver against current in breeding season. Common.

European Pilchard   **p189**
Sardina pilchardus   Sardina
25cm. Seen in shoals during summer, close to shore, especially in bays and harbours. In cold weather descends to greater depths. Survives in brackish water. Well known food-fish. Smaller specimens are called Sardines (Maltese *Nemusa*). Common.

Order Iniomi

Deep-water luminous fish.

Family Synodontidae
Elongate, with deep mouth bearing many teeth. Eyes are dorsally placed on the head. 1 species.

Atlantic Lizardfish   **p189**
Synodus saurus   Skalm
30-40cm. Lives close to shore but in deep water. Resembles a rowlock (hence Maltese name), with numerous needle-like teeth. Common.

Order Apodes

Snake-like with a smooth skin. Dorsal, caudal and ventral fins continuous.

Family Anguillidae
With microscopic subcutaneous scales. Pectortal fins small. 1 species.

Eel p189
Anguilla anguilla Sallura
40-90cm. Can live in sea water, brackish water and even in fresh water. Mostly active by night, lies concealed in mud or sand during the day. Often swims against current in streams, ending up in wells in the vicinity of bays and harbours. Sometimes introduced intentionally to control insects and other animals found in well-water. Scales are invisible and form part of skin tissue. Changes considerably in shape and appearance as it grows. Common.

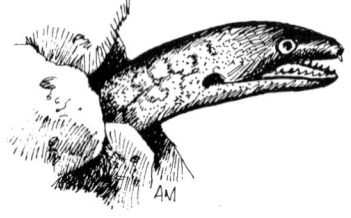

Mediterranean Moray

Family Muraenidae
Pectoral fins absent. 2 species.

Mediterranean Moray p189
Muraena helena Morina
100-120cm. Hides in holes and fissures in rocks, with head protruding. Found even in deep water. Mostly nocturnal. Bite can be dangerous. Common.

Family Congridae
Eyes slightly elongate. Skin has smooth appearance. Pectoral fins small. 2 species.

Mediterranean Conger p189
Conger conger Gringu
100-250cm. Very variable in colour, depending on habitat and depth. Mostly nocturnal, found in both shallow and deep waters, down to hundreds of metres. Younger eels normally found near shore; adults prefer deep water. Common.

Order Beloneformes (= Synenthognathi)

Elongate, slender fish with a single soft-rayed dorsal fin.

Family Belonidae
Very long body, with both upper and lower jaws very long and pointed. 2 species.

Garfish p189
Belone belone Msella
50-80cm. Often forms large shoals at surface in deep water. Moves inshore after winter. Sometimes leaps out of water. Common.

Family Exocoetidae
Pectoral fins are very large. The ventral lobe of the caudal fin longer than the dorsal. 2 species.

Flying Fish

Flying Fish p189
Cheilopogon heterurus Rondinella Komuni
20-30cm. Glides for short distances above surface, often in small groups, using large wing-like pectoral fins. Common.

Order Microcyprini

Very small fish with a single, posteriorly placed, soft-rayed dorsal fin. Mouth small.

Family Cyprinodontidae

Mouth short, directed upwards. Dorsal fin opposite ventral fin. The tail is rounded. 1 species.

Killifish   p189
Aphanius fasciatus   Bużaqq

Male 5-6cm, female 6-7cm. Lives in brackish water in small, shallow inlets. Has become rare in some localities and in some areas has disappeared. Very common, however, at Ghadira and Is-Simar nature reserves. Male more colourful. Maltese race probably endemic. Frequent.

Order Solenichthys (= Syngnathiformes)

Weak swimmers, the mouth elongate and trumpet-like.

Family Macroramphosidae

Oval, with a slender, elongate mouth. 1 species.

Snipefish   p189
Macroramphosus scolopax   Bekkaċċa tal-Bahar

10-15cm. Forms small shoals in deep water. Feeds on microscopic organisms. Frequent.

Family Syngnathidae

Body covered with bony plates. The mouth is narrow and tubular. 9 species.

Short-nosed Seahorse

Short-nosed Seahorse   p189
Hippocampus hippocampus   Żiemel tal-Bahar Halqu Qasir

10-15cm. Swims in a vertical position, with head directed downwards in horse-like fashion. Not easily visible, as it attaches itself to Posidonia leaves swaying in the currents. The eggs laid by the female are collected by the male and carried in an anteriorly-placed pouch, where they remain until they hatch and the young are partly developed. Scarce.

Deep-nosed Pipefish   p189
Syngnathus typhle   Gremxula tal-Bahar Halqha Għoli

30-35cm. Often enters inlets where water is made brackish by rainwater runoff. However, it is most frequently found among Posidonia, where it assumes a vertical position. Hardly visible as it closely resembles Posidonia leaves. Frequent.

Order Gadiformes (= Anacanthini)

Caudal fin rounded, soft-rayed. Scales minute.

Family Merlucciidae

Posterior dorsal fin almost touching anterior dorsal and caudal fins. 1 species.

Hake   **p189**
Merluccius merluccius   Marlozz
35-70cm. Lives in open water at depths of hundreds of metres. Young occur
in shallow waters. Common in certain years.

Family Gadidae
Have a short beard-like process below the mouth. 8 species.

Three-bearded Rockling   **p189**
Gaidropsarus vulgaris   Ballottra tat-Tikek
35-42cm. Lives in deep water, down to 100m, but often seen among rocks
and seaweed in the shallows, especially the younger fish. Frequent.

Order Allotriognathi (= Lampridiformes)

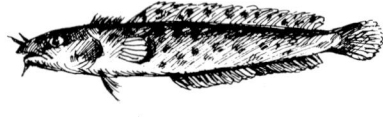

Three-bearded Rockling

Elongate and laterally flattened. Long, soft-rayed dorsal fin. Scales minute
or inconspicuous.

Family Trachypteridae
Laterally flattened; high profile anteriorly, tapering gradually towards the
tail. 2 species.

Ribbonfish   **p189**
Trachypterus trachypterus   Fjamma
100-150cm. Lives in very deep waters, down to 400m. Rarely seen.

Scalloped Ribbonfish   **p189**
Zu cristatus   Fjamma Rasha Kbira
30-90cm. Young sometimes seen close to shore. Adults rarely encountered.
Scarce.

Order Zeomorphi (= Zeiformes)

Laterally flattened, with a relatively high profile. Mouth telescopic and can
be considerably elongated.

Family Zeidae
Body short and high, the head occupying one third of the length. Mouth large.
1 species.

John Dory   **p189**
Zeus faber   Pixxi San Pietru
20-50cm. Lives in open water, but young can be seen inshore among rocks
and seaweed during summer. Very high profile and is so flattened laterally
that it does not have the appearance of a fish when viewed from the front or
rear, a feature it exploits in order to approach prey. Often has stout bone-like
structure behind eye. Frequent.

Family Caproidae
Short, high body, with a very small mouth. 1 species.

Boarfish   p189
Capros aper   Pixxi Trumbetta
5-12cm. Lives in deep water. Often caught accidentally with other fish.
Scarce.

Order Percomorphi

A large and varied group. The anterior part of the dorsal fin is rigid.

Family Serranidae
Live among rocks; many species change sex from female to male. Have three
spines at the edge of the operculum. 11 species.

Dusky Grouper   p189
Epinephelus guaza   Ċerna
100-150cm. Solitary. Lives in crevices, holes and caves on rocky bottoms.
Adult may be found at depths down to 300m. Feeds on all types of animals
found among the rocks. Has decreased in numbers in recent years. Frequent.

Comber   p191
Serranus cabrilla   Sirran
20-30cm. Lives among weed-covered rocks, not far from shore, also found
at depths down to 50m. Hermaphrodite, capable of self-fertilisation. Common.

Brown Comber   p191
Serranus hepatus   Hanżir Burqax
10-13cm. Found on all types of bottom. Hermaphrodite. Frequent.

Brown Comber

Painted Comber   p191
Serranus scriba   Burqax
20-28cm. Seen mostly in shallow waters all year round. Usually solitary.
Hermaphrodite. Common.

Family Moronidae
Two separate dorsal fins. The first ray of the posterior dorsal fin is rigid while
the others are soft. 2 species.

European Seabass   p191
Dicentrarchus labrax   Spnotta
100cm. Generally found singly in deep waters. Young venture near shore
in shoals. Outside Malta, found also in brackish water and estuaries. Scarce,
but increasing due to aquaculture.

Family Apogonidae
Small fish with large eyes. The anterior dorsal fin with rigid rays. Only the
first spine of the posterior dorsal fin is rigid. 1 species.

Cardinal Fish   p191
Apogon imberbis   Sultan iċ-Ċawl
9-13cm. Prefers deep, rocky bottoms, where it hides in holes and cracks.
Emerges in small groups, mostly at night. Sometimes seen in shallow
waters. Common.

Family Carangidae

Fast-swimming, open water migratory species with forked tails. Two separate dorsal fins, the anterior one sometimes much reduced. 12 species.

Vadigo   p191
Campogramma glaycos   Serra
45-60cm. An open water species which feeds on other fish and on molluscs. Resembles young Amberjack. Scarce.

Blue Runner   p191
Caranx crysos   Sawrella Imperjali Denbha Iswed
30-50cm. Resembles young Amberjack or Shrimp Scad. Frequent.
> The **Shrimp Scad** *Alepes djedaba* (Sawrella Imperjali Ċatta) does not have a black tail. It entered from the Red Sea through the Suez Canal and is spreading steadily.

False Scad   p191
Caranx rhonchus   Sawrella Imperjali tat-Tikka Sewda
30-50cm. Prefers open sea. Frequent, occasionally common.

Pilotfish   p191
Naucrates ductor   Fanfru
30-40cm. Appears in small shoals, swimming near the surface in open water. Often found under seacraft, rafts, large fish, turtles, flotsam and *kannizzati* (raft-like bunches of palm leaves used in *lampuki* fishing). Common.

Greater Amberjack   p191
Seriola dumerili   Aċċola
80-100cm. Seen in small shoals, often in the company of other fish. Young amberjack (Maltese *Ċervjola*) are less frequently encountered. Tail often bears vertical stripes. Frequent.

Mediterranean Horse Mackerel   p191
Trachurus mediterraneus   Sawrella Ghajnejha Kbar
25-35cm. Forms shoals in open water. Approaches shore in summer but swims out to deeper waters in winter. Frequent.

Family Coryphaenidae

Fast-swimming, migratory, pelagic species. A single dorsal fin runs the length of the entire body. 2 species.

Common Dolphin-fish   p191
Coryphaena hippurus   Lampuka
50-100cm. Swims at the surface in large shoals. Likes to stay under seacraft and other floating objects. Preys on other surface-dwelling fish. In older fish, head does not remain pointed. Commercially important. Common.

Family Mullidae

Bottom-dwellers. The profile of the head is generally vertical, with two barbels below the snout. 2 or 3 species.

Common Dolphin-fish

Striped Red Mullet   p191
Mullus surmuletus   Trilja tal-Faxxi
20-30cm. On rocky bottoms, singly or in small groups, in waters down to

100m deep. Long barbels are used to disturb mud and sand to reveal the small animals on which it preys. Changes colour on being taken out of water. Young bluish, found mostly in shallow waters. Frequent.

Family Sparidae
Coastal species. Laterally flattened, with hard, generally silvery, scales. A single dorsal fin, with hard anterior rays and soft ones at the back. Strong teeth. 19 species.

Bogue   p191
Boops boops   Vopa
15-30cm. Forms shoals in open water, also encountered in shallows among rocks and Posidonia. Attracted to light. Young swim closer to the surface. Common.

Common Dentex   p191
Dentex dentex   Denċi Komuni
40-55cm. Prefers rocky bottoms in both shallow and deep waters, even down to 150m. Young stay closer to shore in shallow waters. Preys on fish and squid. Frequent.

Annular Sea Bream   p191
Diplodus annularis   Sparlu
10-20cm. Prefers deep waters. Also seen in small shoals in bays and inlets all year round, especially in summer. Common.

Zebra Sea Bream   p191
Diplodus cervinus   Sargu Imperjali
30-35cm. Lives close to shore among rocks, also found at depths down to 200m. Frequent.

Sharpsnout Sea Bream   p191
Diplodus puntazzo   Mogħża
20-30cm. Likes weed-covered, rocky bottoms. Generally solitary, but young usually swim in shoals near shore. Feeds on algae and the occasional mollusc at depths down to 40m. Frequent.

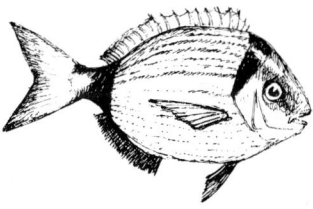

Common Two-banded Sea Bream   p191
Diplodus vulgaris   Xirgien
20-30cm. Forms small shoals among rocks and seaweed near shore, generally in shallow waters. Often enters bays and inlets with brackish water. Frequent.

Common Two-banded
Sea Bream

Saddled Bream   p193
Oblada melanura   Kahlija
15-25cm. Swims in shoals, grazing on algae on shallow rocky bottoms near shore. Also forms shoals in open water. Frequent.

Pandora   p193
Pagellus erythrinus   Paġella
20-30cm. Found on all types of bottom, mostly among rocks. Also found at depths down to 100m. When caught or threatened, red stripes appear briefly on tail. Common.

Red-banded Sea Bream   **p193**
Pagrus auriga   Pagru Hamrani
20-40cm. Found singly on rocky bottoms, feeding on small snails near shore.
Rare.

Common Sea Bream   **p193**
Pagrus pagrus   Pagru
30-40cm. Grazes on the bottom, at depths down to 100m. Young have bluish
spots, and are more spiny, especially around the eyes and gills. Common.

Salema   **p193**
Sarpa salpa   Xilpa
25-35cm. Seen all year round in small shoals in shallow water, grazing on
algae among rocks. Common.

Gilthead Sea Bream   **p193**
Sparus aurata   Awrata
30-40cm. Found all year round in small shoals on all types of bottom, close
to shore in summer and further out in winter. Also found in bays where
water is often brackish. Feeds on snails, crabs and small bivalves. Common.

Family Centracanthidae
Silvery fish with small teeth. 4 species.

Small-spot Picarel   **p193**
Spicara flexuosa   Arżnell
10-15cm. Forms shoals, mostly on deep muddy or sandy bottoms down to
depths of 100m or over. Common.

Family Pomatocentridae
Small fish, with a single dorsal fin, with a short, rigid section in front and soft
at the back. The tail is forked. 1 species.

Damsel Fish

Damsel Fish   **p193**
Chromis chromis   Ċawla
7-11cm. Found in small groups near rocky shores, down to depths of about
20m. Very young fish are a bright, luminescent blue, and when nearly
mature have blue markings round the fins. Common.

Family Labridae
Dorsal fin single, with hard anterior and soft posterior sections. Lips soft and
robust teeth. Multicoloured fish which can change hue according to sex,
season and temperature. Remain close to the shore, feeding in waters of
shallow or medium depth. 21 species.

Rainbow Wrasse   **p193**
Coris julis   Gharusa
14-22cm. Swims among seaweed and rocks near shore. Colour variable,
depending on sex, age, depth and temperature. In time, females change into
males, growing bigger and changing colour. Not a true hermaphrodite,
because it never has simultaneous male and female functions. Common.

Cuckoo Wrasse   p193
Labrus bimaculatus   Parpanjol
20-30cm. Lives among rocks and seaweed. Male more brightly coloured, with white head markings during mating season. Frequent.

Green Wrasse   p193
Labrus viridis   Tirda
30-40cm. Found among coastal rocks and seaweed. Male larger than female. Feeds on algae and small animals. Common.

Black-tailed Wrasse   p193
Symphodus melanocercus   Tirda Denbha Iswed
10-13cm. Found among rocks and seaweed. There are sexual differences in colour, the male being more brightly coloured during mating season. Rare.

Peacock Wrasse   p193
Symphodus tinca   Tirda Mirlija
18-25cm. Found among rocks and seaweed. Marked colour changes take place during the change from female to male. Common.

Ornate Wrasse   p195
Thalassoma pavo   Lhudi
16-20cm. Grazes among rocks and seaweed, and also found in holes on rocky shores, coming to surface in small groups at sunset. Male more brightly coloured than female. Change from female to male takes place as fish grows, accompanied by colour changes. This process probably does not take place if the temperature is unfavourable. Common.

Family Scaridae
Scales very large. Teeth strong and fused together. 1 species.

Parrotfish   p195
Sparisoma cretense   Marzpan
25-35cm. Grazes on encrusting algae, even on vertical rock faces. Scales very large in comparison to other fish. Sexes differ in colour. Frequent.

Parrotfish

Family Trachinidae
Flattened. Eyes and mouth directed upwards. The anterior spines of the dorsal fins, as well as spines on the gill covers are venomous. The lateral scales are diagonally arrayed. 4 species.

Greater Weever   p195
Trachinus draco   Sawt Kbir
20-30cm. Lies on sandy bottoms, generally in deep waters down to 100m, although often encountered on shallow sand. Dorsal fin venomous. Scarce.

Family Uranoscopidae
Head robust and square. The eyes are placed dorsally, looking upwards, with concealed electric organs behind them. 1 species.

Stargazer   p195
Uranoscopus scaber   Żondu
15-25cm. Seen all year round, sometimes at depths over 80m. Buries itself

in sand, with only mouth exposed, feeding on small creatures attracted by lure on its jaws. Scarce.

Family Trichiuridae

Elongate and laterally flattened, with a dorsal fin running the length of the whole body. Teeth strong. 2 species.

Large-eyed Hairtail   p195

Trichiurus lepturus   Xabla Denbha Rqiq

100-200cm. Generally found in deep waters, in small groups. Feeds on other fish, crabs, and squid. Rare.

Family Scombridae

Swift, migratory fish. Elongate, streamlined, strong swimmers covered with minute scales. Finlets of fine spines near the tail, both dorsally and ventrally. 9 species.

Atlantic Bonito   p195

Sarda sarda   Plamtu

45-60cm. Generally seen in shoals in open water. Comes inshore just before summer. Frequent.

Chub Mackerel   p195

Scomber japonicus   Kavall Ghajnejh Kbar

25-35cm. Forms large shoals at the surface, especially in calm seas, descending to greater depths in rough weather. Frequent.

Atlantic Bluefin Tuna   p195

Thunnus thynnus   Tonn

150-250cm. Migrates in shoals at the surface in summer. Keeps to greater depths in winter. Tunnynet fishing no longer practised due to species' decline. Formerly common. Frequent.

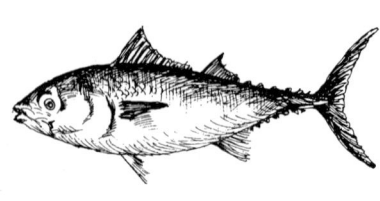

Atlantic Bluefin Tuna

Family Istiophoridae

Upper jaw is long and cylindrical, not flattened as in Swordfish. Caudal fin with two keels on each side. 1 species.

Mediterranean Spearfish   p195

Tetrapterus belone   Pixxispad Qasir

140-200cm. Generally swims in groups in open water. Feeds on small fish. Scarce.

Family Xiphiidae

Upper jaw is very long and flattened like a sword, not tubular. Caudal fin has a single keel on each side. 1 species.

Swordfish   p195

Xiphias gladius   Pixxispad

200-300cm. Upper jaw sword-like. Wreaks havoc among shoals of smaller fish which form its prey. Frequent.

Family Gobiidae

Small fish with eyes very close together at the top of the head. Live along the coast. The ventral fins are sucker-like and serve for attachment to rocky substrata. 10 species.

Rock Goby   **p195**
Gobius paganellus   Mazzun tal-Port
10-12cm. Lives in coastal shallows among rocks and also on sandy or muddy bottoms. Frequent.

Family Callionymidae
Small fish which show sexual differences in size and colour. Eyes close together at the top of the head. Bottom dwellers. 4 species.

Black-spotted Dragonet   **p195**
Callionymus risso   Wiżgha tat-Tikek Suwed
4-6cm. Lives on muddy or sandy bottoms, at depths down to 100m or more. Unusual in shallow waters. Hardly visible. Rare.

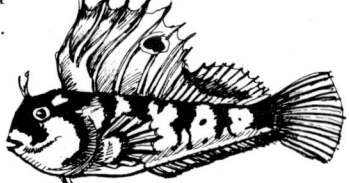

Family Blennidae
Small fish found in coastal shallows. Skin apparently without scales. Head profile is almost vertical, with close-set eyes at the top. 7 species.

Butterfly Blenny

Butterfly Blenny   **p195**
Blennius ocellaris   Budakkra ta' l-Għajn
10-15cm. Found among seaweed on bottoms of mixed sand and rock. Hides in holes in the rock, at depths of up to 50m. Frequent.

Family Ophidiidae
Elongate fish, with dorsal, caudal and ventral fins united. The eyes are near the snout, which has two barbels below. 2 species.

Bearded Ophidion   **p195**
Ophidion barbatum   Ballottra tal-Ħama
15-20cm. On rocky bottoms at depths down to 80m or more. Young generally found among Posidonia in bays. Scarce.

Family Sphyraenidae
Elongate and shallow-bodied, laterally flattened. The mouth is long and pointed, with numerous sharp teeth. The two dorsal fins are well separated. 1 or 2 species.

Barracuda   **p197**
Sphyraena sphyraena   Lizz
40-70cm. Seen in shoals throughout year in open water, at the surface or in deep water. Frequent.

Head of Barracuda

Family Mugilidae
All species morphologically similar. Stout, slightly flattened laterally. The scales are prominent and the mouth very small. Can survive in brackish water. 6 species.

Thick-lipped Grey Mullet   p197
Chelon labrosus   Mulett Kaplat
30-50cm. Found in groups in bays and harbours, even in brackish water and near sewage outfalls. After the rains, often found in waters made brackish by runoff. Sometimes swims against flow and is trapped in rock pools. Scavenger. Very common.

Order Scorpaeniformes (= Scleroparei)

Head spiny and prominent, with large eyes. Tail not forked.

Family Scorpaenidae

Head bony, thick-set and spiny, with large eyes near the top. The spines of the dorsal fin are venomous. 4 species.

Rockfish   p197
Helicolenus dactylopterus   Ċippullazza ta' l-Għajn
20-30cm. Usually lives at depths of 200m. Frequent.

Black Scorpionfish   p197
Scorpaena porcus   Skorfna Sewda
14-20cm. Found among rocks and seaweed, feeding mostly during the night. Can produce sounds similar to those made by a gecko. Common.

Red Scorpionfish   p197
Scorpaena scrofa   Ċippullazza
30-40cm. Largest scorpionfish. Lives among rocks at depths down to 100m or more. Young occur in shallower waters near shore. Dorsal fin poisonous. Common.

Red Scorpionfish

Family Triglidae

Elongate, with a robust head. Eyes near the top of the head, mouth directed downwards. The pectoral fins with ventral finger-like processes. 7 species.

Red Gurnard   p197
Aspitrigla cuculus   Żumbrell Għadma
25-30cm. Found mainly in waters exceeding 100m, but often seen near shore. Feeds on crabs, cuttlefish and small fish. Common.

Piper Gurnard   p197
Trigla lyra   Għadma
25-40cm. Generally lives in deep waters, even exceeding 200m, but often approaches shore in summer. Feeds on crabs, cuttlefish and small fish. Common.

Family Peristediidae

Two bony protuberances above the mouth. Skin bony all over. 1 species.

Armed Gurnard   p197
Peristedion cataphractum   Pixxikornutu
20-30cm. Found on sandy and muddy bottoms, even at great depth. Two anterior horn-like projections are used to sift through sand or mud for prey. Common.

Family Dactylopteridae
Head robust, rectangular. The pectoral fins are greatly enlarged. 1 species.

Flying Gurnard   p197
Dactylopterus volitans   Bies
30-40cm. Lives on sandy or muddy bottoms, usually in shallow water. Pectoral fins large and wing-like, looking like a decorated fan when fully opened. Does not 'fly' above surface like Flying Fish, but opens its 'wings' when threatened and to swim. Feeds mostly on crabs, cuttlefish, squid, snails and small fish. Frequent.

Order Heterosomata (= Pleuronectiformis)

Very flat, lying on their side on the bottom. On hatching, they resemble normal fish, but on reaching a length of 2cm, one eye starts changing position until it comes to lie on the same side as the other eye. At the same time the dorsal fin extends to the head and the body becomes flattened.

Turbot

Family Scophthalmidae
Flat and oval. Lie on their right side, both eyes are located on the left side in the adults. The left side also bears patches of harsh, bony scales, which are absent from the right (ventral) side. 2 species.

Turbot   p197
Psetta maxima   Barbun Imperjali
40-50cm. Lies on the bottom, partly buried in sand or mud, with only the eyes showing. Found even at depths in excess of 50m. Scarce.

Family Soleiidae
The eyes are on the right side, and they therefore lie with this side uppermost. 7 species.

Four-eyed Sole   p197
Microchirus ocellatus   Lingwata ta' l-Ghajnejn
15-20cm. Found singly or in small groups, often at depths below 100m. Markings near tail resemble eyes. Frequent.

Common Sole   p197
Solea vulgaris   Lingwata Komuni
40-50cm. Found at depths of around 20m, going deeper in winter. Frequent.

Order Discocephali (= Echeneiformes)

Elongate. The head is flat with dorsal sucker-like organs for attachment to larger fish and other animals.

Family Echeneidae
Head generally flattened; the anterior dorsal fin rays form a sucker near the head, which is used for attachment to large fish, turtles and seacraft. 2 species.

Common Remora   p197
Remora remora   Remora Komuni
20-30cm. Attaches itself to fish and turtles, thus moving around without having to swim. Feeds on its host's ectoparasites and any food fragments. Scarce.

Order Plectognathi (= Tetraodontiformes)

Laterally flattened, with a high profile. Mouth small, and the gill-slit is also very small.

Family Balistidae
Laterally flattened, the first spine of the dorsal fin strong and enlarged. 1 species.

Grey Triggerfish   p197
Balistes carolinensis   Hmar
30-40cm. Lives among rocks and seaweed near shore, feeding on small organisms, as its mouth does not open widely. Rapidly loses the blue colour when taken out of water. Frequent.

Grey Triggerfish

Family Molidae
No visible scales. The mouth, eyes and pectoral fins relatively small; body large and oval. The dorsal and ventral fins are narrow but very long. 2 species.

Ocean Sunfish   p197
Mola mola   Qamar
100-200cm. Normally found in deep waters, but occasionally ventures to the surface. Rare.

Order Xenopterygii (= Gobiesociformes)

Small, with soft spines. The ventral fins form a sort of sucker for attachment to the rock.

Family Gobiesocidae
Mouth elongate, skin without evident scales, with a ventral sucker. 3 species.

Connemara Suckerfish   p197
Lepadogaster candollei   Buwahhâl Rasu Twila
5-7cm. Found close to shore on rocks and pebbles in the shallows. Common.

Order Pediculati (= Lophiiformes)

Dorso-ventrally flattened. Skin without evident scales; mouth gaping, with numerous teeth. The first dorsal spine is on the head and has a tassel-like tip.

Family Lophiidae

Eyes on top of the head. The male is not small and parasitic, as in related oceanic species.

Greater Angler Fish   **p197**

Lophius piscatorius   Petriċa Kbira

80-100cm. Lies buried in sand in both shallow and deep waters down to 200m or more. Eyes exposed. First dorsal spine has tassel-like lure which sways in the current to attract prey. Frequent.

Greater Angler Fish

AMPHIBIANS

The amphibians (Class AMPHIBIA) are divided into three Orders, two of which (Caudata and Anura) are present in Europe. Amphibians are vertebrates with a soft, moist skin without scales. The skin is permeable to water and most amphibians are therefore limited to humid habitats. The internal temperature of amphibians varies according to the ambient temperature.

Most amphibians lay their eggs in water. When the larvae, known as tadpoles, hatch, they do not resemble the adults. They spend some time in the water, feeding almost incessantly, and later metamorphose into tiny adults. About 45 European species are known.

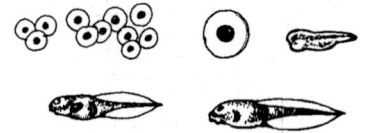

FROGS and TOADS
Order Anura

The Order Anura includes the frogs, robust amphibians which lack a tail. The hind legs are much longer than the forelegs, and this enables many species to leap considerable distances. The mouth and eyes are large. 1 species.

Family Discoglossidae

Painted Frog
Stages of development
from egg to adult

Painted Frog   p199
Discoglossus pictus   Żring

7cm. The only Maltese amphibian. Colour very variable: olive-green, grey, yellow or brown, sometimes reddish, with darker, pale-bordered markings. Pale stripe sometimes present on the back; ventral surface always whitish. Found in localities where fresh water is present, whether flowing or stagnant. Prefers shallow pools in valleys, and water reservoirs, where it rests in the water leaving the head above the surface. In summer it lies concealed in damp places. Lays around 500 eggs in a layer held together by a gelatinous covering. Egg-mass often becomes attached to vegetation, stones or the sides or bottom of the pool. Each egg grows to a diameter of about 4mm before hatching. Young (tadpoles) have a long tail and do not resemble adult. Tadpoles spend 5-8 weeks in the water, breathing through gills. In time, lungs develop, enabling them to breathe air. Hind legs develop before forelegs. Tail shortens and eventually disappears. Diet also changes gradually from vegetable matter to insects and other small animals. Common.

REPTILES

The reptiles (Class REPTILIA) include animals adapted to living in dry, terrestrial habitats. The skin has a **scaly covering** which is waterproof, and which is not permeable to oxygen, as in amphibians. Respiration takes place by means of efficient **lungs**.

The body temperature varies according to that of the environment. Reptiles are most active in warm conditions. When the temperature is low, they seek shelter in holes in the soil, beneath stones or in cracks in the rock, where they remain dormant throughout the cold spell.

In Malta, reptiles do not remain dormant for long periods since winters are relatively mild. On hot days they emerge from their retreat in order to bask in the sun and warm up their bodies. In summer, on the other hand, when temperatures tend to rise considerably, they emerge early in the morning and in the evening. They thus avoid the extreme midday temperatures and manage to maintain a more or less constant body temperature. This system of temperature regulation differs from that found in birds and mammals, where the body temperature is regulated internally. The advantage of the reptilian system is that they require less food to survive, since they use up less energy for temperature control.

Loggerhead Turtle
underside

Most reptiles lay eggs. Species which lay hard-shelled eggs, such as geckos, do so in dry places, while those which lay soft-shelled eggs do so in sand, soil or leaf litter. On hatching, the young look like miniature adults and are generally able to fend for themselves immediately. In some species, such as the Ocellated Skink, the eggs hatch while still in the mother's body, which gives birth to fully formed young.

TURTLES
Order Testudines

This Order comprises land tortoises, freshwater terrapins and marine turtles. The body is covered with a **carapace** (shell) consisting of bony plates. 3 species, all marine.

Family Dermochelyidae

Leathery Turtle   p199
Dermochelys coriacea   Fekruna Sewda
180cm. The only marine turtle whose carapace is covered with skin. Because

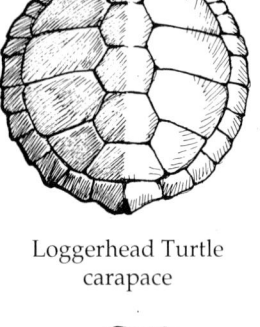

Loggerhead Turtle
carapace

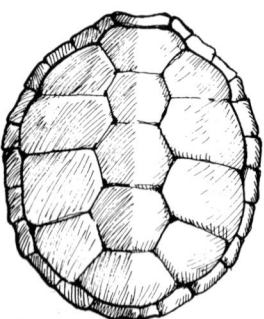

Green Turtle
carapace

of this the carapace is softer than that of other turtles. Does not breed in the Mediterranean, but probably enters accidentally during its migration near the Straits of Gibraltar. Rare.

Family Cheloniidae

Loggerhead Turtle   p199
Caretta caretta   Fekruna Komuni
100cm; 70cm in Maltese waters. Weight 180kg. Reddish-brown carapace is heart-shaped, head rather large with a strong beak. In deep waters it feeds on jellyfish and other animals, and near the shore it also takes crabs, sea-urchins and molluscs. Eggs are laid on sandy beaches from late May to late August, in four clutches, not always on the same beach. Clutch consists of 80-100 eggs which hatch in 20-60 days, depending on sand temperature. Bred at Ramla l-Hamra in Gozo up to the 1930s. Scarce.

Green Turtle   p199
Chelonia mydas   Fekruna Ħadra
110cm. Weight up to 230kg. Carapace more oval than in Loggerhead. Colour more olive-green. Prefers shallow waters with Posidonia. Lays four clutches in June-August, with about 120 eggs in each clutch. Very rare.

LIZARDS, GECKOS and SNAKES
Order Squamata

Reptiles with a scaly skin. This large Order is subdivided into two groups: the Sauria (lizards, geckos etc.) and the Ophidia (snakes). Saurians are animals with a relatively long tail, and almost all have eyelids. Ophidians are legless and crawl on their belly. Their eyes cannot close as eyelids are absent.

Family Gekkonidae
Small, stout lizards with large head and eyes, and with a rather soft, warty skin. Generally nocturnal, although they are also active by day in warm countries. Some can produce sounds. The toes are clawed, and have a ventral covering of short hook-like hairs which enable them to cling to smooth walls, ceilings and even panes of glass. The pupil of the eye is vertical. The skin can become darker or lighter. Most species lay 1-2 hard-shelled eggs, usually inside cracks in walls. 2 species.

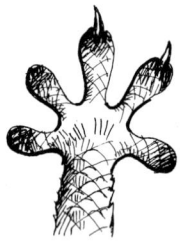

Moorish Gecko
foot

Moorish Gecko   p199
Tarentola mauritanica   Wiżgħa tal-Kampanja
15cm. Flat and broad. Can be distinguished from other geckos because only the third and fourth toes bear claws. Found near the coast in warm, dry places. Lives in rubble walls, rocks, cliffs, disused buildings and walls of houses. Mostly seen in the evening and at night, especially near street or garden lamps, where it preys on insects attracted by the light. Often basks in the sun during the day. Common.

Turkish Gecko
foot

Turkish Gecko   p199
Hemidactylus turcicus   Wiżgħa tad-Djar
10cm. Rather slender with pale, translucent skin. All toes bear claws, unlike Moorish Gecko. Prefers warm places both near the coast and inland. Also

present on the smaller islets. Lives in rubble walls, on rocks and cliffs, cave mouths and trees, as well as inside houses. Feeds on insects and spiders. Usually emerges at dusk, rarely during the day. Lays 2 eggs which hatch in 2-3 months. Very common.

Family Chamaeleontidae

Lizards which are very well adapted to live in trees and shrubs. The toes of both fore and hind limbs, as well as the tail are ideally suited to clasp twigs and branches. Their movements are slow and deliberate. The large, bulging eyes are covered with skin except for a small central aperture. The two eyes can be pointed in different directions independently. They catch insects using their tongue which has a sticky tip, and which they shoot out towards their prey. They can change colour depending on physiological state, background, and air temperature. 1 species.

Mediterranean Chameleon   p199

Chamaeleo chamaeleon   Kamaleont

Mediterranean Chameleon
catching fly

30cm. Normally greenish or brown with paler markings. Colours can turn lighter or darker. When threatened, apart from changing colour, it puffs up its body and opens its mouth wide to look larger and more fierce. Female leaves the trees in order to lay eggs in a hole dug near the base of the trunk; the eggs are then covered with soil. Adapted for life in wooded areas, but often seen in garigue habitats. Was introduced in the 19th century by protestant missionaries who used to bring specimens over from North Africa, then released in the gardens of what was later to become the Jesuit college of St. Ignatius in St. Julians. Has since spread to all parts of the island of Malta. Also occurs on Gozo. Frequent.

Family Lacertidae

Slender lizards with a long tail. Male is generally larger than female. The scales of the head and abdomen are large. Feed mostly on insects, but also on fruit and vegetable matter. Extremely active, but only by day. They love basking in the sun, and hibernate in countries with cold winters. All lay eggs. 1 species.

Maltese Wall Lizard   p199

Podarcis filfolensis   Gremxula ta' Malta

28cm. Four Maltese subspecies are known:
maltensis (islands of Malta, Gozo and Comino) - generally greenish, and often speckled;
filfolensis (Filfla) - blackish with blue or pale blue spots: the largest of the four races;
kieselbachi (Selmunett) - very variable in colour, from brown to grey with small black spots, and a yellow belly;
generalensis (Fungus Rock) - reddish below, with bluish flanks.
Females and young lack the bright colours of the males, and are generally brownish. Male shows territorial behaviour, claiming a small patch of land and threatening other approaching males. During their threat display, the males puff themselves up, tremble and raise their heads to display the bright colours below the neck. When a female approaches, the male makes similar movements, which now serve to attract the female for eventual mating. This takes place in spring, soon followed by the laying of 1-2 eggs in the soil or under a stone. Eggs normally hatch between June and mid-August. Endemic to Malta and to the islands of Linosa and Lampione, where a fifth subspecies occurs. A separate race probably exists on Kemmunett. Very common.

Family Scincidae

Robust lizards with large, smooth, shiny scales. Neck generally thick, head small and body and tail slightly elongate. Legs very short, in some species absent, making them look more like snakes than lizards! They prefer warm climates, and live on the ground. Active by day but generally remain concealed. Feed on insects and other small creatures. Some species are viviparous, retaining the eggs inside their bodies until hatching. 1 species.

Ocellated Skink   p199
Chalcides ocellatus   Xahmet l-Art

30cm. Fawn with rows of black spots on back, flanks and tail. Legs short, and when moving crawls on its belly. Found on cultivated ground or in sandy localities, where it hides in cracks at the base of walls or beneath stones. Gives birth to 2-3 young. Common.

Family Colubridae

One of the largest Families of snakes. They are diurnal species, and with few exceptions have a round pupil. The head is covered with large, flat scales. Most species lay eggs. 4 species.

Algerian Whip Snake   p199
Coluber algirus   Serp Ahdar

100cm. Colour ash-grey or brown with darker head, often with dark bands on the back. Belly whitish. Hunts small animals by day in dry, rocky habitats, also in disused buildings and piles of stones. Probably introduced from North Africa by cargo ships. Not found elsewhere in Europe. Rare.

Western Whip Snake   p199
Coluber viridiflavus   Serp Iswed

150cm. The largest snake. Black, often with a greenish tinge. Belly light grey, sometimes yellowish. Young are pale ash-grey with olive-green head until their fourth year, when they start to take on the adult colours. Found mainly in dry areas among stones and vegetation, but encountered in most habitats. Also climbs trees, and likes basking in the sun. Feeds on lizards and other reptiles and often takes smaller snakes, mice, frogs, young birds and large insects. Mating begins in March and the female lays 5-15 eggs in June or July. Hatching occurs 6-8 weeks later. Common.

Leopard Snake   p199
Elaphe situla   Lifgha

100cm. Ash-grey or yellowish with numerous black-bordered reddish-brown spots. Eyes also reddish. Found mostly on the ground among stones and vegetation in garigue habitats and field verges. Active by day, but often seen at dusk. Feeds on small animals. 2-7 eggs are laid. Scarce.

Cat Snake   p199
Telescopus fallax   Teleskopu

100cm. Slender, with broad, flattened head. Ash-grey, brown or yellowish brown, with darker markings. Eyes with vertical pupil. Prefers areas with rocks and boulders, under which it retreats during the day. Hunts lizards and small mice, generally at dusk, also at night in summer. Poisonous. Venom, however, is weak and injected by back teeth of upper jaw, thus only effective on small prey which can be swallowed whole. 7-8 eggs are laid. Rare.

Western Whip Snake
head

Cat Snake
head

BIRDS

Over 9000 species of bird are known worldwide, all grouped in the Class AVES, within the Phylum CHORDATA. The first birds evolved from reptilian ancestors about 150 million years ago.

Birds are covered in **feathers**, a feature found in no other animal. Feathers are modified reptile scales; in fact birds still retain reptile **scales** on the legs. Feathers help birds fly, give them their distinctive appearance and coloration, and assist in maintaining a constant high body temperature. Birds take good care of their plumage, and the feathers are generally moulted once a year.

A bird's body combines lightness with strength. Apart from a specialised bone-structure, birds have a unique respiratory system which enables them to make the best use of available oxygen.

The mouth consists of a **beak** or **bill**, a most important structure. It is used for pecking, picking and breaking up food, carrying materials, nest-building, piercing, scratching, preening, feeding the young and defense. The beak is very variable in size and structure, depending on the particular needs of the species. Similarly, the legs and feet of birds vary greatly.

The visual powers of birds are unmatched. Some species can see and catch minute insects in flight. Others can detect their prey from a considerable distance. The position of the eyes varies among species.

Birds lay eggs, thus avoiding the necessity of a lengthy period of gestation which would encumber flight. Eggs vary in size, colour and shape. The size of the clutch is also variable, as is the type of nest: some species do not build a nest at all. Nestlings are generally of two types; those hatched as weak, naked chicks, such as those of the Corn Bunting, and those which have a covering of down when hatched. The latter include species such as the Quail, whose young start walking and looking for food shortly after hatching; ducklings take to the water within a few days of hatching.

Because of the great variation in size, colour, song and habits, bird behaviour is often spectacular.

An important aspect of bird behaviour is migration. In spring and autumn, large flocks of birds migrate from one part of the world to another in order to make the best of climatic conditions and food resources in the different seasons. Most birds which breed in northern countries fly southwards in the autumn and return in spring. Some European species fly as far as South Africa, where they spend the winter months, while others only fly as far

Different beak shapes

south as the Mediterranean. Thus, besides the resident species, Malta's avifauna includes winter residents and spring and autumn passage migrants. A total of about 370 species have so far ben recorded, this figure including some very rare or accidental visitors.

GREBES
Order Podicipediformes
Family Podicipedidae

Aquatic. Dive frequently, remaining underwater for considerable periods in order to catch small fish and aquatic insects. Have a tail-less appearance. The legs are placed far back in the body, with lobed, rounded toes, an adaptation for diving and swimming. They moult towards late winter and become more colourful, especially around the head. Sexes are similar. 3 species.

Black-necked Grebe   p201
Podiceps nigricollis   Blongun Sekond
28-34cm. Appears in autumn and winter in bays and harbours and at the Ghadira and Is-Simar nature reserves. Spring plumage is black with reddish underparts, with small yellow plumes behind eyes. Wings have white markings, conspicuous in flight. Dives for food, but also catches insects at the surface. Frequent, in small numbers.

SHEARWATERS, PETRELS etc.
Order Procellariiformes
Family Procellariidae

Seabirds, only coming ashore to breed. Feed on fish, cuttlefish and squid. Sexes are similar. 3 species, one of which is accidental.

Cory's Shearwater   p201
Calonectris diomedea   Ċiefa
45-56cm, wingspan 100-125cm. Occurs March-October, coming ashore at night. Breeds in colonies in cliffs and boulder screes overlooking the sea. Lays single egg in May, chick leaving the colony in October. Call resembles wailing cry. Seen in large numbers by day not far from land in strong winds, especially northerlies. After breeding, flies out into the Atlantic through Straits of Gibraltar. Common.

Mediterranean Shearwater   p201
Puffinus yelkouan   Garnija
32-38cm, wingspan 78-89cm. Occurs December-July, approaching land by night. Breeds in colonies in same habitat as Cory's Shearwater, but more covertly. Single egg laid in March . Young leave colony in July. Rarely seen from land. After breeding, migrates to the Bosphorus and into the Black Sea. Common.

Mediterranean Shearwaters

Family Hydrobatidae

Small seabirds, black with a white rump. Out at sea by day, only coming to land at night in the breeding season. Breed in holes, normally on islets and stacks. Feed on small fish and other similar-sized sea fare. Sexes are similar. 2 species, one of which is very rare.

Storm Petrel p201

Hydrobates pelagicus   Kanġu ta' Filfla
14-17cm, wingspan 36-39cm. Occurs March-September. Keeps at sea, coming
to land at night during breeding season. Nests in holes among boulders on
Filfla, recently rediscovered in Gozo. In the 18th century, historian Agius de
Soldanis wrote that the species bred in one locality on Gozo. Single egg laid
in May-June. Young leave colony by September. Common.

Storm Petrel

CORMORANTS and PELICANS
Order Pelecaniformes
Family Phalacrocoracidae

Water birds. Large, black birds which dive in pursuit of fish. Stand erect on
the rocks, often with wings spread open in order to dry quickly. Sexes are
similar. 2 species, one of which is very rare.

Cormorant p201

Phalacrocorax carbo   Margun
80-100cm, wingspan 130-160cm. Single birds seen in small numbers October-
February along coast and in harbours. Numbers increased in recent years.
Frequent.

HERONS, STORKS etc.
Order Ciconiformes
Family Ardeidae

Wetland birds. Some species live on the seashore. Medium to large birds with
small head, large pointed beak, long neck which is folded backwards in flight,
and long legs. They feed on fish, frogs, small reptiles, large insects and other
small creatures. Often migrate in flocks. Sexes are similar. 10 species, two of
which are very rare.

Little Bittern p201

Ixobrychus minutus   Russett tas-Siġar
33-38cm, wingspan 52-58cm. Passage migrant. Smallest heron. Female and
first year birds different from adult male. Lies concealed among reeds in
valleys. Often heard calling at night while in flight. Frequent in spring,
scarce in autumn.

Night Heron p201

Nycticorax nycticorax   Kwakka
58-65cm, wingspan 105-112cm. Spring and autumn migrant, often in flocks.
Looks neckless, because neck is kept folded between head and shoulders.
First year birds differ from adults, having dark brown plumage with pale
spots and streaks. Frequent.

Little Egret p201

Egretta garzetta   Agrett Abjad
55-65cm, wingspan 88-95cm. Occurs in spring and autumn, singly or in
small flocks. Frequent.

Grey Heron   p201
Ardea cinerea   Russett Griż
90-98cm, wingspan 175-195cm. Spring and autumn migrant, often in large
flocks. Single birds sometimes seen in summer and winter. Frequent.

Purple Heron   p201
Ardea purpurea   Russett Aħmar
78-90cm, wingspan 120-150cm. Spring and autumn migrant, sometimes in
flocks. Slightly smaller and more slender than Grey Heron. First year birds
yellowish-brown. Frequent, but declining.

Family Threskiornithidae
Neck extended during flight. Wingbeats swift and very frequent. Feed on
small aquatic animals. Sexes are similar. 2 species.

Glossy Ibis   p201
Plegadis falcinellus   Velleran
55-65cm, wingspan 80-95cm. Occurs March-April and in autumn, sometimes
in small flocks. Appears black from a distance due to dark brownish-red
plumage and bronze-coloured wings. Bill long and curved downwards.
Scarce.

Teal

SWANS, GEESE and DUCKS
Order Anseriformes
Family Anatidae
Includes swans, geese, ducks and mergansers. Most species feed on terrestrial
and aquatic plants and seeds. Domestic ducks were bred from wild stock.
Male ducks (drakes) are generally more brightly coloured than females.
They have a direct flight with rapid wingbeats. Large flocks of ducks are often
observed at sea, flying by without coming to land. About 28 species, some of
which are very scarce or rare.

Teal   p201
Anas crecca   Sarsella
34-38cm. Smallest duck. Occurs from autumn to spring. Sometimes seen in
winter, flying at sea in small flocks. Frequent.

Mallard   p201
Anas platyrhynchos   Kuluvert
51-62cm. Occurs in autumn and winter in numbers which vary greatly from
year to year. Often seen in spring. Frequent.

Pintail   p201
Anas acuta   Silfjun
Male 61-76cm, female 51-57cm. Single birds and small flocks appear from
autumn to spring. Frequent.

Garganey   p201
Anas querquedula   Sarsella Ħamra
37-41cm. Spring and autumn migrant. Large flocks often seen in spring.
Slightly larger than Teal, with more streamlined flight. Frequent.

Mallard feeding

BROADWING RAPTORS

Order Accipitriformes
Family Accipitridae

Birds of prey. They lack the pointed wings typical of falcons. Sexes are different in some species. 17 species, many of which are scarce or rare.

Honey Buzzard   p203

Pernis apivorus   Kuċċarda

52-60cm, wingspan 135-150cm. Occurs in spring and autumn, often in small groups, especially in the afternoon. Autumn birds mostly come from Scandinavia. In the evening, seeks out wooded areas. Feeds mostly on wasp larvae. Male has greyish head, with less bars than female on underwing. Immature birds mostly dark brown, but colour of head variable, sometimes white. Frequent.

Honey Buzzard

Black Kite   p203

Milvus migrans   Astun Iswed

55-60cm, wingspan 135-155cm. Passage migrant, often in small groups. Feeds on small animals, especially carrion, and on organic waste. Tail shallow-forked. Sexes similar. Scarce in autumn, rare in spring.

Marsh Harrier   p203

Circus aeruginosus   Baghdân Ahmar

48-55cm, wingspan 110-125cm. Spring and autumn migrant. Flies low over plains, hillsides and marshes, hunting mice, reptiles, birds and other small animals. Quarters and soars with wings held erect in a shallow V configuration. Sexes different. Common.

Montagu's Harrier   p203

Circus pygargus   Baghdân Griż

43-50cm, wingspan 98-110cm. Passage migrant. Has same diet as Marsh Harrier. Sexes different. Frequent in spring, scarce in autumn.

Family Pandionidae

Pale bird of prey. It hovers and dives into the water for fish. 1 species.

Osprey   p203

Pandion haliaetus   Arpa

55-69cm, wingspan 145-160cm. Spring and autumn migrant, especially in April and September. Autumn birds are mostly of Finnish or Swedish origin. Sexes similar. Scarce.

FALCONS

Order Falconiformes
Family Falconidae

Raptors with pointed wings and relatively long tail. Generally prey on small reptiles, rodents, birds and large insects. 12 species, five of which are very rare.

Kestrel   p203

Falco tinnunculus   Spanjulett

33-39cm, wingspan 65-80cm. Occurs in spring and autumn, and in small numbers in winter. Occasionally nests on inaccessible cliffs. Formerly bred even in bastions. Frequently hovers while hunting for prey. Sexes different. Common.

Red-footed Falcon p203
Falco vespertinus Żumbrell
28-31cm, wingspan 65-75cm. Passage migrant, usually in small flocks. Often perches on overhead wires. Hovers and takes dragonflies and other large insects on the wing. One of the smallest falcons. Sexes totally different. Frequent in spring (in some years very scarce), scarce in autumn.

Hobby p203
Falco subbuteo Seqer tal-Ħannieqa
28-35cm, wingspan 70-84cm. Spring and autumn migrant. Resembles Peregrine, but smaller. Feeds on large insects, and birds such as hirundines and swifts, which are taken on the wing. Sexes similar. Frequent.

Peregrine p203
Falco peregrinus Bies
39-50cm, wingspan 95-115cm. Passage migrant in small numbers, sometimes nesting on sea cliffs. Formerly resident and a regular breeder. The subspecies *brookei* breeds in the Mediterranean. Renowned for its swiftness and strength, catching duck- or dove-sized birds in mid-air. Sexes similar. Scarce.

Hobby chasing Swallow

PHEASANTS, QUAILS etc.
Order Galliformes
Family Phasianidae

Keep to the ground, often concealed in vegetation. Feed on seeds, leaves, roots and also insects. 1 species.

Quail p203
Coturnix coturnix Summiena
16-18cm. Spring and autumn migrant, small numbers also occurring in winter. Attempts to breed in spring and early summer with little success. Cock slightly different from hen, with a distinctive call. Frequent, sometimes common.

CRANES, RAILS etc.
Order Gruiformes
Family Rallidae

Fowl-like birds of small to medium size. Generally found in marshes and wetlands, many keeping themselves concealed. Mostly heard calling at night. Feed on insects and other small invertebrates. Sexes are similar. 8 species, one of which is very rare.

Water Rail p203
Rallus aquaticus Gallozz tax-Xitwa
22-28cm. Occurs in autumn and winter, occasionally in spring. Favours reed-filled watercourses. Call resembles the squeal of a pig. Scarce.

Spotted Crake   p203
Porzana porzana   Gallozz tat-Tikki
22-24cm. Spring and autumn migrant. Smaller than Water Rail, with shorter bill. Solitary, most active at daybreak and dusk. Scarce.

Moorhen   p203
Gallinula chloropus   Gallozz Iswed
32-35cm. Spring and autumn migrant, often wintering in wetland areas. Some pairs are resident and breed in pools and water-filled quarries. Tail is constantly jerked. Toes very long, enabling it to walk over surface vegetation. Bobs head when swimming. Frequent.

Coot   p203
Fulica atra   Tiġieġa tal-Baħar
36-38cm. L:argest rail. Occurs in autumn and winter. A small number overwinter annually at Ghadira and Is-Simar nature reserves. Feet lobed and flattened. Scarce.

Coot taking off

WADERS
Order Charadriiformes
Family Recurvirostridae
Birds of saltmarshes and coastal areas. Elegant birds, with long neck and legs which enable them to wade in fairly deep water in search of insects and other invertebrates. 2 species.

Black-winged Stilt   p205
Himantopus himantopus   Fras-Servjent
34-40cm. Passage migrant, often in small flocks. Black markings on head very variable, and both sexes can have pure white head. Male has glossier and darker back. Scarce in spring, rare in autumn.

Family Burhinidae
Birds of plains and open spaces. The short bill is rather thick and the eyes are large. Also active by night. Feed on snails, slugs, insects and the occasional mouse or other small animal. Sexes are similar. 1 species.

Stone Curlew   p205
Burhinus oedicnemus   Tellerita
40-44cm. Spring and autumn migrant. Formerly bred, last recorded in 1911 at L-Ahrax tal-Mellieha. Scarce.

Family Charadriidae
Birds of plains and coastal areas, with short bill and a characteristic pattern of markings. Mode of feeding is unlike that of other birds. They generally run for short distances, then stop abruptly to peck at their food, usually consisting of insects and other invertebrates. Sexes are similar. 13 species, some of which are scarce and others are very rare.

Little Ringed Plover   p205
Charadrius dubius   Monakella
14-15cm. Spring and autumn migrant, also appearing in winter and summer. Bred for the first time in 1995 at Ghadira nature reserve. Occurs on shores and open spaces such as airport grounds. Common.

Lapwing

Dotterel   p205
Charadrius morinellus   Birwina
20-22cm. Autumn migrant, also occurring in winter and spring. Frequently heard while flying overhead. Summer plumage is brighter. Frequent.

Golden Plover   p205
Pluvialis apricaria   Pluviera
26-29cm. Passage migrant October-March, some birds overwintering at the airport. Neck and breast black in summer plumage. Feeds mostly on insects and other small invertebrates. Frequent.

Lapwing   p205
Vanellus vanellus   Venewwa
28-31cm. Autumn and winter migrant, sometimes in large flocks. Mostly occurs during cold spells with northerly winds. Sometimes frequents the airport grounds for a few days, as it likes open spaces. Frequent.

Family Scolopacidae
Shore and marsh birds. Vary from small, short-billed waders like the stints, to large long-billed species such as the curlew. Sexes are similar, except Ruff and Phalaropes. They call frequently in flight. They forage for food at the edges of marshes and pools, probing the mud repeatedly with their beak to pry out small invertebrates. 32 species, some of which are very rare.

Little Stint   p205
Calidris minuta   Tertuxa
12-14cm. Spring and autumn migrant. Winter plumage light grey, darkening to brown in summer. Common.

Curlew Sandpiper   p205
Calidris ferruginea   Beggazzina Hamra
18-23cm. Passage migrant. Bill long and downward-curved. Distinct summer and winter plumages. Feeds on invertebrates, often immersing head completely in water. Common in spring, scarce in autumn.

Dunlin   p205
Calidris alpina   Beggazzina tat-Tiżż
16-22cm. Autumn migrant, sometimes appearing in spring and winter. Stocky appearance with longish bill. Summer and winter plumages different. Frequent.

Ruff   p205
Philomachus pugnax   Girwiel
Male 26-32cm, female 20-25cm. Spring and autumn migrant. In summer, male's neck adorned with 'ruff' of brown, black or white feathers (in Malta rarely seen in this condition). In autumn and winter, difference between male and female (reeve) is in size only. Legs vary from green to flesh-coloured, even orange. Usually occurs in small flocks near pools and at airports. Frequent.

Snipe   p205
Gallinago gallinago   Bekkaċċ
25-27cm. Occurs September-May, especially in spring and autumn. Bill very

long. Conceals itself in vegetation along valley watercourses and marshes. Flight zigzagging. Frequent.

Woodcock   p205
Scolopax rusticola   Gallina
33-35cm. Autumn migrant, sometimes occurring in winter. Lies concealed in ground vegetation, flying out at dusk and dawn. Eyes set high in the head for maximum field of vision while feeding. Scarce.

Woodcock

Spotted Redshank   p205
Tringa erythropus   Ċuvett
29-32cm. Spring and autumn migrant. Rarely seen in summer plumage. Scarce.

Redshank   p205
Tringa totanus   Pluverott
27-29cm. Spring, summer and autumn migrant. In flight, white edge of wing conspicuous. Legs red. Frequent.

Greenshank   p205
Tringa nebularia   Ċewċewwa
30-35cm. Spring and autumn migrant. Legs green and bill long and slightly upcurved. Call can be heard from considerable distance. Frequent.

Green Sandpiper   p205
Tringa ochropus   Swejda
21-24cm. Spring and autumn migrant. Resembles Wood Sandpiper, but wings darker, with more white on tail. Occurs mostly near fresh water, especially pools in valleys. Call melodious and liquid. Frequent.

Wood Sandpiper   p205
Tringa glareola   Pespus tal-Baħar
19-21cm. Spring and autumn migrant. Smaller and paler than Green Sandpiper. Very vocal when alarmed. Frequent.

Common Sandpiper   p205
Actitis hypoleucos   Beggazzina tar-Rokka
19-21cm. Occurs all year round, especially in spring and autumn. Often frequents seashore. Constantly bobs body when perched or walking. Frequent.

Family Laridae
Gulls. Seabirds, generally having white underparts and grey or blackish backs. Sexes are similar, but immature birds usually have a distinctive brownish plumage. Breed in colonies on the coast, on small islands in lakes and on sea cliffs. Feed on various aquatic organisms and also on garbage. 12 species, some of which are very rare.

Mediterranean Gull   p207
Larus melanocephalus   Gawwija Raśa Sewda
36-38cm, wingspan 98-105cm. Seen at sea from December to mid-March. Enters harbours when strong winds are blowing. Colour of head and beak different in summer. Immatures differ from adults. Frequent, in some years common.

Yellow-legged Gull

Black-headed Gull   p207
Larus ridibundus   Gawwija Rasha Kannella
38-44cm, wingspan 94-105cm. Occurs November-April, especially in mid-winter. During strong winds, hundreds seek shelter in ports and harbours. Immature plumage different from adult. Common.

Yellow-legged Gull   p207
Larus cachinnans   Gawwija Prima
55-67cm, wingspan 130-158cm. Occurs all year round, in greater numbers during winter. Breeds in small colonies on cliffs on the southern coast and on Filfla. The largest Maltese breeding bird. 2-3 eggs laid in March. Young are on the wing from late May. First year birds differ from adults, and take about four years to assume adult plumage. Feeds on flotsam, fish, shellfish, crabs and even other birds. Colony at Ta' Ċenċ declined drastically in recent years. Common.

Family Sternidae
Terns. Slender, elegant seabirds, some frequenting ponds and marshes. Fly about and hover over the water and dive for fish. Sexes are similar. 9 species, most of which are scarce or rare.

Sandwich Tern   p207
Sterna sandvicensis   Ċirlewwa tax-Xitwa
36-41cm, wingspan 98-105cm. Occurs in autumn and winter. Medium-sized tern with long, slender wings. Scarce.

DOVES and PIGEONS
Order Columbiformes
Family Columbidae
Medium-sized birds, rather stocky, with a small, round head. Calls are a melancholy cooing. Feed on seeds and grain. Sexes are similar. 6 species, two of which are rare and another, the Rock Dove, breeds locally, but has interbred extensively with feral pigeons.

Turtle Dove   p207
Streptopelia turtur   Gamiema
26-28cm. Passage migrant. Large numbers often arrive during the night and at daybreak. Formerly more numerous. Following spring migration, some pairs attemp to breed in woodland areas, but rarely succeed. Common in spring, scarce in autumn.

CUCKOOS
Order Cuculiformes
Family Cuculidae
Slender, solitary birds, with long tail and narrow wings. Parasitic breeding habits, the hens laying their eggs in the nests of other species. Toes are opposed, two pointing forwards and two backwards. Sexes are similar. Flight resembles that of birds of prey. They feed on insects and caterpillars. 2 species, one of which is very scarce.

Cuckoo   p207

Cuculus canorus   Daqquqa Kahla

32-34cm. Passage visitor. Occasionally breeds, parasitising other birds' nests. Female lays eggs singly in nests of smaller birds. On hatching, young cuckoo pushes out eggs or nestlings of host species and remains the only occupant of the nest. It is cared for and fed by the foster parents. Occasionally, adult females and immatures have a rufous phase. Frequent in spring, scarce in autumn.

OWLS
Order Strigiformes
Family Tytonidae

Face heart-shaped. Hunt by night for rats, mice and small birds. Sexes are similar. 1 species.

Barn Owl   p203

Tyto alba   Barbaġann

33-39cm, wingspan 85-93cm. Individual birds may reach Malta in autumn. Nests in holes in cliffs and even in bastions. Has a shrill, shrieking call. Formerly frequent and resident, it has now been virtually wiped out. Very rare.

Family Strigidae

Owls of various sizes, generally brownish or greyish. Sexes are similar. Fly out to hunt at dawn and at dusk. 4 species, one of which is accidental.

Scops Owl   p203

Otus scops   Kokka

19-20cm. Spring and autumn visitor, with individual birds overwintering. Hides in trees. Feeds on large insects. Frequent.

Short-eared Owl   p203

Asio flammeus   Kokka tax-Xaghri

34-42cm. Occurs in spring and autumn, occasionally in winter. Sometimes breeds, last recorded on Comino in 1983. Nest constructed on ground among vegetation. Likes open country, hunting at dawn and at sunset. Feeds on rodents, also taking birds and other small animals. Scarce.

Chick of Cuckoo
ejecting egg from host nest

NIGHTJARS
Order Caprimulgiformes
Family Caprimulgidae

Nocturnal birds, with long tail and wings, large eyes and a gaping mouth. Beak and legs small. Rest on the ground or on logs, but do not perch on trees. Catch insects in mid-air. 3 species, two of which are very rare.

Nightjar   p207

Caprimulgus europaeus   Buqrajq

26-28cm. Spring and autumn visitor. Has a silent flight. Long whisker-like bristles at sides of mouth; middle toe comb-like. Very well camouflaged among leaves, branches, dry grass and stones. Male has white patches on wings and tail. Formerly common. Frequent.

SWIFTS
Order Apodiformes
Family Apodidae

Adapted for an aerial life with long, narrow, sickle-like wings. Flight rapid. Catch insects in their large mouth. Sexes are similar. 6 species, one of which is common and three are very rare.

Flock of Swifts

Swift   p207
Apus apus   Rundun
16-17cm, wingspan 42-48cm. Occurs March-October, mainly May-August. Often flies in flocks. Outside breeding season, often spends months on end in flight, flying at high altitudes at night, resting on the wing. Common.

BEE-EATERS, ROLLERS etc.
Order Coraciiformes
Family Alcedinidae

Colourful birds with eye-catching patterns. Beak large. Generally frequent ponds, streams and marshes. Sexes are similar. 1 species.

Kingfisher   p207
Alcedo atthis   Ghasfur ta' San Martin
16-17cm. Solitary, occurring in summer and autumn, less frequently in winter, round the coast and in localities such as Ghadira and Is-Simar. Often flies inland near freshwater pools in dammed watercourses. Flight is straight, swift and low over water. Dives into water from the air or from convenient perch to catch fish and aquatic insects. Frequent.

Family Meropidae

Slender, elegant and colourful. Beak and tail are quite long. They stay in large groups, calling frequently as they hunt large insects, which are caught in mid-air. Sexes are similar. 2 species, one of which is very rare.

Bee-eater   p207
Merops apiaster   Qerd in-Nahal
27-29cm. Wingspan 44-49cm. Migrates in flocks, calling frequently. Central tail feathers much longer than others. Frequent in spring, scarce in autumn.

Family Coraciidae

Colourful, stout birds of medium size, with a strong beak. Perch on trees and overhead lines, flying to the ground to pick large insects and other small animals. Sexes are similar. 1 species.

Roller   p207
Coracias garrulus   Farruġ
30-32cm. Spring and autumn migrant. Generally solitary. Scarce.

Family Upupidae

There is only one species in this Family.

Hoopoe   p207
Upupa epops   Daqquqa tat-Toppu
26-28cm. Passage migrant. Has a crest of feathers, usually kept lowered, but

raised when alarmed. Very conspicuous black and white pattern in flight. Beak long, thin and curved downwards, used to pick insects from cracks and crevices. Frequent in spring, scarce in autumn.

WOODPECKERS
Order Piciformes
Family Picidae

Climb tree trunks, feeding on insects and their larvae. Nest in holes in tree trunks. 2 species, one of which was only recorded once.

Wryneck   p207
Jynx torquilla   Bulebbiet

16-17cm. Spring and autumn migrant, a few overwintering. Remains concealed, but often seen on open ground feeding on insects. Occasionally raises crest-like feathers on head. Tongue extremely long, used to search for insects in holes and crevices. Toes opposed, two pointing forwards and two backwards. Call shrill and shriek-like. Frequent.

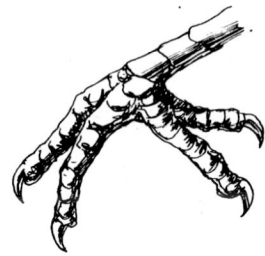

Foot of Wryneck

PASSERINES
Order Passeriformes
Family Alaudidae

Ground-dwelling birds of open country. Generally well camouflaged, mostly brown-streaked. Feed on seeds and insects. Sing in flight. Sexes are similar. 13 species, some of which are very rare.

Short-toed Lark   p207
Calandrella brachydactyla   Bilbla

14cm. Summer visitor, March-October. Often sings in flight. Occurs in open country, and nests on the ground in garigue areas, airport grounds and fields, even if cultivated. A shallow depression is dug, generally in the shelter of a plant or stone, and lined into a small nest made of dry grass. Sexes similar, but male's head more brownish. Very common.

Skylark   p207
Alauda arvensis   Alwetta

18-19cm. Arrives in flocks in October-November, and overwinters until March. Frequents open country, feeding in fields and garigue areas. When alarmed, it lies low before flying off. Crown feathers can be raised as a small crest. Formerly common. Frequent.

Family Hirundinidae

Slight, slender birds of the air, flying with great swiftness and catching flying insects on the wing. Sexes are similar. 5 species, one of which is very rare.

Sand Martin   p207
Riparia riparia   Hawwiefa tax-Xtut

12cm. Passage migrant. Smallest hirundine. Tail not deeply forked. Very common in spring, frequent in autumn.

Swallow   **p207**
Hirundo rustica   Huttafa
19-22cm. Spring and autumn migrant. Has occasionally bred. Gathers in large flocks in open country and even roadsides, circling in the air, often close to the ground in search of flying insects. Roosts in large numbers. Likes to perch on overhead lines. Tail deeply forked, with long outer tail feathers. Very common.

House Martin   **p207**
Delichon urbica   Hawwiefa
12-13cm. Passage migrant, breeding occasionally. Cup-shaped nest is made of mud and constructed under ledges or balconies. Behaviour similar to other hirundines. Tail forked. Very common in spring, frequent in autumn (scarce in some years).

Family Motacillidae
Elegant, slender birds, especially the wagtails. Tail is rather long. They are ground-dwelling and generally prefer open country, walking and running in search of insects, spiders and other invertebrates. With the exception of the wagtails, sexes are similar. 11 species.

Tree Pipit   **p209**
Anthus trivialis   Diżż
15cm. Spring and autumn migrant, often in flocks. Call is characteristic "dzzz... dzzz". Common.

Meadow Pipit   **p209**
Anthus pratensis   Pespus
14.5cm. Arrives in October and overwinters until March. Closely resembles Tree Pipit, but call is different. Common.

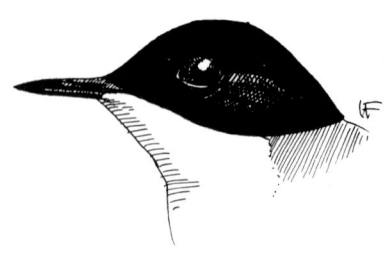

Yellow Wagtail
Black-headed subspecies

Yellow Wagtail   **p209**
Motacilla flava   Isfar
17cm. Spring and autumn migrant, generally in flocks. Prefers valley watercourses and cultivated fields, picking out insects and other invertebrates. Various subspecies occur, in which males have different head colour; females are similar. Roosts in large numbers in reed-filled valleys. Very common.

Grey Wagtail   **p209**
Motacilla cinerea   Zakak tad-Dell
18-19cm. Occurs September-March. Rather solitary, unlike Yellow Wagtail. Usually seen singly along watercourses. In March throat turns black, and yellow of breast and underparts becomes brighter. Common.

White Wagtail   **p209**
Motacilla alba   Zakak Abjad
18cm. Arrives in October and overwinters until March. Found mostly near farmsteads, hunting for insects on dunghills. Also in open countryside. Roosts in very large flocks, main roosts being the trees in Great Siege Square in Valletta and Ghajnsielem Square in Gozo. In spring the black patch on the breast extends to the throat. Very common.

Family Prunellidae
Unobtrusive, rather stout birds with a slender bill. Frequent woodland fringes and alpine habitats. Sexes are similar. 2 species.

Dunnock   p209
Prunella modularis   Żiemel
14.5cm. Arrives in October and overwinters. Hunts for invertebrates on irrigated land, never far from groves. Common.

Family Turdidae
Includes both arboreal and open country species, but all come down to the ground in search of worms, insects and spiders. Some also eat fruit. Sexes are similar in some, in others not. All renowned songbirds. 27 species.

Robin   p209
Erithacus rubecula   Pitirross
14cm. Arrives in October and overwinters until March. Establishes territory, which it actively defends. Sexes similar. Sings frequently. Very common.

Nightingale   p209
Luscinia megarhynchos   Rożinjol
16.5cm. Spring and autumn migrant. Seeks the cover of woodland and overgrown valleys. More often heard than seen. In spring frequently heard singing. Common.

Bluethroat   p209
Luscinia svecica   Kudirross Blu
14cm. Spring and autumn migrant, sometimes in winter. Skulks in thick vegetation. Two subspecies occur - white-spotted and red-spotted. Blue breast lacking in female. Scarce.

Black Redstart   p209
Phoenicurus ochruros   Kudirross Iswed
14cm. Arrives in late October and overwinters until March. Frequents cliffs, hills, bare valleys, fortifications and buildings. Regularly quivers tail. Female paler than male. Common.

Redstart   p209
Phoenicurus phoenicurus   Kudirross
14cm. Spring and autumn migrant. Frequents groves and wooded valleys. Regularly quivers tail. Female lacks bright colours of male, but tail has same reddish colour. Common.

Whinchat   p209
Saxicola rubetra   Buċaqq tas-Silla
12.5cm. Spring and autumn migrant. Keeps to open country, perching on low vegetation. Small but stout. Female duller than male. Common.

Stonechat   p209
Saxicola torquata   Buċaqq tax-Xitwa
12.5cm. Autumn migrant, overwintering until March. Frequents open country, where it often perches on shrubs, uttering distinctive 'pebble-clinking' call. Small and stout, with a relatively large head. Female's head paler than male's. Common.

Stonechat

Wheatear

Wheatear   p209
Oenanthe oenanthe   Kuda
15-16cm. Spring and autumn migrant. Occurs in open country, where it keeps to the ground, or perches on rocks, walls or bushes. Displays white on tail in flight. Female's plumage duller than male's. Common.

Black-eared Wheatear   p209
Oenanthe hispanica   Kuda Dumnikana
14.5cm. Spring and autumn migrant. Same habits as Wheatear. Two subspecies occur. Frequent.

Rock Thrush   p209
Monticola saxatilis   Ġanbublu
19cm. Spring and autumn migrant. Frequents cliffs, screes and rocky hillsides. Scarce.

Blue Rock Thrush   p209
Monticola solitarius   Merill
20.5cm. Resident. Retiring in habits, frequenting cliffs and screes, especially near the sea, and rocky hillsides. Has melodious song. Frequently seen on bastions or derelict buildings in the countryside. Nests in holes and crevices in cliffs, sometimes even in walls, large boulders by the sea or abandoned buildings. Female lacks blue of male. The national bird. Formerly common. Frequent.

Blackbird   p209
Turdus merula   Malvizz Iswed
24-25cm. Arrives in autumn, overwintering until March. Seeks cover of wooded areas and overgrown valleys. Female duller than male. Frequent.

Fieldfare   p209
Turdus pilaris   Malvizzun tal-Qtajja'
25.5cm. Winter visitor, especially during very cold spells. Frequently calls in flight. Sexes similar. Scarce.

Song Thrush
breaking snail shells

Song Thrush   p209
Turdus philomelos   Malvizz
23cm. Autumn migrant, overwintering until March. Often calls in flight. Song often heard in March. Found mostly in wooded areas and overgrown valleys. Feeds mostly on snails, breaking shell against rock. Common.

Redwing   p209
Turdus iliacus   Malvizz Ahmar
20cm. Occurs in late autumn and winter, mainly during cold spells. Prefers woodland habitats. Scarce.

Family Sylviidae
Birds of trees, undergrowth and reeds, generally small. Feed on insects, but some species are fruit-eaters. Sexes are similar in some, in others not. 41 species, some of which are very rare.

Cetti's Warbler   p211
Cettia cetti   Baghal ta' l-Gholliq
14cm. Resident, mostly found along watercourses in the cover of thick

vegetation. Song short but powerful. Bird more often heard than seen. Started breeding in the 1970s, now widespread. Nest, generally built in Bramble, is made of grass and dry leaves of reeds, and lined with finer dry leaves and dark feathers. Sexes similar, male slightly larger. Frequent.

Fan-tailed Warbler   p211
Cisticola juncidis   Baghal ta' l-Imrewha
10cm. Widespread resident. Started breeding in 1970s. Prefers open country. Nest constructed from spiders' webs and dried vegetation and shaped like wide-necked bottle. Male often calls incessantly (a repetitive 'tsip...tsip...tsip') as it patrols its territory, especially February-June. Common.

Sedge Warbler   p211
Acrocephalus schoenobaenus   Baghal tas-Simar
13cm. Spring and autumn migrant. Often sings in spring. Seeks cover of dense vegetation or reeds in damp valleys or along watercourses. Frequent.

Reed Warbler   p211
Acrocephalus scirpaceus   Baghal tal-Qasab
12.5cm. Migrant. Frequents reedbeds in damp valleys. Occasionally breeds at Salina and Is-Simar. Common in autumn, scarce in spring.

Great Reed Warbler   p211
Acrocephalus arundinaceus   Baghal Prim
19cm. Spring and autumn migrant. Keeps to reedbeds in damp habitats. Creaky song often heard in spring. Frequent.

Icterine Warbler   p211
Hippolais icterina   Bekkafik Isfar
13cm. Passage migrant. Arboreal, often warbling in spring. Common in spring, scarce in autumn.

Spectacled Warbler   p211
Sylvia conspicillata   Bufula Hamra
12cm. Resident, frequenting open country. Male's song often heard in breeding season, as it guards territory. Nest built in low-growing shrubs. Female has duller colours than male. Formerly common. Scarce.

Subalpine Warbler   p211
Sylvia cantillans   Bufula Passajra
12cm. Spring and autumn migrant. Frequents trees and shrubs of the maquis. In autumn, feeds regularly on figs and blackberries. Female lacks bright colours of male, which loses rufous breast in autumn. Common.

Sardinian Warbler   p211
Sylvia melanocephala   Bufula Sewda
13cm. Resident. Widespread in countryside, also in urban gardens. Nests in all types of shrubs and small trees. Male often sings in fluttering display flight. Female lacks black head of male. Very common.

Sardinian Warbler
in display flight

Whitethroat   p211
Sylvia communis   Bekkafik Ahmar
14cm. Passage migrant. Resembles Spectacled Warbler, but larger. Common in spring, scarce in autumn.

Garden Warbler p211
Sylvia borin Bekkafik
14cm. Spring and autumn migrant. Arboreal. In autumn often seen in Fig trees and Bramble, feeding on the ripe fruit. Shy and inconspicuous. Sexes similar. Common.

Blackcap p211
Sylvia atricapilla Kapinera
14cm. Occurs from autumn to spring. Frequents woodland, and in late winter found mostly near Ivy, feeding on the ripe berries. Sings frequently in winter and spring. Male's crown glossy black, female's and juvenile's is brown. Common.

Wood Warbler p211
Phylloscopus sibilatrix Vjolin Ħadrani
12.5cm. Passage migrant. Prefers trees. Feeds on insects and larvae among tree foliage. Often flies out to catch flies and mosquitoes on the wing. Common in spring, frequent in autumn.

Chiffchaff p211
Phylloscopus collybita Vjolin tax-Xitwa
11cm. Occurs from autumn to early spring. Same habits as Wood Warbler, but smaller and not so green. Very evident along valley watercourses. Often sings on sunny winter days. Common.

Willow Warbler p211
Phylloscopus trochilus Vjolin Pastard
11.5cm. Spring and autumn migrant. Same habits as Wood Warbler and Chiffchaff. Sings frequently in spring. Common.

Goldcrest p211
Regulus regulus Bufula tal-Qamar
9cm. Occurs late October to late March. Frequents groves of Pine, Cypress and Tamarisk, picking out insects from foliage. Frequent.

Firecrest p211
Regulus ignicapillus Bufula tat-Toppu Ahmar
9cm. Occurs late September to mid-April. Same habits as Goldcrest. Frequent.

Head of Goldcrest

Head of Firecrest

Family Muscicapidae
Legs short, not used for walking or hopping. Perch on branches, watching out for flies and mosquitoes which they take on the wing. 5 species.

Spotted Flycatcher p211
Muscicapa striata Żanżarell tat-Tikki
14cm. Passage migrant. Likes to perch on the highest branches, from where it flies out to catch insects on the wing. Some pairs nest every year. Common in spring, scarce (occasionally frequent) in autumn.

Collared Flycatcher p211
Ficedula albicollis Żanżarell tal-Kullar
13cm. Passage migrant. Perches on low branches, from where it flies out after insects. Female's pattern duller than male's. Common in spring, scarce in autumn.

Pied Flycatcher   p211
Ficedula hypoleuca   Żanżarell Iswed
13cm. Passage migrant. Same habits as Collared Flycatcher. Common in
spring, scarce in autumn.

Family Oriolidae
Robust but not large. Generally brightly coloured. Arboreal birds which feed on
insects and fruit. 1 species.

Golden Oriole   p213
Oriolus oriolus   Tajra Safra
24cm. Spring and autumn migrant. Call melodious. Often feeds on fruits of
Loquat and Mulberry in spring. Female greenish. Frequent.

Family Laniidae
Long-tailed and strong-billed birds which feed on large insects and other
birds. Perch on high branches watching out for their prey. 4 species.

Woodchat Shrike   p213
Lanius senator   Kaċċamendula
19cm. Spring and autumn visitor. One or two pairs breed almost annually.
Perches on top of trees, flying to the ground to take large insects. Sexes
similar. Frequent.

Family Sturnidae
Generally dark with a rather short tail. 3 species, two of which are very rare.

Starling   p213
Sturnus vulgaris   Sturnell
21cm. Arrives in autumn, generally in large flocks, and overwintering.
Congregates in flocks in open country, perching on overhead lines and trees.
Roosts in huge flocks, especially in *Ficus* trees, such as those of the Palace
courtyard in Valletta. Spotting on plumage more evident in winter than in
spring. Sexes similar. Some pairs have recently started breeding. Very
common.

Family Passeridae
Beak adapted for seed eating. Gregarious birds, except during the breeding
season. Also found in urban areas. 4 species, two of which are rare.

Spanish Sparrow   p213
Passer hispaniolensis   Ghammiel tal-Bejt
15cm. Resident and widespread. Builds clumsy nest in ventilators, holes in
walls and cliffs, telegraph poles, drainpipes and trees. Gathers in flocks,
especially after breeding season, often roosting in great numbers in trees
such as large *Ficus*. Feeds on seeds, insects and other invertebrates, also
scavenging from rubbish dumps. Very common.

Spanish Sparrow
having a dust bath

Tree Sparrow   p213
Passer montanus   Ghammiel tas-Siġar
14cm. Resident, but less widespread than Spanish Sparrow. Usually nests
in holes and narrow crevices in walls of rural buildings, also on the outskirts
of towns and villages. Despite name, does not nest in trees, as does Spanish
Sparrow. Sometimes migrants appear in autumn. Sexes similar. Frequent.

Family Fringillidae

Songbirds, with bill adapted for seed-eating. Males generally brightly coloured, unlike the duller females. Passage migrants, appearing in late autumn, winter and even spring. 13 species, three of which are rare.

Chaffinch p213

Fringilla coelebs   Sponsun
15.5cm. Autumn visitor, also overwintering. Some pairs remain until spring and nest in wooded areas. Common.

Serin p213

Serinus serinus   Apparell
11cm. Occurs from mid-autumn to spring in numbers which vary greatly from year to year. Often seen in small flocks on cultivated land and in gardens. Has occasionally bred. Common.

Greenfinch p213

Carduelis chloris   Verdun
15cm. Occurs in autumn, winter and spring, singly or in small flocks. Frequents wooded areas and orchards. Call a characteristic wheeze. Has occasionally bred. Common, especially in autumn.

Goldfinch p213

Carduelis carduelis   Gardell
14cm. Occurs from autumn to spring. Feeds on thistle seeds in open country. Has occasionally bred. Sexes similar. Frequent, especially in autumn.

Siskin p213

Carduelis spinus   Ekru
12cm. Occurs from mid-October to December, occasionally until March. Likes Groundsel seed. Frequent (in some years common, in others scarce).

Linnet p213

Carduelis cannabina   Ġojjin
14cm. Autumn migrant, also overwintering. Sometimes migrates in large flocks. Some pairs are resident, breeding especially on Gozo. Prefers open country. Male has red forehead and breast in spring. Common.

Crossbill p213

Loxia curvirostra   Kruċjat
17cm. Occurs July-October, frequenting pinewoods. Bill crossed, used to extract pine seeds from cones. First year birds and females lack red colour of adult male. Rare, but frequent in some years.

Hawfinch p213

Coccothraustes coccothraustes   Taż-Żebbuġ
18cm. Occurs October-November, occasionally until March. Sizeable finch with strong, robust beak. Scarce, occasionally frequent.

Hawfinch

Family Emberizidae

Tail longer than that of finches, bill is short and conical. Males generally more brightly coloured. 15 species, some of which are scarce or rare.

Ortolan Bunting   p213
Emberiza hortulana   Ortolan

16.5cm. Spring and autumn migrant. Establishes short term territory in open, sparsely wooded ground. Scarce.

Corn Bunting   p213
Miliaria calandra   Durrajsa

18cm. Resident. Prefers open country with few trees. Builds nest on the ground, among herbage or in low shrubs. Characteristic monotonous jingling song, always given from an exposed perch. Gathers in flocks in summer, frequenting freshwater pools. Sexes similar. Formerly more common. Frequent.

Corn Bunting

MAMMALS

The Class MAMMALIA comprises about 4500 species of vertebrate animals. They are capable of cooling down in hot weather and warming themselves in cold conditions, in this way keeping their body temperature constant at about 36 °C.

Mammals care for their young, providing them with food, especially at the beginning of their life. The females carry the developing embryos inside their body until birth, and then provide nutrients in the form of milk produced in specialised glands called **mammary glands**.

Mammals are covered with **hair**, have a **bony skeleton** and a relatively large brain. In fact the highest degree of behavioral complexity in the Animal Kingdom is found in the mammals.

The Class MAMMALIA is subdivided into 19 Orders. The most primitive is the Monotremata, represented by two species that lay eggs. In all the other Orders the species are live-bearers.

Mammals exhibit great variety in morphology and behaviour. They occur on land, in water and even in the air. Some are herbivores, obtaining their food by grazing. Others use their claws to capture and tear their prey. They include species which can leap considerable distances and others which can run swiftly for long distances or which lead an arboreal life, climbing and swinging among the branches with great skill. There are mammals which spend part or all their life in the water, while others are capable of flight, catching their prey in mid-air. Some mammals lead solitary lives and others live in groups, colonies or large herds.

Pygmy White-toothed
Shrew

INSECTIVORES
Order Insectivora

The first mammals to appear on earth, around 234 million years ago. They are all quite small, never larger than a rabbit. They walk on their heels and have five toes on each foot.

Family Erinaceidae
Terrestrial mammals covered with hard, spiny hairs. Slow-moving and generally nocturnal. 1 species.

Vagrant Hedgehog   **p215**

Erinaceus algirus   Qanfud

20-25cm (+ tail 2.5-4cm). Head with pointed snout, small round ears and a body-covering of rigid, spiny hairs parted over the head. Acute sense of hearing and smell. Nocturnal. Feeds on snails, slugs, insects, worms and small vertebrates such as frogs and lizards. Does not hibernate, but not active at temperatures below 20 ℃. Gestation lasts just over a month. Litter of 2-4 young between May and October. Common.

Vagrant Hedgehog
in defence posture

Family Soricidae

Resemble mice, although they are not related. Snout is long and pointed. Active by day and night. 2 species.

Pygmy White-toothed Shrew   **p215**

Suncus etruscus   Ġurdien Geddumu Twil

3.5-5.2cm (+ tail 2.5-3cm). Smallest mammal in the world. Greyish-brown tending to dirty grey ventrally. Teeth white. Has a few bristle-like hairs on snout and tail. Ears rather large and prominent. Hides under logs and stones, in open country and woodland, often in rubble walls. Mostly nocturnal, feeding on small invertebrates. Litter of 2-5 young in spring or autumn, following gestation of 4 weeks. Becomes inactive when temperatures drop considerably or food is scarce. Not known from Gozo. Frequent.

Sicilian Shrew   **p215**

Crocidura sicula   Ġurdien Geddumu Twil ta' Għawdex

5-7cm (+ tail 2.8-4.2cm). Dark grey dorsally, becoming white ventrally. In young, the dark grey changes to white abruptly. Identified in 1989, having been formerly mistaken for another species. Found only on Gozo and Sicily, and known from Malta since the Pleistocene (1.5 million years ago). Formerly present also on the island of Malta. Females already pregnant in March and give birth to 5 young, with probably more than one litter. The subspecies *calypso* occurs on Gozo and is endemic. Frequent.

BATS

Order Chiroptera

The only flying mammals. Their wings are formed from skin stretched over the elongated bones of the hand. Bats transmit rapid, high-pitched sounds, the echo of which helps them locate and catch their insect prey. The squeaking one hears at a bat roost has nothing to do with echo-location, but is used for communication among individuals.

At sunset, bats fly in search of flying insects. Some species eat their prey in flight. Others carry the prey to a suitable place where they hang upside down and eat it. During the night they rest, hunting again at dawn. Bats catch flying insects by curving wings and tail forwards to form a bag.

Male bats mate with more than one female. Mating takes place in autumn, but actual fertilisation takes place in spring. There is usually one offspring, sometimes two, generally every year. In summer the females gather in colonies to give birth. Females generally take four years to reach sexual maturity, while males reach maturity earlier.

Family Rhinolophidae

Bats with horseshoe-like lobes on their face which vary in form from one species to another. They sleep hanging upside down with the wings folded around the body. 2 species, one breeding and one migratory.

Lesser Horseshoe Bat   p215

Rhinolophus hipposideros   Farfett il-Lejl tan-Naghla Żghir
4-5cm (wingspan 19-25cm). Smallest species in this Family. Sets out about one hour after sunset, and flies through most of the night. Found all year round, generally singly, sometimes in small colonies. Remains dormant in deep caves during winter; may be found in abandoned buildings during the warmer months. Feeds on moths, mosquitoes, beetles and spiders. Frequent.

Head of
Lesser Mouse-eared Bat

Family Vespertilionidae

Smooth-faced, with an appendage in the ears, known as the **tragus**. 8 species, four of which breed and some others are rare.

Lesser Mouse-eared Bat   p215

Myotis blythi   Farfett il-Lejl Widnet il-Ġurdien
6-7.5cm (wingspan 30-40cm). One of the largest species. Found all year round in certain deep caves, singly or in small colonies numbering about 20. Colonies with about 100 individuals occur in two localities. Flies out at dusk, frequenting cultivated land, edges of woodland and areas around open water reservoirs. Catches insects in the air, also on the ground. Formerly common. Frequent.

Grey Long-eared Bat   p215

Plecotus austriacus   Farfett il-Lejl Widnejh Kbar
4-5.5cm (wingspan 25-30cm). Ears very long. Found mostly near cultivated land and in inhabited areas. Sleeps in cracks in walls and rock faces and in winter is dormant in caves and tunnels. Catches insects in flight. Females reach maturity in two years and in late June congregate in groups of about 10 to give birth. The single young is tended for 6-7 weeks. Some individuals are probably migrants. Frequent.

Head of
Grey Long-eared Bat

Pipistrelle   p215

Pipistrellus pipistrellus   Pipistrell
3.5-5cm (wingspan 18-24cm). Smallest and most widespread bat in Europe. Ears short and rounded. Tragus short and blunt. Tail short and wings slender. Found in inhabited areas, valleys, cliffs and woodland. Roosts in small groups in crevices in trees, walls, old houses and bastions. Flies out soon after sunset, catching small insects on the wing. Can consume up to 3500 mosquitoes in one night. Females congregate in late spring to give birth. Litter generally one, occasionally two, every two years. Young fly at about 20 days. Each male mates with up to 10 females. Common.

CARNIVORES
Order Carnivora

Mammals with strong jaws and sharp, cutting teeth for tearing flesh. Most have glands which secrete a strong-smelling liquid to mark their territory. They are slender, with a flexible tail and generally long legs adapted for running. Even those with short legs can run very fast for short distances. They have acute senses of sight, smell and hearing, and show complex behaviour. Many species are solitary, although the young are cared for by the mother for some time after birth.

Family Mustelidae
Small carnivores. Body is long and slender, and the legs are short; capable of climbing. Claws are not retractable, unlike those of cats. Female is generally smaller than the male. 1 species.

Head of Weasel

Weasel   p215
Mustela nivalis   Ballottra
20-31.5cm (male); 17.5-18cm (female) (+ tail 3-6cm). Smallest carnivore. Long and slender, with short limbs, long neck and small head. Found in all rural habitats. Hunts by day and night, feeding mainly on rodents, rabbits and nestlings. Solitary. Gives birth in April-May and, when food is plentiful, again in July-August. Gestation 34-37 days, with litters of 4-6. Young tended by the mother. Females smaller than males. Not found on Gozo and Comino. Very scarce.

DOLPHINS and WHALES
Order Cetacea

Marine or riverine animals. Forelimbs have evolved into flipper-like organs while the hind limbs have disappeared. Tail is paddle shaped with a central constriction, and is moved up and down to propel the animal forward at great speed. They have a strong sense of hearing, but vision and smell are weak. A blowhole is situated on top of the head. They come to the surface to breathe, but can remain underwater for up to one hour.

Family Delphinidae
Small dolphins. Very agile swimmers. Jaws are toothed and the snout pointed, with a prominent dorsal fin and a constriction in the middle of the paddle-like tail. 7 species.

Common Dolphin   p215
Delphinus delphis   Denfil
200-250cm. Snout pointed and streamlined, dark with a whitish tip. Flanks bear yellowish-brown patches. Seen in small schools, frequently breaking surface. Often swims near ships. Mating in July-October. Gestation 10 months. Young born the following summer. Males longer than females. Frequent.

Bottle-nosed Dolphin   p215
Tursiops truncatus   Denfil Geddumu Qasir
250-410cm. Back dark grey, underside light grey. Snout short, lower jaw protruding further than upper. Vertebral column curved backwards. Seen in schools which often number 100. Mates in summer. Gestation 1 year. Young reaches full maturity after 12 years. Frequent.

RODENTS
Order Rodentia

Mammals with teeth adapted for gnawing, although some species are insectivorous and others omnivorous. Incisors kept sharp by gnawing.

Family Muridae
Rats and mice. Tail virtually hairless and often longer than body. Senses of hearing and smell are very acute. 4 species.

Wood Mouse   p215
Apodemus sylvaticus   Ġurdien tar-Raba'
9.5-11cm (+ tail 7-11.5cm). Very similar to House Mouse, but has larger eyes and ears. Tail long and thin, hind legs pale, long and slender and larger than those of House Mouse. Yellowish-brown, tinged with grey above and silvery-grey below. Prefers woodland habitats, also found in gardens and inhabited areas. Hearing and vision acute. Nocturnal. Feeds on seeds, snails and insects. Produces up to four litters annually, each numbering 4-7 young. Gestation 19-20 days. Young born in March-October, but mostly in July-August. Scarce.

Brown Rat   p215
Rattus norvegicus   Far tal-Kampanja
21.5-29cm (+ tail 17-23cm). Like Black Rat, but ears shorter, thicker and more furry. Tail shorter and thicker. Eyes small. Lives in urban habitats: in rubbish dumps, drains, farms and food stores. Mostly nocturnal, but often seen by day. Lives in social groups, communicating with the other members by sound. Gestation 3 weeks. Up to five litters annually, with a maximum of 15 young (mostly 7-9). Very common.

Black Rat   p215
Rattus rattus   Far Iswed
15-24cm (+ tail 11.5-26cm). Eyes larger than those of Brown Rat. Ears and tail virtually hairless. Tail long and slender. Lives in inhabited areas, in holes and tunnels, also among trees and reeds. Nocturnal and omnivorous, preferring fruit and vegetables. Gestation 3 weeks. 3-5 litters annually, each with up to 16 young. Sexually mature at 3-4 months. Very common.

House Mouse   p215
Mus musculus   Ġurdien ta' l-Imramma
7.5-9cm (+ tail 5.5-10cm). Found in houses, farms, warehouses, fields and groves. Omnivorous. Offspring produced all year round. Gestation 19-20 days. When food is abundant, produces up to 10 litters annually, each with 5-6 young. Sexually mature at 6 weeks. Lives up to 3 years. Mostly nocturnal. Can squeeze through apertures as little as 1cm in diameter. Territorial. Hearing and smell good, but vision less acute. Very common.

House Mouse

RABBITS and HARES
Order Lagomorpha

Herbivorous. Tail very short and nostrils can be closed by flaps of skin.

Family Leporidae
Ears long. Hind legs longer than forelegs. Fast runners. 1 species.

Wild Rabbit   p215
Oryctolagus cuniculus   Fenek Salvaġġ
34-45cm (ears 6-7cm). Eyes large and prominent, hind legs long. Tail short, curved upwards, dark above and pale below. Tail is very visible when the animal runs. Female smaller than male. Generally pale sandy brown or greyish with white underparts. Comes out to graze at daybreak and at dusk. Incisors chisel-like. Feeds on grass and also digs for roots. Stamps its hind legs as a sign of alarm. Found in open countryside, in garigue and in screes, living in colonies. Excavates deep burrows in which it builds its nest. Male mates with more than one female. Gestation 28-33 days. More than 3 litters annually, with 3-12 young in each (mostly 5). Young emerge from burrow after 3 weeks. Common.

Wild Rabbit

Glossary

abdomen - in arthropods, the posterior division of the body, composed of a number of similar segments; in mammals, that region of the body below the diaphragm, containing the viscera (intestines, etc).

annual - plants which complete their life cycle, from germination to seed production and death, within one year.

annulus - a ring-like structure surrounding the stalk of some mushrooms.

antenna (pl. antennae) - head appendage in certain arthropods usually taking the shape of a multi-segmented filament and normally having a sensory function.

anther - that part of the stamen (usually at its apex) inside which pollen is produced.

axil - in the context used in this book, it is the upper angle between the base of the leaf and the stem.

biennial - plants which complete their life cycle, from germination to seed production and death, within two years.

bifid - split into two, e.g. a bifid stigma consists of two branches arising from the apex of the style.

biodiversity - the total diversity of life on the planet including species, varieties within species, and the ecosystems they form part of.

bract - an inflorescence leaf; typically different from a foliage leaf.

byssus - in the bivalve molluscs, hair-like filaments which are used to attach the animal to a substratum.

calcareous - containing calcium carbonate (limestone).

cap - the usually umbrella-shaped top of a mushroom; scientifically known as the pileus.

carapace - in crustaceans, the shield-like anterior portion of the exoskeleton which covers a number of the anterior body segments; in turtles, the thick bony 'shell' covering the back of the animal.

cartilage - skeletal tissue of certain vertebrates which consists of cells embedded in a resilient matrix containing abundant collagen fibres.

catkin - a hanging, elongated inflorescence carrying small, often unisexual flowers; this falls off after pollen and/or seeds have been released; typical of wind-pollinated trees.

cell - the basic unit of life, consisting of a mass of cytoplasm bounded by a cell membrane, and, in plants and some other forms, also by a cell wall.

chelicera (pl. chelicerae) - the first pair of appendages of arachnids; used for grasping.

chlorophyll - a group of green pigments which are used to trap light energy for use in photosynthesis.

chrysalis - an alternate name for pupa.

cilium (pl. cilia) - fine hair-like structure projecting from the surface of certain cells, usually present in great numbers.

colony - strictly speaking, an association of individuals whose bodies are confluent (as in many corals); however, also used to describe a group of animals living together in a co-operative manner (as in termites, ants and some bees and wasps).

columella - in gastropod molluscs, the axis round which the shell spirals.

compound leaf - a leaf which is divided into several leaflets, each of which is individually attached to the leaf axis.

compound-palmate - a palmate leaf made up of several separate leaflets.

compound-pinnate - a pinnate leaf made up of several separate leaflets.

cotyledon - the first leaves occurring in the seed.

dichotomous - a type of branching in which the axis repeatedly divides into two branches.

ectoderm - in the embryos of animals, the outer body layer which in the adult develops into epidermis, nervous tissue and nephridia.

ectoparasite - parasite living on the external surface of the host.

elytron (pl. elytra) - the thick, tough front wing of beetles, which is modified as a protective cover for the delicate hind wings.

embryo - the developing organism resulting from the fusion of a sperm cell and an egg cell.

endemic - species which occur naturally only in a defined geographical area, e.g. species found only in the Maltese Islands are said to be endemic to the Maltese Islands.

endoderm - in the embryos of animals, the innermost body layer which in the adult develops into the gut and associated structures.

entire - a leaf margin which is even, i.e. not toothed, cut or lobed.

exoskeleton - a skeleton situated on the outside of the body.

filament - in a flower, the usually filiform structure which subtends an anther.

flagellum (pl. flagella) - long, thread-like structure possessed by certain cells, which executes lashing or undulating movements.

floret - a small individual flower from a compact inflorescence.

gills - in plants, sheet-like structures on the underside of the cap of a mushroom, on which the spores are produced; scientifically known as lamellae.

herbaceous - plants which do not form compact woody tissues.

hermaphrodite - an individual which is capable of producing both male and female gametes.

hybrid - the product of cross-breeding between different species or races.

hypha (pl. hyphae) - the filaments which make up the bodies of fungi.

indigenous - species which occur naturally in a geographical area and which have not been introduced by human intervention; also referred to as native.

inflorescence - a shoot which is specialised to bear flowers.

integument - the outer covering of the body of an animal.

invertebrate - an animal that is not a member of the Subphylum VERTEBRATA of the Phylum CHORDATA; one that does not possess a vertebral column (backbone).

involucre - a collection of bracts crowded around an inflorescence as in the Apiacae and Asteracae.

labellum - the specialised lower inner petal of an orchid.

lamina - the flat portion of a leaf; the leaf blade.

lanceolate - a leaf blade which is widest at or below the middle and tapers at both ends, typically two to four times as long as broad.

larva (pl. larvae) - stage between the egg and the adult form in the life cycle of certain animals; the larva may be vastly different in morphology and behaviour from the adult; some animals have more than one larval form in their life cycle.

leaflet - one of the leaf-like appendages of a compound leaf.

mantle - in molluscs, that part of the body surface which encloses the viscera and which secretes the shell.

medusa (pl. medusae) - free-swimming form of many cnidarians, having a bell- or umbrella-shaped body.

metamorphosis - period of rapid change in which the final larval form of certain animals transforms into the adult form.

midrib - the central 'vein' of a pinnate leaf.

moulting - in birds, the seasonal process of replacing old feathers with new ones.

mycelium - the food-absorbing body of a fungus consisting of a dense mass of filaments permeating the food source.

native - an alternative word for indigenous.

naturalised - an organism which, though of alien origin, manages to run wild and establish self-sustaining populations.

nauplius - the first larval stage of many crustaceans.

operculum - in gastropod molluscs, a horny or calcareous structure used to block the aperture of the shell.

organic - produced by a living organism.

ovary - the central part of the flower which contains the ovules; grows to become the fruit.

ovipositor - organ on the abdomen of female insects through which the eggs are laid, frequently used to deposit eggs in otherwise inaccessible places, such as the tissues of animals or plants.

ovules - the bodies carried within the ovary which, after fertilisation, grow to become seeds.

ovum (pl. ova) - the female sex cell or gamete, usually large and non-motile.

palmate - a leaf with several principal (or primary) veins, all of which arise from the petiole.

pappus - the feathery appendage attached to the tiny fruits of many Asteraceae and some other plants, which is used for dispersal.

parapodium (pl. parapodia) - leg-like outgrowth from the body wall of polychaete annelids which bears chaetae and which is normally used for locomotion in active forms.

parasite - an organism which lives on or in another species, known as the host; the parasite derives nourishment from the host, which is more or less harmed by this association.

parthenogenesis - development of the female egg into an individual without fertilisation by the male.

pedipalp - the second pair of appendages of arachnids; may be grasping, sensory or locomotory, depending on the group.

perennial - plants which take more than two years to complete their life cycle.

periostracum - in molluscs, the outermost layer of the shell, which is made of an organic matrix.

petal - one of a group of floral parts which immediately surrounds the stamens; normally the most conspicuous part of the flower, being often distinctively shaped and coloured, and serving to attract pollinators.

petiole - a stalk subtending the leaf blade; leaf stalk.

photosynthesis - the process carried out by most plants (a notable exception being the Fungi) whereby light energy, absorbed by pigments known as chlorophylls, is harnessed to convert water and carbon dioxide into sugars, from which the plant can then produce all its requirements; a by-product of photosynthesis is oxygen, which the plants release.

pinnate - a leaf with a single principle (or primary) vein, the midrib, which has secondary veins branching out of it.

pinnatifid - pinnate leaves which are cut into lobes reaching roughly half way to the midrib.

pollen - minute dust-like particles formed in the anthers; each pollen grain contains male reproductive structures; pollen is conveyed to the stigmas by various means such as wind or insects; the pollen grains then germinate, forming a tube which enters the ovule permitting fertilisation of the female parts.

polyp - sessile form of many cnidarians, having a tubular body usually with a crown of tentacles round the mouth.

proboscis - in certain insects, an elongated mouthpart used for sucking up liquids.

pupa (pl. pupae) - stage in the life cycle of certain insects, during which the larva transforms into the adult form.

radula - in molluscs, a long, ribbon-like structure bearing numerous transverse rows of teeth on its surface, and which is used to rasp off food.

rhizome - horizontal, typically underground stem, which roots at the nodes, and typically bears terminal shoots; plants which spread by means of rhizomes are described as being rhizomatous.

rosette - a group of leaves crowded around a short axis.

sepal - one of the outermost segments of a flower; usually green, serving to protect the flower bud; sepals collectively form the calyx.

sessile - attached permanently to the substratum, or only moving for very limited distances from its point of settlement.

siliqua (pl. siliquae) - the fruit typical of the Brassicaceae; pods with two short chambers, separated by a partition; a short siliqua is known as a silicula.

simple leaf - a leaf which is not divided into leaflets.

sperm - the male sex cell or gamete, usually smaller than the female gamete and motile.

spicules - elements made of mineral substances in the body of certain animals; usually function as skeletal structures.

spikelet - one of the units of the inflorescence of a grass, consisting of one or more florets plus associated bracts.

sporangium (pl. sporangia) - structure which contains spores.

spore - an asexual reproductive body, most often unicellular, produced by most plants, and which potentially grows into a new plant.

stamen - the part of the flower which is designed to produce, carry and release pollen; typically consists of a stalk-like portion, the filament, which subtends the anther.

stigma - part of the flower, usually on top of the ovary, the function of which is to receive the pollen.

stipule - a small leaf-like appendage occurring at the base of the leaves of some plants, e.g. the Fabaceae and Rosaceae.

stridulatory structures - structures on the body of certain insects, which the animals rub together to produce sound.

style - a stalk which subtends the stigma.

substratum (pl. substrata) - the underlying surface on which an animal moves, burrows or is attached.

succulent - plant structures, mainly leaves and stems, which are fleshy due to the storage of water.

symbiosis - broadly speaking, an intimate association between different species, typically used as means to obtain nourishment; the term is more often used (as in this book) to denote an association which is apparently of benefit to both partners.

tendril - a branched or unbranched filiform structure which can twine around, or stick to, suitable supports used by climbing plants.

thorax - in insects, a group of three segments behind the head which bear the legs and, where present, the wings; in mammals, the cavity bearing the heart and lungs.

tragus - a lobe growing upwards from the lower border of the ear of certain bats.

trifid - split into three, e.g. a trifid stigma would have three branches arising from the apex of the style.

trifoliate - a compound leaf with three leaflets.

tuber - a swollen underground plant organ (root or stem) which is used for storage of food.

umbel - an inflorescence wherein the flowers all radiate from the apex of the subtending stalk; may be compound, as in the Apiaceae, where a large number of small umbels all arise from the apex of a subtending stalk.

vascular plant - a plant supplied with an internal system of tubes primarily as a means of transport for water, minerals and food produced by photosynthesis.

vertebrate - an animal that is a member of the Subphylum VERTEBRATA, of the Phylum CHORDATA, characterised, amongst other things, by a vertebral column (backbone).

volva - a cup-like structure found at the base of the stalk of some mushrooms.

zygote - the fertilised egg cell.

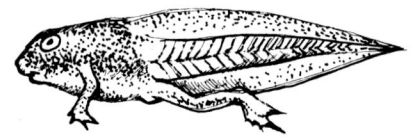

Reference and Bibliography

Arnold, E.N. & Burton, J.A. 1978. **A Field Guide to the Reptiles and Amphibians of Britain and Europe.** London:Collins.

Askew, R.R. 1988. **The Dragonflies of Europe.** England: Harley Books.

Baldacchino, A.E., Lanfranco, E. & Schembri, P.J. 1990. **Appuntamenti man-Natura.** Malta: Merlin Library.

Baldacchino, A.E. & Schembri, P.J. 1993. **Ir-Rettili u l-Amfibji tal-Gżejjer Maltin.** Valletta: Soċjetà għall-Istudju u l-Ħarsien tan-Natura - SSCN.

Blamey, M. & Grey-Wilson, C. 1993. **Mediterranean Wild Flowers.** Great Britain: Harper Collins.

Bon, M. 1987. **The Mushrooms and Toadstools of Britain and North-western Europe.** Great Britain: Hodder and Stoughton.

Borg, J. 1927. **Descriptive Flora of the Maltese Islands.** Malta: Government Printing Office.

Borg, J. 1976. **Street Trees in Malta.** Malta: Men of the Trees (Malta).

Brown, V.K. 1983. **Grasshoppers. Naturalists' Handbook 2.** Cambridge: Cambridge University Press.

Cachia, C., Mifsud, C. & Sammut, P.M. 1991. **The Marine Shelled Mollusca of the Maltese Islands (Part One: Archaeogastropoda).** Malta: Grima Printing & Publishing Industries.

Cachia, C., Mifsud, C. & Sammut, P.M. 1993. **An Annotated Check-list of the Marine Mollusca of the Maltese Islands.** Austria: EVMG.

Cachia, C., Mifsud, C. & Sammut, P.M. (in print) **The Marine Shelled Mollusca of the Maltese Islands (Part Two: Mesogastropoda).**

Campbell, A.C. 1982. **Hamlyn Guide to the Flora and Fauna of the Mediterranean Sea.** Middlesex, England: Hamlyn Publishing Group Ltd.

Chinery, M. 1986. **Insects of Britain and Western Europe.** Britain: Domino Books.

Corbet, G. & Ovenden, D. 1990. **The Mammals of Britain and Europe.** London: Collins.

Cramp, S. & Simmons, K.E.L. (eds.). 1977-83. **The Birds of the Western Palearctic. Vol. I-III.** Oxford: Oxford University Press.

Cramp, S. (ed.). 1985-92. **The Birds of the Western Palearctic. Vol. IV-VI.** Oxford: Oxford University Press.

Cramp, S. & Perrins, C.M. (eds.) 1993-4. **The Birds of the Western Palearctic. Vol. VII-IX.** Oxford: Oxford University Press.

Gilbert, F.S. 1986. **Hoverflies. Naturalists' Handbook 2.** Cambridge: Cambridge University Press.

Giusti, F., Manganelli G. & Schembri, P.J. 1995. **The Non-marine Molluscs of the Maltese Islands.** Torino, Museo Regionale di Scienze Naturali.

Harde, K.W. 1981. **A Field Guide in Colour to Beetles.** London: Octopus Books.

Harris, T. 1982. **The Natural History of the Mediterranean.** Great Britain: Pelham Books.

Haslam, S.M., Sell, P.D. & Wolseley, P.A. 1977. **A Flora of the Maltese Islands.** Malta: Malta University Press.

Higgins, L.G. & Riley, N.D. 1976. **A Field Guide to the Butterflies of Britain and Europe.** London: Collins.

Humpries, C.J., Press, J.R. & Sutton, D.A. 1981. **Trees of Britain and Europe.** England: Country Life Books.

Jones, D. 1983. **The Country Life Guide to Spiders of Britain and Northern Europe.** England: Country Life Books.

Lanfranco, E. 1969. **A Revised Check-List of Maltese Algae.** Pietà: National Press.

Lanfranco, G. 1993. **Ħxejjex Mediċinali u Oħrajn fil-Gżejjer Maltin.** Malta: Media Centre Publications.

Lanfranco, G.G. 1969. **Field Guide to the Wild Flowers of Malta.** Malta: Progress Press.

Lanfranco, G.G. 1969. **Maltese Mammals (Central Mediterranean).** Malta: Progress Press.

Lanfranco, G.G. 1993. **The Fish Around Malta (Central Mediterranean)** Malta: Progress Press.

Luther, W. & Fielder, K. 1976. **A Field Guide to the Mediterranean Seashore.** London: Collins.

Lythgoe, J. & G. 1971. **Fishes of the Sea - The Coastal Waters of the British Isles, Northern Europe and the Mediterranean.** London: Blandford Press.

Macdonald, D. & Barret, P. 1993. **Mammals of Britain and Europe.** London: Collins.

Polunin, O. & Huxley, A. 1987. **Flowers of the Mediterranean.** London: Hogarth Press.

Reidl, R. 1991. **Fauna e Flora del Mediterraneo.** Italia: Muzzio.

Sammut, P.M. 1984. **A Systematic and Synonymic List of the Lepidoptera of the Maltese Islands**. Keltern: Verlag Erich Bauer.

Schembri, P.J. 1993. Physical geography and ecology of the Maltese Islands: a brief overview. In **Options Méditerranéennes Serie B: Études et Recherches N˙7. Malta: Food, Agriculture, Fisheries and the Environment.** France: CIHEAM.

Schembri, P.J. The Fauna of the Maltese Islands: a review and analysis. In Ellul-Micallef, R. & Fiorini, S. (eds.) **Collegium Melitense Quartercentenary Celebrations (1592-1992)**. Collected papers. pp. 541-573. Msida, Malta: University Press.

Schembri, P.J., & Baldacchino, A.E. 1992. **Ilma, Blat u Ħajja.** Msida: Malta University Services Ltd.

Schembri, P.J., Lanfranco, E., Farrugia, P., Schembri, S. & Sultana, J. 1987. **Localities with Conservation Value in the Maltese Islands**: Environment Division, Ministry of Education.

Schembri, P.J. & Sultana, J. (eds.) 1989. **Red Data Book for the Maltese Islands**. Malta: Department of Information.

Schober, W. & Grimmberger, E. 1989. **A Guide to Bats of Britain and Europe.** England: Hamlyn Publishers Group Ltd.

Schönfelder, I. & P. 1990. **Wild Flowers of the Mediterranean.** London: Collins.

Sommier, S. & Caruana Gatto, A. 1915. **Flora Melitensis Nova.** Firenze: Stab. Pellas.

Sultana, J. & Gauci, C. 1979. **L-Agħsafar.** Valletta, Malta: Is-Soċjetà Ornitoloġika - MOS.

Sultana, J. & Gauci, C. 1982. **A New Guide to the Birds of Malta.** Valletta, Malta: The Ornithological Society - MOS.

Valletta, A. 1971. **The Butterflies of the Maltese Islands**. Malta: A. Valletta.

Valletta, A. 1973. **The Moths of the Maltese Islands.** Malta: A.Valletta.

Zammit-Maempel, G. 1977. **An Outline of Maltese Geology**. Malta: G. Zammit-Maempel.

Index of English names

Index of scientific names